Aidan Duff

Aidan is a coach and facilitator. Together with his wife, Beth, he runs **gentle leadership** a personal development company based in rural Aberdeenshire, Scotland. Having witnessed the crushing nature of autocratic or paternalistic management styles, they are committed to introducing Values-Centred Leadership concepts to their clients and find joy in seeing how organisations blossom when they adopt a more soulful approach to managing people.

Aidan and Beth love horses. Eight years ago they purchased Chelsea and have transformed the mare from being unpredictable and suspicious of humans into a magnificent creature who is bursting with generosity of spirit and determination to repay kindness. Inspired by Chelsea, they offer a programme of experiential learning called **the red horse speaks** where horses join them to teach their human friends about leadership and communication.

They are inspired by the techniques of Lance Secretan and Monty Roberts seeing similar results on people and horses alike. This book reflects their experiences.

Aidan Duff

The Gentle Way

Lipstick Publishing

Lipstick Publishing
West Knockenbaird Croft,
Insch, Aberdeenshire.
Scotland AB52 6TN

www.lipstickpublishing.com
admin@lipstickpublishing.com

This paperback second print 2006

First Published in Great Britain by
Lipstick Publishing 2005

ISBN: 1-904762-22-0

Printed and bound by Antony Rowe Ltd, Eastbourne

Dedication

This book is dedicated to Beth and Chelsea.

Read on – you'll soon know why.

Acknowledgements

I would like to thank my wife Beth for being a constant source of encouragement and enthusiasm. As I wrote this book, she never failed to appreciate each day's output and I will always remember her excitement whenever she came home at the end of a day, from work or from her sessions with our two horses Chelsea and Susie, ready to read and enthuse over the next batch of pages. Writing 'The Gentle Way' with Beth at my side has been an exercise in joy. I cannot express adequately how much this buoyant source of support has meant to me. Beth was also my 'horse' consultant, sharing with me every scene of Chelsea's story. Parts of that story are based on Beth's real-life experiences with Chelsea, dutifully recorded in a most amazing journal.

Beth and I would like to thank Lance Secretan for being the initial inspiration behind this entire project. Lance and his wonderful support team have been the spark that ignited our Calling to work with horses and humans, and the breath that fanned that spark into life. Thank you Lance for the way your presence has changed our lives for the better since we first attended your annual Higher Ground Community gathering in July 2000. With Lance's kind permission I have used, in chapters 12 and 14, some phrases from his own work 'Blueprint for New Leadership'. Why change perfection?

We would also like to thank all those people who were with us at King View, Ontario, in November 2000, especially Susan Nind, our project 'midwife' and mentor, Ron Szymanski, our adviser and friend, and Denise Szymanski, our friend-in-fun, now sadly missed, who lived every moment to the full and inspired us with her zest and beauty. Thanks too to T. Kay Rix, our friend and supporter, and 'wee' Debbie Zins, our friend and laughter-merchant. Nor can we ever forget John Pollock whose presence and support was simply there, all the time, loving and encouraging, unchanging and authentic.

Thank you too to those Secretan Associates and attendees at the Higher Ground Community gathering in July 2001,who read the early chapters of 'The Gentle Way' and made such helpful comments, particularly Leonore Clauss, who is wisdom itself, and Anne Brooks whose comments touched my heart.

I will always be grateful to Aileen Gibb and all the wonderful ladies from Inspirational Coaching International. Aileen encouraged me to do what

I am doing today. So thank you, Aileen, and your team from iC International (hi, girls!), for all you have done in recent years to support me.

Thank you too Sydney Morley, 11 years old, for allowing me to share with my readers your lovely poem 'Totally for Sure' (origin unknown).

Chelsea, our gorgeous chestnut mare, wishes to join Beth and me in thanking Jackie Mather, who shared with Beth so much of Chelsea's schooling and the subsequent fun of competition with her. You knew how to listen to our equine friend and became her loved companion. She gives you a nicker of affection and thanks.

And finally, of course, we want the world to know how much we love Chelsea, and Susie too. Our two horses, so different in character, have one thing in common – a determination to repay us for all our efforts in making this world a kinder place for them. Animals know, don't they? Life would simply not be the same without these two wonderful creatures. They now help us as teachers in our **red horse speaks** programme.

Thanks too to Willow and Sophie, our cats, who 'helped' so much in the book writing process. I'm delighted to say that my second laptop has survived the attentions of these two lovable creatures. Unlike my first, whose keyboard could not survive their continual and affectionate scrutiny! Farewell, dear Sophie. We won't forget you. Welcome 'SP'. I see you are determined to pick up the mantle of scrutineer-in-chief!

CONTENTS

Chapter 1

Chelsea's First Fan

The slippery foal's first experience of life was to smell, hear and feel the comforting presence of its mother. The earthy mustiness of the Irish Draught mare enveloped the spindly-legged chestnut foal in a wash of security. It heard a quiet throaty whickering as the mare's nose gently nuzzled her head and ribs. Immediately the bond was established and a sensation of pure love and caring caused the newly born foal to raise its head to the world and look at the wonders that surrounded it.

Dark, liquid eyes peered protectively down over velvet-soft nostrils. The nudging and nuzzling continued, encouraging the foal to struggle tentatively to her feet. Ungainly legs wobbled and she slipped down on her haunches, clumsiness combining with beauty – a picture of innocent weakness and determination. The mare whickered again in pride and caressed her newborn with her nose. Again the foal struggled to stand. Now instinct gave her the determination to succeed. In later years that same determination would become her trademark – that spirited approach to the first hour of life was a foretaste of her true character.

And so a perfect creature came into this world. She found her mother's teats and began to suckle, ungainly yet without faltering. Love and nourishment welcomed her to the small world of the stable. The compacted straw on which she stood smelled both acrid and warmly sweet. She lifted her head and tottered against the wooden partition that divided her box from the adjacent one, in which she heard the contented munching and grinding of a horse eating hay. The larger world outside would soon be hers to explore, especially as the warmth of a late spring afternoon gave promise of a world of fields and wildlife, of new growth and of freedom. Her first home was a stud farm nestling within idyllic green Irish countryside close to Killarney.

It was not until six months passed that the name 'Chelsea' was adopted. Eric, one of the stable lads, fell in love with the chestnut foal – her combination of silky-coated beauty and impetuous joie de vivre attracted the young man from the first day he saw her. "She's one of my charges," he stated with determination, running his hand lovingly down her shoulder and fixing the stud owner with a steady and determined stare.
Mr. O'Sullivan nodded appreciatively as he returned the look, knowing that any other course of action was unnecessary and unfair. He liked horses and

only employed those who felt the same. Such a pairing would serve the needs of all concerned. One of the filly's ears twisted towards him waiting for the reply, the other continued to monitor Eric's anxious breathing.

"Right you are, lad. She's yours. I know you'll take good care."

"Thank you, sir, I'll be doing that alright." Then a pause as Eric summoned his courage for the final request. "May I ask one more thing, sir?"

A small smile and a barely perceptible nod encouraged Eric to continue. "It's her name, you see. 'Gentle Sea Breeze' is fine enough but I'd like to use 'Chelsea' as her stable name. Would that be in order, Mr. O'Sullivan?"

"Why's that, Eric?"

"It's close enough, if you see what I mean and …"

"…and you're a Chelsea fan. Is that it?"

"Aye, sir, Dad always supported them before he moved here from London." Eric was half English, although his parents had returned to his mother's hometown of Killarney many years ago. Eric was as Irish as they come but he loved following the English football league and threw his support behind his father's team.

"Looks like you're going to be the fan of another Chelsea. Go for it, son."

Both ears went forward as Eric's head nudged her neck. Eric's green eyes met one of Chelsea's dark brown eyes. It looked deeply into his mind, but it touched deeper than that – into his soul.

"Thanks, Mr. O'Sullivan." Eric led the filly away, preparing to turn her out into the small paddock where the other foals were grazing in the early morning sun.

"But Eric," the voice followed the pair. "Don't forget your other charges. She's not to become a pet."

Eric turned, raised a hand in recognition and smiled, but whispered to Chelsea, "I love you girl – your number one fan and that's for sure." And so a relieved and contented young man watched as the little filly trotted exuberantly into the field, dipped her head and bucked with joy, then trotted again – a perfect elevated trot – her tail arched upwards defiantly. "You're a beaut, girl, that's for sure, but I'll bet you'll be a handful."

Chelsea spooked at a blowing paper packet, reared up and snorted before cantering back to the herd. "And a drama queen, that's also for sure." Eric leaned on the gate and sighed with the pure pleasure of life. Then he remembered that his duties called and he turned happily towards the long shed and put his mind to mucking out. At that moment, his connection to another creature carried him to a higher plane – a sense of love and peace filled him and time changed pace. The morning passed in a flash and Eric could not explain how he had achieved it all in the time. Nonetheless, the rows of boxes were ready, fresh, knee deep straw bedding laid down in place of the previous night's soiled and compacted layers. Chelsea's box received extra attention.

He returned to the paddock with his lunch, sat on the gate and munched an egg and tomato sandwich as he watched the young horses. The others grazed peacefully whilst Chelsea rolled in the warm grass, reaching that exquisite moment when her spine supported her for just an instant before the momentum of the roll threw her onto her side, one way then the other. She stood up and shook herself deliciously before looking around. Catching sight of Eric, she stared intently in his direction for a while before dipping her head sideways and cantering around the field. Her silky mane and tail flowed freely and Eric smiled as he saw the chestnut colours gleam in the midday sun. "A redhead, just like me," he thought, realising that his own temper was never far from the surface. "I'd better watch out."

During the second perfect year, before Chelsea was backed, Eric looked forward to his early morning greeting from her. He loved to be first in the yard, to quietly slide open the huge doors and listen for the rustling sounds of horses rousing themselves. He especially liked it when he'd catch Chelsea lying on the deep straw bed, resting on her side, raising her head from the straw as he approached her box and rising to her feet to receive the customary carrot. Eric was also bitten twice – petulant little nips as he over-vigorously brushed her tender spots. Her sturdy frame and soft coat had developed magnificently, but she was no coarse-haired cob.

Eric had many such occasions to recall how accurate his assessment of her fiery nature had been – sensitive to touch and touchy by nature. "She certainly wants me to know who's boss," he mused on the two occasions she had nipped his backside. But Eric loved her all the more, for being "human" as he put it. He also realised that this same fire and determination could one day be harnessed by the right owner. She'd be a winner at something but she'd need the right owner – one who would be prepared to invest time and effort and, above all, love. "My God, if you did that for her, there's nothing she wouldn't do for you. But if …" He stopped himself. The alternative prospect sent a shiver of dread down his spine.

Chelsea had a white Turkish crescent on her forehead. It curved like the top of a flashing question mark between the dark brown eyes. Below the crescent, a thin trace of white continued down the left side of her face in a barely noticeable broken line. Eric kissed the end of her nose where a faint spot of white down-like hair completed the pattern. He murmured encouragement and eased the bit into her mouth. At nearly two years of age, Chelsea had not yet been backed, but she had very quickly accepted the bit after initial puzzlement and concern. A bond of trust had developed between the two and although Chelsea always needed gentle cajoling, she now recognised that, with Eric, no harm would ever be done. So, the strange ways of humans were tolerated with a mixture of stolid acceptance on bad days and amiable cooperation on most other days. Today was just such a day. She stretched forward and opened her mouth in what seemed like a forced yawn. The bit slipped easily into the waiting mouth and Eric ran a hand up her face drawing the straps over her ears. He then buckled and adjusted them, and finally he stood in front of the chestnut face and looked into two attentive eyes.

"Let's straighten things up for you, girl – get you all nice and comfy." His fingers fussed with the straps that crossed her nose and forehead and lightly patted the head that he loved so much. She blinked to the movements but didn't show concern. Eric recalled the difficulties that other horses had shown, and he smiled. Chelsea too was not always such an angel, but she never misbehaved with Eric. He'd seen others, clumsier than himself, trying to put a bit into her mouth. Sometimes she'd begin her ploy of non-cooperation by turning her back. If that was not possible, she'd turn her head in disdain. Finally, her mouth would stay closed in a grumpy frown. But never with Eric. His ritual of caressing and requesting never failed to win her over. "Humans don't like being taken for granted, lass. So why should you?" And so Eric learned that he should ask nicely. In return, Chelsea recognised the ritual and always cooperated.

Leading her by the reins, Eric walked towards the waiting trailer. Its ramp was down and a hay net was tied up inside. "What we'll do now Chels is walk you straight in, no stopping, no getting used to the idea, just walk you in as if it was your box at night. Can we give it a go? OK?"

As they approached the ramp, Chelsea's only reaction was to dip her head in interest and examine it briefly, without stopping. They strode up and stopped by the hay net. A bored snort blew into Eric's face. Her way of saying, "What's all the fuss?"

To be sure – it was no fluke. Eric loaded her three more times, remembering the dramas that often accompanied this learning exercise for some other horses. But he realised that loading would cause no fears for the chestnut filly and he felt confident that tomorrow, when they repeated the same process for real, he could rely on Chelsea. Eric had been granted permission to take her to a local show where Chelsea would be shown 'in hand'. This was not normally allowed. Horses from the stud were reared and backed for selling on. Nothing more. Time and effort was not put to showing or competing. But Eric had prevailed in his request, asking if he could take Chelsea in his own time using his father's car and trailer. Showing her in hand required no more training than what he'd already done with the filly and he was certain that Chelsea would behave, and catch the eye of the judge. Not that that mattered though. Eric's eye for quality was a match for anybody and his own certainty was all that really mattered.

The next day, horse and lad set off for the showground. The twenty-minute journey caused Chelsea to sweat up a little. Eric registered the fact that Chelsea was an anxious traveller so he led her gently out of the trailer and walked her for fifteen minutes, talking quietly and confidently about the sights and sounds of the showground. Soon anxiety was replaced by excitement and interest, the noises and smells new and intriguing. A loudspeaker thundered out details from the show-jumping arena, music filled the air in between the commentaries, and the waft of burgers carried everywhere. They returned from their circuit of the showground, back to the trailer that Eric had intentionally parked well away from the hubbub. He tied her lead rope to the trailer and removed the rug.

Chelsea nibbled from the hay net but soon lost interest in eating. Her breathing was heavier than normal, in anticipation of the new experiences to come. For the first time ever, she sensed the importance of an occasion, a feeling that would never fail to fill her in the years ahead whenever she was asked to compete. Eric recognised the tension and talked quietly as he groomed the filly. "Aye, Chels, it's a big day. Just walk with me at my pace. We're going to show off today. You're a beaut lass and I love you. Easy does it, I know you don't like being brushed. Let's make you really shine out." And so the companionable chattering went on. Her breathing remained heavy with anticipation but her trust in Eric never wavered. Not even when he left her for a few minutes, tethered by the hay net, while he went to collect his number.

Outside the show ring, a few owners had already assembled in the collecting area, walking their horses in large circles or trotting them up and down in straight lines. For many horses this was the first time they were being shown and there was an air of skittering excitement. Some pulled at their lead ropes, anxious to keep moving; a few stood quietly beside their owners. One young gelding reared and backed away from some invisible demon. Eric and Chelsea approached the collecting ring and observed these goings on with interest. They passed a burger van, now busy with trade. "Sizzling and steam," thought Eric as he watched the eager faces of the customers. He looked forward to his own visit to the van shortly.

With that final thought, Eric led Chelsea into the collecting ring to wait for their class to be called. They walked about with a few of the other competitors. Some stood and watched an earlier class in the show ring as the judge put the competitors through their paces, studying them with a keen eye, running her hand over backs, down over hocks and gently over ears in a final gesture of calming affection. Soon it was time for Chelsea's class and Eric walked her into the show ring with the others. He was pleased to hear a murmur of admiration from a small group of bystanders, picking Chelsea out for special praise. The judge smiled at the competitors and once again went through the routine for the new group – asking them all to walk in a circle around her. She made her first assessment and Chelsea was called in second, much to Eric's delight. The judge then called each competitor in turn to show its paces before being examined carefully. When it was Chelsea's turn, Eric saw pleasure in the judge's face. Did he just imagine it or was she taking extra time, particularly when handling the filly's gleaming coat, extending the pleasure of the moment in recognition and appreciation of true class?

Once again they walked around as a class. Now the judge eyed them for a final time, comparing their conformation, paces and presence. She seemed to take forever to make up her mind but this time she pointed at Chelsea first and asked her to take the winner's position, close to the side of the show ring, a short distance from the back of the burger van. Eric's flood of pride was short lived. As the other horses lined up ready to receive rosettes, a single loud explosion cracked viciously from the gas cylinder that fed the van's cookers; a tongue of flame lanced upwards hurling a shard of metal from the canister's neck.

In perfect synchronisation, the six horses reared backwards and their handlers ducked instinctively. Two of the young horses broke loose and galloped across the arena snorting in fright, their lead ropes flying loosely between their front legs. One of the handlers was shouldered brutally by the charge and fell heavily. The remaining horses reared and skittered in alarm, edging from the source of the explosion. Their handlers anxiously held onto the ropes, backing away with their charges as they composed themselves and tried to calm and control the agitated beasts.

Chelsea had reacted with the others. The instinctive backward step that preceded her rearing saved her from more serious injury as the metal shard sliced cruelly across her face, just beneath the level of the eyes where the ridge of bone is barely covered with flesh. She half turned against the pain, barging Eric who stumbled and fell into a seated position, momentarily releasing the lead rope. Chelsea's momentum continued, her front legs straddling the fallen lad. Once again, instinct took over and she avoided trampling her companion. Instead she paused, giving Eric the chance to grab the very end of the rope. This would have been pulled brutally from his grasp as she reared upwards but, as soon as she felt the slack tighten, she responded immediately, falling back onto her front legs. For a moment she stood, snorting in confusion and fear, looking down at Eric. Their eyes met and a droplet of blood fell between the two of them, landing on Eric's cheek.

The confusion lasted for several minutes. Handlers soothed agitated horses, people ran to catch the loose animals, the standby ambulance staff rushed to the fallen handler – an elderly lady whose collar bone was fractured and who was showing alarming signs of shock. Nobody noticed Eric and Chelsea, simply because the two were the quietest and most composed. Neither did Eric notice the melee that surrounded them. Instead his attention was devoted to the anxious filly – she was now breathing heavily. With his handkerchief he wiped the runnel of blood that seeped from the nick below her white crescent. Then, with one hand on the lead rope and the other dabbing the wound, he relied on his voice to calm her. "Eeeaasy, there, eeeaasy," he repeated over and over, stretching the word in one long and calming tone.

That day Chelsea won her first competition but above all, she won the unwavering admiration of a young man, wise beyond his years, whose deep knowledge of horses told him that Chelsea's behaviour was exceptional. Something inexplicable, a sort of inner power coupled with true intelligence and trust had carried her through that experience. She had flinched and faltered, naturally and instinctively, but she had composed herself quickly. What Eric would never fully appreciate was the extent to which Chelsea's magnificence that day was the early reward for his own efforts with her. The true rewards of love and gentleness.

Only one person noticed them slip away from the arena. As Eric was placing the protective boots and tail guard on her, getting ready for the short journey home, the judge stood to one side, unobserved, letting the pair complete their preparations. With Chelsea rugged and ready for loading, Eric looked up and saw the lady who smiled in kindness and admiration – the sort of moment that needs no words. Then she patted Chelsea lovingly on her neck before laying the same hand on Eric's shoulder.

"Well done to the two of you. I'm seeing something special here. Treasure this moment, boy. You've achieved something that's not possible for just anybody – a true bond of trust with a horse is a precious thing. It's a powerful thing. But it's the power of gentleness. Thank you for showing me." She handed Eric the winner's rosette. "That horse will win more, lots more, but none will be as meaningful or as memorable as this one. Treasure it."

On the short trip home, Eric reflected on this comment. Chelsea had behaved magnificently. Why? He replayed the events of the day in his mind, thinking of love and trust, of quietness and confidence, and of calming words and caresses.

"She's right, you know," he spoke to himself now, thinking of the judge's own words, the ones that had struck a chord deep within him. "She's right – it all boils down to the power of gentleness. I'll learn from that, even when dealing with humans. Surely, gentleness is the greatest strength."

Chapter 2

"Will you be my Friend?"

James was alone, crouching on the cool concrete floor of the veranda. He picked up 'Baldy' and cradled the bear in his arms, soothing the ragged bundle as torrents of rain thrashed upon the corrugated iron roof. Outside, sheets of water occasionally gusted against the fine mesh of the mosquito gauze, breaking into tiny pearls before gently spraying his solitary figure. As droplets of water spattered the five-year-old boy and his toy companion, he whispered, "I didn't mean to leave you behind, Baldy. It's all right now, only rain. I'll look after you." The simpering quaver in his voice betrayed the fact that the words were a hollow attempt to build up his own morale.

Another searing tongue of lightning tore from the glowering black envelope that shrouded the hilltop settlement of Kololo. Instantly, a responding clack of thunder hurled its venom at the land below and, with a scream, James ran into the adjoining room and crawled behind a sofa, between the angle of the backrest and the cold whitewashed wall. There he cowered and waited for the storm to pass, comforting Baldy and thus himself.

James was born in Uganda. His parents were expatriates: his father a civil engineer, often based on construction sites away from their home in Kampala; his mother a lost soul whose early fear of living in a strange land, away from the familiar comforts of England and family, had eventually hardened into a dull acceptance of her burden which was eased only by regular forays to the drinks tray and a small, tight circle of friends whose main interests were bridge and gossip.

For this reason, James was a child who had not yet experienced the full love and companionship of attentive parents or chattering, playful friends. He was a solitary child, alone through circumstance. His gentle nature and kindly dark brown eyes would easily have attracted playmates were it not for the fact that a permanent hideous scar ravaged his face, from one ear across his cheek to the upper lip, ending just beneath a twisted, deformed nose. Only one attempt at surgery had been made to rectify this cruel travesty of the human feature. It was too soon to know whether further attempts would be considered – certainly not until his return to a country whose medical facilities could provide some small hope.

At first, the children of his parent's friends were told to include James, to act normally and, sadly, to ignore the child's appearance. Yet not one ever looked directly at James' face without betraying dismay and disgust. Not one ever mentioned his misfortune, fearful of his reaction. And so, eventually, the impossible facade had given way to a gradual exclusion of James from the group. It was easier to do. James accepted that he was different, but wondered why everybody tried to ignore the fact. However, his loving disposition could not be suppressed and he adopted, not surprisingly, a second hand bear whose dishevelled appearance and loose button eye had instantly attracted his gentle caring nature.

Now, he cowered behind the sofa and lavished Baldy with affection and concern. He looked at the large bald patch on its chest, remembering how the bear had first arrived with a failing growl. "You press here," his mother had said, pointing to the chest. "See, hear him growl." A tinny wail was the only response.

"That's not a growl, that's a squeak," James had noted, trying again without luck to see if he could find a better spot to press.

Eventually, Baldy's growl failed completely and James resorted to major surgery, gently anaesthetising the bear with a handkerchief dipped in gin before clipping the offending area with his mother's sewing scissors. Then, using the sharpest kitchen knife possible, he had cut a small incision in the bear's chest, enough to find and repair the growl. The operation was unsuccessful, leaving a permanently mute bear and a bald patch that never seemed to grow back. Baldy's knowing smile always reminded James that the attempt was nonetheless appreciated and the bond between the two was ever more firmly established.

As soon as the afternoon storm passed, James' mother took them shopping. She needed to buy another dress for herself and Nesta, the maid, was not available to look after James, who happily accompanied his mother, excitedly pointing out his favourite sites as they drove the short distance to the centre of Kampala. The warm smell of hot pavements after rainfall hung in the air and once again crickets started their incessant chirruping. They passed the golf course where a huge anthill was surrounded by cheerfully flaying Africans, swatting and collecting the myriad of flying ants that had been enticed out by the rain. These were edible, providing a rich source of protein and a remarkably palatable taste.

The shopping centre of Kampala comprised one main street, with cracked pavements and rutted tarmac roads. The air of dilapidation was accentuated by water filled potholes. Tendrils of steam started to hover lazily over the main road as the late afternoon sun broke through overcast skies and immediately began to bake the hard messy surfaces. James' mother parked the car and hurried to the main store, calling James, who had fallen behind, his constantly alert eyes having spotted a movement behind one of the flaked concrete pillars that supported the protective awnings to the pavements. His mother ignored his distraction and strode hurriedly into the shop, anxious to make her purchase as quickly as possible and return to the comfort of home and refreshment.

James glanced up at his mother's disappearing figure and checked himself. He eyed the pillar again seeing tiny, stick-like arms playing with an elastic band. He rounded the column and saw, sitting at the pavement edge, a small black boy no older than himself. The child was dressed only in a single, foul, cotton T-shirt, filthy with stains and dust. His distended stomach bulged from below the shirt. Nothing else covered the waif's body and James clearly saw the stump of one leg carelessly protruding over the edge of the pavement. The other leg was complete but, like the arms, it was thin and fragile, dusted in grime. It seemed hardly significant that the boy's body was unclothed beneath the waist. Such lack of privacy seemed insignificant compared with the scab-ridden stump of leg. James was horrified. He understood with an instinctive concern that the child was terribly handicapped and undernourished. Worst of all, he understood that the child was homeless, probably abandoned on the street to induce sympathy and maybe to glean a few coins from passers-by. Nobody stopped. Africa can be frightening in its seemingly callous disregard for hardship and suffering. Africans walked by, glancing with more interest at the unusual sight of a disfigured white child than at the simpering, incomplete figure of the undernourished black boy.

"Jambo." James used the accepted word of greeting quietly, stretching out a tentative hand to touch the boy's arm. The boy looked up, his black eyes wide and tear-stained, mucus crusted beneath his nose. More tears welled in the eyes and the frail arms rose slightly, before falling back in alarm and fear.

"Don't be scared; Baldy will look after you." James knew his words would not be understood, so he stretched out his hand, offering the bear in greeting. Baldy's mischievous grin caught the boy's attention. Without smiling, he raised his hand again and touched the bear's head.

"Baldy likes children like us," James continued before very slowly sitting down beside the boy. They said nothing for some minutes; it didn't matter – the silence was friendly and the two of them held the bear. Then James put an arm around the frail black shoulders and hugged the tiny frame.

"Will you be my friend?"

For the first time the boy looked long and intently at James' ravaged features. Then, his own face cracked open in a genuine smile of warmth, without a vestige of repulsion. His arm came up and fell lightly on James' shoulder.

Thus they sat, observed by a single African waiting in a car nearby. He shook his head in wonder and glanced down at his lap where a handgun lay. Across the street stood another man leaning casually against the shop front, waiting for the white woman to emerge. He too held a gun, hidden in a pocket, ready to use if she attempted any form of resistance. He glanced back at his accomplice, checking to see if the car's driver was ready to make good their eventual escape. Surprised, he saw the man leave the vehicle and walk thoughtfully across towards him. Strangely, his compatriot walked with an air of unhurried ease, without tension. His hands were empty, unprepared for the robbery.

The two men met just as Helen Anderson appeared in the doorway, anxiously looking for her son. The man with the gun signalled with angry eyes to his friend, who raised his hand and quickened forward.

"Hapana," he said urgently. "No!"

The white woman walked unwittingly past the two Africans, spotted James and ran to grasp his arm, a look of disdain crossing her face as she saw, and smelled, the black boy.

"Come on James, it's time to go."

"Coming, Mummy," her son replied, "but Baldy wants to stay with my new friend."

Later that year, James started school. He nervously clung to his mother's hand as they walked from the car on the first day. His thin brown legs were partly covered by oversized khaki shorts into which was tucked a crisp new white shirt. The green and white striped school tie, the first tie he had ever worn, hung chaotically from his neck. It drooped below the waistline of his shorts, too long for such a small frame. This item of clothing was not mandatory, but his mother had insisted, at least for the first day. "Just to make sure you look right, like the other children."

Beneath the wide brimmed hat, ideal for protection against the sun, his disfigured face was hidden in shadow. James was nervous, but not because he dreaded school. He only worried about the other children's reaction to his face. Even so, his natural exuberance and friendliness could not be suppressed that easily. He saw a tearful blonde girl leave a car and walk into the main hall where she was welcomed by a teacher and placed in the appropriate group.

"Why is she crying, Mummy?" he said. "Is she sad? I hope she's OK."

"Don't worry, James, she's probably a little nervous. But she'll settle in. Look, there's Mrs. Reid, let's say 'Hello'."

They approached James' teacher, who stood below a large sign saying 'Class 1B'. As the two ladies chatted, James saw the blonde girl again, sitting on the floor under a sign 'Class 1A'. She looked lost as she waited for the round up of all newly arriving classmates to be completed. Their eyes met and James smiled. He edged across the yard or two gap that separated them.

"Hello, are you scared?"

"No! Well akshly, yes." Mary's voice betrayed a feeling of dread. Her first day at school.

"I'm not," said James. "Mummy says we'll have fun and play for the first week. And that's forever. Why are you sitting there?"

"Cos I'm in this class." Mary pointed to 'Class 1A'. Neither of them understood the characters. "What happened to your face?" No disgust, just a natural interest and relief at not being alone.

"Mummy says I was born this way but the doctors will mend it when we go back to England. I like you."

Mrs. Reid swept James up lovingly and he said his goodbyes to his mother. There then followed a strange process called 'Assembly' where a huge man in a black gown said things that James did not understand, then prayed to God before telling them all to work hard in the new term. All the older children left for their classes. Classes 1A and 1B remained behind and the huge man said, "Hello" and some other stuff that made no sense again.

"Follow me Class 1B." Mrs. Reid led her troop down a long corridor. James looked at Mary and wished that he was Class 1A.

As Mary sat on the bench in front of a small table at the back of her classroom, she looked around in awe at blackboards and notice boards and the large teacher's desk at the front of the room. Suddenly she felt a small push in her side and turned to see James climb over the bench from behind her. He squeezed onto the bench, pushing another girl along a few inches. Half an hour later a fraught Mrs. Reid put her head round the door and saw the missing boy. During that time James and Mary had said nothing to each other. But they felt comfortable.

Mary spoke just once, putting up her hand and squeaking, "Here, Mrs. Lacey," as instructed, in response to the register call. James did not have to say anything – his name was not called.

"But I like Mary. Why can't I be in Class 1A?"

Mrs. Reid could not be angry at such honest exuberance.

"You don't always get what you want, James. Sometimes, especially at school, YOU DO WHAT YOU'RE TOLD." He had learned his first lesson.

"Can I play with Mary outside of school?"

"Yes, James, and you can play with her during break times. I'll see Mrs. Lacey and make sure she tells Mary." Mrs. Reid smiled lovingly and regretted that she would not have the confidence to speak to the headmaster in order to have James reassigned. For Betty Reid had been brought up with a respect for, yes, even a fear of, authority. And, after all, that was the way things had always been.

That first week had been great fun. The plasticene and paint, paper and glue, and games and 'PE' thrilled James. At times his enthusiasm burst like a joyous bubble as one idea after another flooded out. To start with a general melee filled the classroom as all the children gained confidence and expressed themselves in an incoherent babble of noise. But, after Mrs. Reid had clapped her hands sternly, to regain their attention, they began to realise that "one at a time" meant just that and up went hands to attract her attention. Very often, James never even knew the answer but still his hand would shoot into the air and he would burble cheerful responses to the questions. All this was tolerated for a while but, as the weeks passed, James experienced hurt. On one occasion, Mrs. Reid, unwittingly, stifled a particular flow of chatter.

"Don't be silly, James." They had been talking about animals, in something called alphabetical order, and Mrs. Reid wanted to know if anyone had seen a 'B for bear'. James started to say that he once lived with one, called 'Baldy', but it had now gone to stay with his black friend, the one with only one leg.

Later James asked, "Why are we all white in this school?"

"This is the Nakasero Primary School for Europeans, James. The black children are too poor to come here and the Asian children have their own ways of being taught. But you will be allowed to play football against the Asian boys. Our schools always have football competitions."

"But why can't we be with them all the time?" He wasn't thinking of the Asian boys. His mind went back to his friend with one leg, the only other child ever to have hugged him.

"That's enough, James. Now, children, who has got a C for cat in their home?"

As the months went by, James learned to restrain his questions, to speak only when asked, and to stop thinking that the answer to questions lay in his imagination. Instead, "Listen to me children" … "Don't interrupt" … "Now, all together, A, B, C …" and "No, you can't" began to replace lively chatter, the world of imagination where anything was possible and, worst of all, the complete lack of fear in coming forward with ideas and opinions.

Inevitably, also, a small group of his classmates started to pick on his features. Playground taunts drove him from joining in the group games.

"There goes 'Juggly', run for it." The chant "James is ugly, James is ugly" had been condensed to "Juggly."

Mary, now his best friend, clucked crossly at the taunts and they would share the same swing, taking turns to push each other. He was still a cheerful child, but he would often watch the games of 'It', envy the rough and tumble of the other boys' antics and hear their shrieks of excitement with a growing feeling of exclusion. Mary was nice, but she was 'just a girl'. And so, for the first time, James joined the world of perceptions and judgments, attitudes and stereotyping. Within that first year at school, he developed layers of complexity, becoming a 'normal' human being.

Chapter 3

Hunting and Jumping

Chelsea seemed to prefer human company to that of other horses. In the field, she enjoyed the company of the other fillies, nuzzling her greetings, grazing close to the herd, squealing in play and mock reprimand, and joining in the drama of group canters. But back in the yard, especially in her box, she would either ignore other horses with a kind equine aloofness or, at feeding time, she would kick crossly at the partition, defending her feed and hay from imagined challenges from Suds and Ollie, geldings in the adjacent boxes.

So, each morning, she accepted with interest, if not always enthusiasm, the new and strange practices that humans seemed intent on imposing. Lunging sessions passed without incident. She accepted the bridle and the lunge line without demur, although boredom very quickly replaced acquiescence when it came to the regime of walks, trots and canters in seemingly endless circles around the schooling arena. Eric wondered if her future owner would want her to do dressage. He made a mental note to speak to Mrs. O'Driscoll who had already agreed to purchase the filly. He would ask her what she intended to use Chelsea for. If necessary, he would tell her that dressage was too constraining for such a free spirit. Immediately, he checked the thought process, realising that he could not interfere even though something, deep within him, wanted to find a reason for the sale to fall through.

Two days ago, Mr. O'Sullivan had asked Eric to bring Chelsea in from the field.

"Take her to the outside school, Eric; I've a lady who's interested."

Eric had guessed who it might be. He remembered, the day before, seeing a lady watching the fillies in the field with interest. She'd not spoken to anybody, just parked her car in the long track that ran beside the field and watched the horses …

Majella was on her way home from work. Still dressed in office clothes, she appeared out of place. The chill of a late autumn breeze made her shiver and regret the impulse to drop by the yard. Then she caught sight of Chelsea. Even at a distance the filly's character stood out. As she raised her head, ears upright, assessing the presence of the newcomer, her crescent flashed brightly in the late afternoon sun and she snorted. At that moment two stable boys emerged with lead ropes, ready to bring the horses in for the night. Immediately, Chelsea trotted away and the lads ignored her, knowing by now that she would only catch once she realised that she was alone in the field.

Eric was occupied with other duties so one of the lads, Sean, eventually returned to collect Chelsea. By now she was alone, standing at the gate anxiously looking towards the yard, aware that the evening feed awaited. Even so, she eyed Sean's approach and turned her back on him at the last moment. Had it been Eric, she would have stood quietly while he clipped the lead rope onto the head collar. Sean was used to this though. He walked to her side and caught her eye, dropping his head so she would understand that there was no challenge. She repeated the process, turning her back on him again. This time, still with his head lowered, Sean slowly took hold of the head collar. Feeling the slight pull of restraint, Chelsea allowed herself to be caught.

Majella liked character in her horses. That simple scene told her enough about Chelsea and she decided to phone Mr. O'Sullivan that night. And so, the next day Eric walked Chelsea around the school whilst the prospective owner discussed terms with Mr. O'Sullivan. Autumn was not the usual time to be making a sale, but Majella O'Driscoll knew that, if she came before the spring, she would get the pick of the horses. Her main interest was hunting although she also put her hand to show-jumping, in local Riding Club competitions. After the coming winter her own horse would be too old to cope with another year of hunting, and she was thinking ahead.

Eric stood to one side, holding Chelsea, ready to walk or trot her as required. He therefore missed the conversation between the two others. Only at the end, when asked to give his opinion about the horse, had he replied simply "She's the best, Ma'am, the best…"

Now, as he recalled the events of the visit, he once again experienced an ache of despair. He'd hoped to have Chelsea's company through her third winter at the stud. His wish was granted. Later that day Mr. O'Sullivan called Eric into his office and explained that Mrs. O' Driscoll wanted to buy Chelsea but that she had agreed that the filly should stay at the stud until she was backed and had started some school work. From now on, though, Chelsea had a new owner who was paying for livery and who should therefore be allowed access to the filly. This arrangement was too good to be true and a rush of relief washed through Eric, purging the emptiness that he had felt for two days.

It was with the same feeling of relief that he took Chelsea into the school and began the process of backing her, something he'd been looking forward to. In the first session he simply spent time running his hands over her back, gradually increasing the pressure. Then Sean held her head whilst Eric slowly leaned over the back, like a sack, flopping his weight slowly across her. She fidgeted and crabbed against Sean, but otherwise regarded the entire process as another strange human experience. By the end of the session, Eric had lifted his feet completely off the ground, his chest and stomach lying fully on the filly's back. Chelsea became accustomed to the weight and accepted the burden with stolid bemusement. However, the carrot and apple were very much more welcomed. Thanking her in the usual way, Eric allowed her to pick the treats from his hand. Then he held her head and kissed the velvet nose. That night he continued to stroke her back and, for the first time, he put a light stable rug over her. He wanted to be sure that she was comfortable so, for an hour, he observed to make sure that she had become accustomed to the experience, watching her munch hay into which he'd hidden a few extra carrots as a distraction. Canny as ever, she'd spotted the trick and enjoyed the game of hide and seek, nosing her way through the hay until she found each carrot. The stable rug was soon forgotten.

Later that night, Eric peered in the box to check again and was delighted to find Chelsea asleep on her side. She raised her head when he quietly replenished the hay. As he slipped out, Eric chuckled, enjoying a wonderful sight. 'Scabby', the yard cat, sidled across the partition, arched her back as she rubbed against his outstretched hand with the side of her head, and then settled comfortably into the manger, after first making two precise circles within it. Later, back in his bedroom, Eric turned out the light and lay back, smiling at the image of Scabby, curled up on top of the hay, eyes peering over the side of the manger at Chelsea who, with a final long sigh, lay her head back onto the straw bedding. The late night news that day had led with another bombing outrage from north of the border, such a complete contrast to the picture of two animals, different in so many ways, accepting each other's presence without condition. Eric spent many hours that winter schooling Chelsea and other horses. Yet he had much to learn from his animal charges.

Within a week, Chelsea had accepted the saddle and Eric was riding her. The hours of lunging had given her an understanding of the various voice commands and she was slowly able to relate these to the subtle pressures that Eric applied with hands and legs. Schooling had been progressing well for several weeks; although the dank coldness of winter rain had forced them to do much of the work in the indoor arena. The progress was marked but it was taking time, not because Chelsea was a slow learner, but because her patience with the entire process was often close to snapping. Each session generally followed the same cycle. The friendly morning greeting was followed by a growing grumpiness as numnah and saddle were produced, her ears flat back as these irritations were placed upon her. Often, a tetchy start to the lesson would then be followed by a short spell of attentive learning and application. Finally, always, there was a period of impetuous rebellion almost as if she was trying to say, "OK, point made, now let's do something exciting."

Eric did not mind at all. He loved feeling the power in her body, even when it was misdirected. Her haunches had begun to muscle up as she started to work properly, learning to power herself from behind for a few strides at a time. The kick of acceleration became stronger as the days passed and it was clear that the one activity Chelsea loved was jumping. Her impatience at the drudgery of the basics would fall away as soon as she saw the jumping poles being assembled. Then her body language would instantly change to "Ah, time for some fun at last."

One day, Mrs. O'Driscoll asked if Chelsea's morning schooling session could be postponed until the afternoon so that she could watch. She had chosen a beautiful clear day, the sort that was perfect for hunting. The damp soil in the outdoor school had turned crisp in the still, freezing air, but it yielded sufficiently to make an ideal riding surface. So, Eric decided to run the lesson outside, very much to Chelsea's liking – she had a clear conviction that hidden monsters lurked within the darker corners of the indoor arena! That afternoon, her mood was vastly improved as she sensed something new, possibly more interesting, was about to happen. Not only had she avoided the drudgery of a morning session, but also now she was outdoors, away from the sinister atmosphere of the poorly lit indoor school, and her spirit was free to soar in the clear open air.

Thus it was that Majella O'Driscoll saw, with joyful appreciation, how well Chelsea had developed. First, Eric walked the filly around the arena stretching her legs in the warmth of the sun. Her head did not toss in boredom and irritation; instead she seemed to concentrate, eyes downward, on each of Eric's commands. He barely spoke, other than to give the occasional click of encouragement and murmur of praise, nor did he use the reins other than to maintain a light contact on the bit whilst his legs nudged and pressed clear signals.

When she trotted, her developing muscles flowed with the sway of her stride and her quarters gleamed and then dulled as she moved in and out of the sunlight, the chestnut colouring seeming to flicker like flames as she passed through the shadows cast by silver birches lining one side of the school. Finally, Majella saw an explosive kick as Chelsea burst into canter and she shouted with pleasure as she witnessed the power, controlled by gentle touches from Eric.

"Well done Chelsea," she called. "And well done Eric, you've brought her along a treat."

That day Chelsea did not get bored. Eric laughed aloud, jubilation almost taking over before he checked himself and concentrated on the lesson. He was experiencing the thrill of a breakthrough, that moment when effort is finally rewarded, when suddenly things come together and become effortless. After weeks of imperceptible progress he was experiencing a surge of achievement as everything fell into place. Chelsea recognised the air of elation, knowing that she had achieved something special. She loved the congratulatory pats and cheerful words of praise from both Majella and Eric, responding to it all with delight and showing no signs of boredom.

Eric dismounted, flushed with exertion and elation. "Shall we jump her, Mrs. O'Driscoll?"

"Give it a go, Eric." Her heart pounded with excitement as she realised that she had, through foresight and determination, purchased something special. Later she would wonder if she could handle Chelsea, but right now the thought was put firmly to one side as she was swept up in the pleasure of the moment. She held Chelsea while Eric assembled the jump. He built a single, small fence but used spare poles and uprights to create a narrow lane leading up to it. So far Chelsea had not been ridden to jump – she had been free to tackle them on her own, to get the feel of the approach with her own instincts.

"Maybe today, I'll ride her." Eric held the thought, hoping that Mrs. O'Driscoll would give him the nod.

Chelsea's ears followed Eric. She was still alive with her own achievements and was now thrilled at the prospect of jumping, the reward she always enjoyed at the end of her sessions. "OK, girl, let's go." Eric removed the saddle and replaced the reins with a head collar. Chelsea was familiar with the routine and trotted beside Eric who held the collar lightly and ran towards the avenue of poles, releasing her at the last moment and urging her forward. She responded with enthusiasm, surging at the fence and soaring over it, clearing the obstacle by a full eighteen inches. They did this several times, Majella and Eric both calling out encouragement and then praising Chelsea as they caught her at the end of each run.

Eventually, Majella made the suggestion that Eric had been hoping for.

"Would you like to ride her over a small jump, Eric?"

The smile never left his face as he set up Chelsea's first 'proper' jump. He quickly tacked her up again, mounted and trotted her around allowing her to adjust once again to being ridden. Then he approached the obstacle and, with a final nudge of encouragement, let her take over. He felt the adjustment of the stride, then a quick surge and the familiar swoop of exhilaration as they soared clear. He steadied her on landing and brought her around for a second attempt. Again, she responded but clipped the cross pole as she rose. It rolled to the ground before they had landed.

"Never mind, I'll put it up, you keep going," Majella called out, and the session continued for a few more minutes, during which time Chelsea and Eric began to form a greater understanding of each other. Sensing her tiredness, Eric called it a day and, together, he and Majella walked Chelsea around the arena, winding her down from the exertions and chattering to each other with enthusiasm. Chelsea was included in the conversation. Her ears flicked one way and another as she picked up the words of praise and joy.

Majella O'Driscoll always kept a journal. Later that evening, she wrote about the day, trying to capture the feelings she felt, the sense of excitement that overcame her and also the joy that she had experienced, and her admiration for the perfect creature.

"This entry will make good reading in the years ahead," she concluded. "Not all days are as intense and moving as today …" Then the pen paused before she let her thoughts flow honestly onto the paper "… But do I DESERVE Chelsea? Will I make full use of her potential and, most important of all, can I cope with her?" Her prescience, the full significance of those words, would soon become apparent.

At the moment that she laid her pen to one side, Eric switched off his TV and lay back in bed looking up at the ceiling. Since he had started caring for Chelsea he had enjoyed his nightly 'think', mulling over the day's experiences. Without realising it, by replaying the day's events in his mind, he was actually teaching himself lessons in horsemanship. Clearly something special had happened today, some sort of breakthrough had occurred. Why? Why, had everything suddenly come together? He remembered how Chelsea had, until today, given limited attention to her schooling, learning, yes, but losing interest too quickly and then becoming tetchy and impatient. "Have I been doing anything wrong before? Was Mrs. O'Driscoll something to do with it? Was it coincidence that all of a sudden things worked so well?"

He couldn't work it out. His love for the young mare and the fairness with which he'd treated her hadn't changed. Her love of him had not been any more intense today. She had simply relaxed and enjoyed the experience, like a sudden release from constraint. And then he realised.

"Yes! Of course! For the first time this winter, she's been schooled outside, free in the open air." And then a series of thoughts came to Eric, all making perfect sense – that creepy dark indoor school, not enough light, echoes when he called out, strange corners where hidden demons could hide. "You're just like a human being, Chels. You need an inspiring environment, to feel free. I'm glad I've got the job I've got. Not like all those poor office workers, just like poor Dad, stuck in their unexciting rabbit hutches."

He remembered visiting his father's office, how the open plan area had been divided into compartments with head-high partitions, how his father had always complained of the environment, the lack of windows and plants.

"Sometimes I can't even think," his dad had said. "All I see are grey partitions and all I hear is chatter and telephones. Yet here, at home, as I look out over those meadows, I get my best ideas and I'm filled with a type of inner peace. It's funny, they ought to let me work from home."

Majella collected Chelsea one mild grey March morning. Her trailer was old but safe. For years she had used it to transport Colleen, her old hunter now due for retirement. But she had never travelled far, limiting herself over the past five years to the local hunt. Colleen, a black Irish Draught Thoroughbred cross, was seventeen years old and, although now retired, she would be retained as Chelsea's companion, and also to compete in a few Riding Club shows. Majella and her husband were both professionals working in Killarney but living in a renovated farmhouse sitting within five acres of land that also held an old dairy. It was ideal for two or three horses, with more grazing than was actually needed, and accommodation for horses during the cold winter nights.

Naturally, Eric was there to help load Chelsea and to bid his farewells. He knew that Mrs. O'Driscoll lived locally and, although he sensed that an era was ending, he could not bring himself to believe that he would never see his beloved mare again. The past four years had passed quickly and had left him with wonderful memories of Chelsea, her courage, her determination to respond to his affection and, most of all, her free spirit, the essence of her character and something he hoped would never be crushed. He walked her into the trailer and tied her beside the hay net. Then he looked straight into her eyes and ran his hands down both sides of her neck whilst kissing her, as usual, on the velvet muzzle.

"Take care, my beauty. Enjoy life and stay lucky with your new owner. I'll see you again. I know I will."

The comment was made with a mixture of hope and certainty. Eric could not bring himself to feel too sad – he knew Chelsea had a good and caring owner and the O'Driscoll's had already assured him that he could visit them 'any time at all'.

"We mean it." What more could he ask for, short of buying Chelsea himself? And that would have been impossible for too many reasons. So the current solution was as good as he could have hoped for. With a final mussing of her ears, he slipped quickly out of the trailer and closed the door.

Majella hugged him briefly and slipped an envelope into his hand. "I got a bargain, Eric, because of your efforts. Let me share a bit of my luck with you. Use this to complete your studies." With that, she climbed into a dilapidated Vauxhall and started the engine.

As usual, Chelsea sweated up during the short journey. This time anxiety made it worse, for her deep intelligence and bond with Eric told her that this was a farewell. So she fidgeted agitatedly in the trailer, breathing heavily and showing no interest in the hay. She was relieved to offload an hour later and, striding down the ramp, looked at her new home with interest. Two hundred yards away, she heard Colleen's whinny of welcome to Majella and froze, peering intently into the distance.

The aging black mare met the shining chestnut. Also in the field was Fergus, a squat and even more ancient Shetland. Chelsea kept a wary distance from Fergus but was soon grazing companionably close to the other mare. Missing Eric, Chelsea now seemed grateful to have company and Colleen's gentle disposition immediately allowed Chelsea to settle. As the weather was mild, both mares were left out that night, clad in warm New Zealand rugs. Fergus needed no such protection!

In no time, Chelsea felt comfortable with her new world and never grumbled on the days when Majella called across to her, lead rope in hand. She always made a point of refusing to be caught, at least for a few minutes, making Majella persevere until, chuckling with amusement, her new owner could at last slip the head collar gently round her neck. But then she'd walk in happily and accept the tack with good nature.

Majella began with a few hacks, putting Chelsea through a series of exercises whilst she assessed the mare's potential. Eric had schooled her well, doing far more than simply backing the horse, so Majella's job was easy and she quickly became comfortable with her new ride. Soon, Chelsea was jumping small obstacles with customary abandon. But what impressed Majella most of all was her power. The transition from walk or trot to canter would always come with an explosive surge. Back in the fields, Majella also experienced Chelsea's early tendency to buck when the boredom of walking and trotting in circles became too much.

"Not a problem," she thought. "Any horse that bucks will be a good jumper. And after all, that's why we got you, Chelsea."

Very soon, Majella tested Chelsea's and her own ability to cope with hunting. They galloped through a nearby wood and across the fields in a mock chase. Chelsea responded with enthusiasm and surged effortlessly over the small obstacles that had been prepared carefully in advance. There were also a few moments of pure exhilaration when Majella realised that she was barely able to control the power beneath her body. She would have preferred an easier ride, especially when she knew what lay ahead, intending to drop back to a gentle canter. But Chelsea maintained her gallop throughout, flying over the obstacles with naive ease and enthusiasm, whilst Majella experienced that delicious mixture of fear and exhilaration. She was not confident enough to fully trust Chelsea's instincts for coping with rough terrain and was relieved when the gallop ended. She remained seated on Chelsea as the horse stood, blowing lightly with her exertions. It was amazing how quickly she recovered, though, and it was Majella who took time, slumped forward in the saddle gasping for breath and waiting for the ache of tired muscles to ease.

"Phew! I'd better keep my fitness levels up through the summer to keep up with you lass," she murmured into the mare's ear. Still leaning forward and wheezing with exertion and emotion, she patted Chelsea's neck.

And so, through that summer, Majella hacked out with Chelsea on a regular basis. She also entered a ten-mile pleasure ride, with limited success because Chelsea simply ignored the word 'pleasure' and set about competing – her typical nature – and a desire to canter and gallop whenever possible meant that Majella had to work hard to hold the pace at an acceptable level. However, Chelsea's recovery time was incredible! The rate of her heartbeat returned to normal levels very quickly and she passed the vet's examination with flying colours. Each time the two went out, they became more familiar with each other's quirks and Chelsea took to the new life with characteristic enthusiasm, never failing to give her all. This worked against her at an early show-jumping competition where, in the Minimus class, whose small fences are designed to give a young horse confidence, Chelsea approached the tiny jumps with her usual full-blooded approach and actually came last, knocking over four poles, simply due to over confidence!

She seemed to dismiss them as ludicrously easy obstacles, beneath her contempt, and hitting them seemed only to give rise to an air of inconsequential disdain! She obviously preferred the greater challenge of the Novice class, which she won with ease on the same day.

Majella smiled with affection as she lined up to receive her rosette. Chelsea had developed another endearing trait, causing much merriment amongst the spectators whenever it was displayed – she had a horror at receiving rosettes! By now she had won several, but she never allowed anybody to pin one on her brow band. Instead, she turned her head away, keeping a wary eye on the potential intrusion. So, once again, Majella accepted a rosette on behalf of Chelsea!

For all her foibles, Majella was beginning to feel a true attachment to the animal, different to the love she felt for dear, faithful Colleen. Nonetheless it was an affection based on admiration and, dare she admit it, there was now a deep respect born out of a sort of fear – not the fear of being harmed, for Chelsea was never vindictive; rather, it was a constant nagging feeling of apprehension that something dramatic was about to happen every time she mounted the mare. Although Majella was never as overtly affectionate as Eric, Chelsea sensed that her new owner's intentions were noble and life with her was going to be fun! And whenever Chelsea realised that a human had her interests at heart, she seemed to respond. With her, it was all or nothing.

The summer passed quickly and, still with that nagging feeling of trepidation, Majella took Chelsea to her first hunt. There is an atmosphere about hunts that is palpable. It transmits itself to horses and hounds so that an air of festive tension pervades the gathering. Chelsea picked this up and skittered and pulled in eager anticipation of something new and excitingly different. Majella took care to hold her back, waiting for the chase to get well underway before joining the more sedate pace of the followers. She avoided the hedges and stone walls, using gates instead, and thus they fell well behind the master and the leading group. To Chelsea, the experience was nothing more than a communal noisy hack, with the sound of hounds and horn always somewhere well ahead in the far distance. So, for both of them, the occasion was a slight disappointment, although Majella had to admit to herself that she was relieved that it has passed without incident.

On the next hunt, Majella determined to push harder. She felt a personal challenge to prove that the feeling of awe she held for Chelsea was ill-founded. She also knew that Chelsea was born to greater things and a sedate hack away from the action would never fulfil her true potential. She shared her concerns with her husband: "After all, I've hunted for years and I did want a horse with character. It was my decision to buy her so now I should harness her potential."

And so there followed a period of months during which Majella became bolder as she and Chelsea took to hunting with shared pleasure. Yet all the time, Majella had to admit that she was never fully in control and it was Chelsea who was always eager to push forward with the leading horses.

Towards the end of the season, on a late winter morning, they assembled for another hunt. Once again Chelsea fidgeted with excitement and her impatience welled to the surface as they hung around waiting for the formalities to be completed. There is a rule of etiquette for hunting that requires all participants to stay behind the master at all times. But something happened that day. A general melee of enthusiasts had gathered around the long iron gate that led away from an access road into the field from which the hunt was to begin. Nobody was to blame. As Chelsea strode through the opening, two waiting horses spooked at each other in excited irritation. As one reared back, the other reacted by crabbing sideways and slammed against the gate pushing it into Chelsea's side. She wheeled in alarm and stumbled heavily against the post that supported the open end of the gate.

In years to come, Chelsea would always carry a patch of white hair where the bruising occurred, making it appear as if she had leant against a newly painted surface. She would always be wary of gates and narrow openings. Today, although not serious, the dull pain of the bruising stayed with her, agitating her heightened level of excitement. Already tense with anticipation, she was now a coiled spring about to be released. Without waiting for Majella's command, she surged forward just as the master's horse began to give chase. The barks and howls of the hounds added to the frenzy and the two horses galloped, side by side, the tension and competitiveness of each transmitting to the other.

Majella felt the thrust of power, realising this was something well beyond her control. As a competent rider she had galloped many times in the past, but never with such unremitting momentum. It was impossible to stop. There was no choice but to sit it out, to try to gain a degree of control, at least in direction, by attempting desperately to point Chelsea towards the easier places to jump, the lower points of hedgerows and the gaps in walls. However, even this failed, so Majella sat up and concentrated on survival! The master's horse was a mature, sturdy creature, built for comfort and endurance, not for speed. It fell behind as the master, realising what had happened, managed to restrain the gelding's charge in the hope that Chelsea would understand that the challenge was over and, herself, ease up. But Chelsea was a pure athlete, young and inexperienced. The running eased the pain in her quarters and she was now charged with adrenalin and acting on instinct, releasing her energy the only way she could.

They approached a three foot stone wall and Majella felt a swoop of terror before suddenly, fatalistically, feeling nothing but a detached interest in what would happen next. As horse and human soared over the obstacle, they saw the ground fall steeply away at the other side and, taken by surprise by the long drop, Chelsea's front legs hit the uneven surface later than she expected causing her to peck on landing, only just managing to stay on her feet. Majella was thrown forward over Chelsea's shoulder and rolled heavily for several yards before coming to a stop beside a small boulder, only inches from crushing her back.

"Two more rolls would have killed me." Majella was amazed at this first thought, coldly objective at the very moment her emotions were running riot.

Later that day, she eased her legs off the floor and lay back on the sofa. A sharp stab from the broken ribs momentarily replaced the dull aching of her body until, at last, her legs stretched comfortably out, their full weight supported by cushions.

"It's too soon to decide," she replied to her husband, Paul. "But I think I agree with you – she's too much to cope with."

Paul was adamant. "Just think about it. Chelsea was born to perform – it's just the way she is. Anyone can see that she's a Rolls Royce among Minis here. It's like asking a high flyer to accept the mundane limitations of a small company when their very being is calling for a challenge in a bigger world. It wouldn't be fair to hold that person back – they just wouldn't give of their best. Nor will Chelsea. She'll always feel constrained by our simple world. And face it, love, you're no professional equestrian! Nor do I want you to be. You'll always be responding to her, not the other way round, the way it should be – you guiding her, in full control."

Within a month, Majella accepted the inevitable. With the help of Henry O'Sullivan she found a buyer for the mare and was delighted with the sale price. Yet, as she handed Chelsea over to her new owner, she felt pangs of regret at her own inability to handle the free spirit that she could so easily have loved.

As the transporter drove away, she saw the name – Edgar Gibson – painted on the side of the vehicle and, remembering still her affection for the headstrong but willing mare, she sent out a brief good luck prayer to

Chelsea. Would a professional showjumper give her the challenge for which she was destined?

That night she phoned Henry O'Sullivan to thank him and let him know that Chelsea had been collected.

"Look out something suitable for me, Henry, this time with a little less of the C-Factor. Oh, and by the way, let Eric know that Chelsea's with Edgar Gibson now, up near Dublin. I know he'll want to keep up to date with her movements."

"Majella, Eric's at college in Dublin. He left us three months ago. But I'll tell his dad to pass the news on."

Majella smiled as she disconnected her mobile phone. She tapped the stubby aerial against her chin thoughtfully. "Well would you believe it! Whatever will be will be."

That night, Eric's father phoned his son with the news. Eric put the phone down and sat on the bed, turning to his girlfriend, Mary, with a huge smile. With one hand on each of her cheeks, he looked into her gorgeous green eyes and kissed her playfully on the nose.

"What's up?"

"Nope, nothing. Just happy!" And the kissing moved to other places.

Edgar Gibson was the yard manager of an equestrian centre five miles west of Dublin. He was a young man, still only in his mid-twenties, whose infatuation was show-jumping. His parents had introduced him to the event when he was a youngster. They were not wealthy but, when they saw the joy in his face as he sat astride that first tiny Shetland pony, they knew that the purchase had been worthwhile and, strengthened by their own love of horses, their main aim in life, since Edgar's sister had died fifteen years ago, was to support their only son in fulfilling his dream. With a simple, down-to-earth philosophy, Patrick Gibson believed deeply that nothing would be achieved unless there was a passion for what you were doing. The death of his daughter had changed him completely, giving him a realisation that what mattered in life was not its longevity but what was done with the time God gave you. With fulfilment would come the confidence and peace of mind to face anything else. Thus further education was not thrust upon Edgar when he announced his desire to become a top class show jumper.

Patrick Gibson believed with utter certainty that this would happen.

"Thoughts are things, son. If you already think yourself to be a champion then you are one." And between them they had plotted his path to success.

"You'll have to work your way into this one. Work with horses, start at the bottom and never lose sight of your dream. If you put the effort in; if you stay alert to life's signals, then it'll happen. Meanwhile, Mum and I will do what we can."

The Liffey Livery Yard was always happy to employ keen youngsters. Edgar started there when he was sixteen and now, ten years later, he managed all the equestrian aspects of the business. Most of the youngsters only stayed for a year or two, working for pocket money, or to fund their studies. Generally, they moved on as better opportunities presented themselves. But Edgar had remained, proving his worth and winning the trust of the Fitzgerald family, the yard's owners. Over the past ten years, Edgar had purchased two horses – a grey mare and a black gelding, both by a winning stallion whose jumping pedigree had been famous in the heady world of Irish and British show-jumping.

It had taken time, but now, at last, Edgar had acquired his third horse – Gentle Sea Breeze. He was delighted with the purchase. Gentle Sea Breeze was no such thing! Gentle she was not, breezy maybe – the chestnut oozed class and athleticism. She fidgeted cantankerously during the long journey north and emerged from the four-horse transporter sweating and breathing heavily.

Edgar had taken his transporter down to Killarney once he was certain that he would make the purchase. Henry O'Sullivan had contacted his parents about the opportunity to buy the horse. He and Edgar's parents were long time friends and Henry had immediately thought of Edgar when Majella had asked him if he knew of any interested buyers.

After viewing the horse and putting her through her paces, Edgar was convinced that she would perfectly meet his need for one more horse with which to compete. Now, as he unloaded the mare, he felt a sense of achievement. Thanks to his hard work and his parent's financial support he had purchased, over the past five years, a superb horse transporter and three top quality horses. Already, his name was becoming known in some of the second-ranked jumping venues. He needed a breakthrough of fortune, sponsorship on a grand scale, to progress up the ladder but he was certain it would happen soon. Every time he achieved a success, like winning a competition, then seeing his name in the papers or, like now, investing in a new horse, he felt a step closer to his dream. But the same driving ambition that caused him to work ceaselessly and single-mindedly towards that dream, had also hardened him. Unlike his father, for whom the intense tragedy of the bereavement had been a turning point, causing a search for deeper meaning in life, Edgar was simply driven by personal ambition. He loved his parents and fully appreciated the immensity of their efforts, but he had a core of stony resolve that did not allow failure to block his way.

A week later, Gentle Sea Breeze was standing in her box eating hay with her back to the door when she heard a familiar voice: "Hey, Chels. Hey, girl."

She whickered with delight and turned to see Eric and Mary, carrots in hand, leaning over the half door. Immediately, she nuzzled his hand, searching for another carrot but also enjoying the smell and familiar contact with her friend.

"Oh, Eric, she's gorgeous," Mary gushed, patting her forehead tentatively.

"I know, I know. Chels, you're a real beaut, my girl." He held her head once again, for the first time in nearly a year, and kissed the nose as if nothing had ever changed.

Edgar approached. He shook Eric's hand in cheerful greeting.

"Glad to meet you, Eric. I heard you were coming – my parents told me. What do you think of her?"

Edgar was proud of Gentle Sea Breeze and he was fishing for compliments. He knew that Eric had originally cared for her and that he was besotted with the mare. So he expected an endorsement of his decision to buy.

"Chels is the genuine article. She'll go to the ends of the earth for the right person, but only the right person."

That was not quite the answer Edgar expected but he continued smiling.

"You called her 'Chels' Why's that?"

"Oh, just an abbreviation of Chelsea. I hope you'll still be calling her that."

"I wasn't sure. It seems a bit, well English if you see what I mean. I was going to think of something with more of an Irish touch."

"Chelsea is the name of Bill Clinton's daughter. He's got Irish roots somewhere in the past."

Eric could not explain why, but it seemed important, for Chelsea's sake, to keep her link with him. The conversation moved on and they discussed her strengths and quirks. All the while, Chelsea's head stayed close to Eric's shoulder and he occasionally stroked her face, especially when making a particularly affectionate comment about her early years.

Edgar listened to Eric with interest. He was delighted to know that his own assessment of her athleticism and jumping potential was well founded. He could not bring himself to feel as emotionally attached to Chelsea as Eric was, but he admired the other, recognising an intensity of feeling that spoke volumes about the young man's authenticity. The two had instantly formed a rapport and Edgar ended the conversation with the hope that Eric would continue to keep in touch. As they parted, Edgar punched Eric's shoulder affectionately.

"I'm going to keep her stable name. If you like it, that's good enough for me. Hope to see you again."

Eric lingered for a moment or two longer, enjoying Chelsea's company. She stood quietly and when, at last, he slipped away, she waited until his departing figure moved out of sight before returning to her hay.

It was Mary who broke the silence. She'd observed the past fifteen minutes with interest and her antennae had picked up something wonderful.

"She's special to you, Eric, I can see that clearly." Her voice did not carry its usual tone of wry humour; instead it was husky with thoughtful admiration. "I've never seen an animal so drawn to a human, not even a dog. It's like you each have a chemistry, searching out each other's company."

"You know, Mary, you're spot on. I've never felt as attached to any living creature as I …". His voice faltered as he realised how the comment might be interpreted.

"That's OK, Eric, there time aplenty for us."

She eyed her ginger-haired companion with renewed respect and realised suddenly that she'd been privileged to catch a glimpse of another person's soul, seeing a grace and authenticity that could never have been assumed. It was there, simply and clearly, shining through the veneer of human niceties like a splinter of light through the leaves of a tree, pure, bright and intense – undeniable. Her heart seemed to be drawn from her chest towards her friend and she resolved, with a determination that only a woman has at these times, not to let Eric out of her life.

"Come on, Chelsea, COME ON!"

The volume of Edgar's urges rose as he pushed the mare through her paces. He thwacked her side sharply with the short whip, feeling her stiffen and then surge forward toward the four-foot fence. Her attention slipped, the surge had taken her too close, and as she attempted to rise she clattered the light poles bringing them down in an untidy mess. Immediately she ducked her head but recovered her balance, and Edgar pulled her sharply to a halt, gasping with impatience.

"For God's sake, Chelsea, concentrate. If I ask for an extra stride, give me one." He slid off the saddle, intending to rebuild the jump, but first went round to face the horse. "What's the matter? I can feel your strength and I know you're up to it. You've proved you can do it. So why all the drama?"

Chelsea eyed Edgar, turning her head slightly to one side, as if trying to pull away from him, and he saw a rim of white around her dark brown eyes. This gave her a maniacal look, panicky and confused. Immediately Edgar regretted the outburst and tried to stroke her face, but she continued to pull her head away so all he could manage was a brief pat on the neck. Then he remounted. Edgar was extremely fit so, throwing one leg over her back, he simply vaulted into the saddle. Once again they returned to the practice jumps, the fallen fence having been re-assembled by Edgar's father.

"Edgar, don't be too hard on her," he called across the school. "Maybe we should take a break before you carry on, let her calm down." For Chelsea was now bucking and snorting and there was no chance that anything would be gained from continuing the lesson. Realising this, Edgar urged her forward, driving her at the fence that she had clattered a few minutes before. She clipped it again, this time only lightly, and one pole rolled to the ground. But, at that, Edgar called it a day.

"Come and have supper with Mum and me tonight. It's time we planned for the future."

That evening, Maureen Gibson removed the lid from the huge bowl in front of her. Steam escaped and misted her spectacles forcing her to turn her head briefly and wait for sight to return before picking up the ladle and stirring it into the food. With the steam came a tantalising aroma and Edgar breathed in deeply and ostentatiously, and sighed with anticipation. He loved Irish stew – close to being his favourite meal, especially the way Mum made it.

Until that moment, the family had been chatting happily. Patrick said grace before turning the conversation to Edgar – asking how he had been doing at the livery yard and what new horses were in. But again there was a pause and they all watched in silent anticipation as Maureen ladled generous portions onto plates and handed one to each of the men. Then Edgar dropped his eyes to his plate and concentrated, mashing potatoes, carrots and turnips into a delicious messy mound. Finally he scooped gravy and pieces of mutton on top of it all before digging his fork into the food and taking a huge mouthful. He gasped at the heat, keeping his mouth partly open and drawing in sharp breaths of cooling air. Raising a hand in apology, it took a few moments for him to speak.

"Thanks, Mum, that's gorgeous, as usual. What'll we do about Chelsea, Dad?"

The ritual of serving the food had delayed them long enough for Edgar to forget his father's original questions. Also, he did only have one thing on his mind just now and he desperately wanted to talk, to tap into the well of knowledge and worldly wisdom that was his father.

"Right, son, let's sum up. Chelsea's been with you for over six months. She came with every recommendation, with spirit as well as ability. I've spoken to Majella O'Driscoll and you know Eric quite well. Both say she's star quality. OK so far? Right, so why has she started to lose concentration, because that's what you say has happened? Remind me again, what's been happening? How's she been doing in the summer competitions?"

"It started OK, Dad. Full of enthusiasm and she won all her Intermediate classes. That's way ahead of most horses her age. She sometimes forgets to concentrate on the small fences, but she really goes for the big ones and, against the clock, she's as strong as any horse I know. But then, in the big league, she seems to have lost interest. I've been pushing her harder at the school because there's a whole new level of difficulty now. I think she's not enjoying it. Loves the easy stuff when she can be queen of the castle, shows off like nothing on earth and goes like a train. I think she's like a genius, like someone who's never had to struggle. Everything comes too easy so there's no inner strength when a real challenge comes along – doesn't like being cajoled, just content to coast. I've tried so hard with the schooling, but ..."

"Can I stop you there, son. What I'm hearing is logical, but it's all one sided. She's taking the blame all the way. Now she's a prima donna, that's for sure, but she's not a quitter. Something is making her lose heart, because that's what it sounds to me. Let's think if it's something that we're doing."

So far, Patrick had had very little say in the way Chelsea had been schooled but his wise head knew that he should not accuse Edgar directly, and he used the 'we' knowingly.

"Well, I've been the same with her as with Ellie and Boots. They're older, I know, but that's no reason why Chelsea can't be pushed just as hard."

"What do mean, 'pushed just as hard'? Is it the amount of time spent schooling, or more what you do when you're working her?"

And so the discussion progressed. Succinct questions followed by answers that ranged from evasion to honest exasperation. It took time and

Maureen cleared the dishes and placed mugs of tea in front of her two men folk. She knew what was happening, having seen Patrick's gentle probing work to great effect in the past. He'd never give direct instructions to others about how they should run their lives, but he challenged and guided the thought process. "Can you explain that in more detail? ... In what way does that work? … How do you feel when she does that? … Is there any other way that you can think of? … How does that make her feel?" And so it went on. An hour later, Patrick summed up. At no time did he impose his own interpretation or ideas.

"Have I got this right, son? Chelsea loved jumping to start with. Perhaps she suffered from a wee bit of over exuberance and charged the fences but at least she gave her all. Then, as you say, when you moved on to the Open fences, you felt that she was too headstrong and needed to be restrained so you stopped giving her her head. Instead you began to dictate the pace, the strides between fences, just as you do with Boots and Ellie. You say it worked well with the older horses, even when they were youngsters but you also say that they've never been hunters. So, it seems to you that Chelsea is a different animal. You've already acknowledged her 'chestnut/redhead' nature and you know she's hunted and has been used to the relative freedom of that sport compared with show-jumping. Finally, you're beginning to wonder if she's finding the routine of work in the school boring and too restraining. She's always pulling too hard and bucking when you restrain her so, as a result, her concentration goes."

"Now, as for the way forward from here, you feel that the answer is to make work more fun. And that's where you're stuck because work is work and there is a limit to what can be done in the school, given your time constraints and the availability of the school."

"That's about it, Dad. It boils down to how we can make schooling more fun for Chelsea. You've been great about listening. I really appreciate it and I feel better just talking. Thanks for taking the time to listen and, especially, for making the effort to understand my feelings. But now I need some advice. What would YOU do?"

"That's a toughie, Edgar. I know horses pretty well and what makes them tick but I'm no great expert on show-jumping. But one thing has come to mind and it may be worth a go."

"What's that, Dad?" Edgar felt open to any suggestion. His single-mindedness had received a severe jolt over the past months and, with that experience, some of his arrogance had been chipped away, like small flakes from a sculptor's stone. Not enough to change his basic character – he needed that same arrogance, or self-confidence, to succeed. But the first rough edges had certainly been rounded and smoothed by his father's gentle coaching.

"Well, we've been talking all this while about 'schooling' and 'the school'. Could we not start talking about 'guiding' and 'the fun session'? Isn't it possible to do some fun work outside of the schooling arena? What about a hack or two with obstacles but lots of gallops in between?"

"That's not getting her tuned to the real thing when it comes along. She'll not be familiar with jumping in a confined area, responding to the commands for stride patterns and tight turns." But already Edgar knew the reply to his own argument. "OK, Dad, I get the point. We mix fun outdoors with sessions inside – get Chelsea's morale back on an even keel. And, I know I should be better about thanking and praising her. Less of the whip 'during' and more of the pat 'afterwards'."

The new approach worked well and, over the following months, Chelsea's usual ebullience returned. Now six years old Chelsea was ready to enter the Dublin International Horse Show and pit herself against the budding contenders for show-jumping's top flight. Edgar had prepared all his horses carefully, for this was the one occasion that mattered above all else. He wanted to be noticed and attract the ever-important sponsorship that would relieve his family of the financial burden of his life of commitment to equestrianism. Boots and Ellie were his solid backup, his 'honour' cards. They had helped to gain him his reputation as a young man with potential. Their steady nature and safe approach to jumping often took Edgar through to jump-offs, but neither had the pace or agility to win against the clock. This was the main reason why Chelsea had been such an attractive prospect – whilst Boots and Ellie were the solid suit, she was to be his trump card.

Edgar was perfectly aware of the risks but the potential gains were massive. If Chelsea kept her concentration, she could beat any other horse. Much depended on the start – her capacity to make silly mistakes always preyed on Edgar's mind but if he could just attune her to the task in hand and start well, he knew by now that she would dig deeply into herself. It wasn't just confidence, either too much or too little; rather it was as though her understanding grew with each fence successfully cleared and she would become increasingly determined to see it through. It was all a matter of avoiding the early mistakes.

The Grade 'C' events always took place over the first few days of the show. Edgar often thought ahead to the events that took place on the final day and visualised himself taking part. "It will happen."

This year, his plan was to transport his horses from the yard to the Show on each of the two days they were scheduled to compete. This meant that Boots would go on the Monday whilst Ellie and Chelsea had both been entered for the main event on the following day. For the first time, Irish Television, RTE, had decided to transmit a Grade 'C' event in recognition of the growing interest in the sport and to encourage young talent. Edgar planned to jump his two best horses in the televised event.

"Boots will be ideal on day one, to calm my nerves and get me used to things."

He liked the big black gelding, always so solid and dependable but never very bright. Nothing upset Boots. However insignificant or important the occasion, with large crowds or empty arenas, he simply did all that was asked of him with an air of bemused disinterest. If he ever won, his only reaction was that of semi-startled puzzlement!

Edgar's strategy worked. Boots DID win in front of a half full arena, quite the largest crowd that had ever watched them. Edgar felt a wash of elation as the final cheer accompanied his clear round, the only one in the competition. He patted Boots' neck vigorously as they cantered around the arena. Boots slowed to a halt as soon as they passed through the exit gate, and then he simply stood, stolidly, blinking with bemusement as Edgar leapt from the saddle and hugged him. It was as if Boots was unable to fully appreciate the full significance of their achievement. "My God, did I win? Oh well, where's the hay?"

"GIBSON CLEAR ON HIS LORDSHIP"

Beneath the headline, the article continued:

> *"He's been spoken about as a potential Irish great. Now Edgar Gibson proves the pundits are right. Knowing that a clear round would win him his first title, he achieved just that with Gracegarth Lord – a solid and fault free round. The young rising star has the world of jumping at his feet and a glittering career awaits."*

Edgar scanned the local evening paper; even with its clichés he read each word with excitement and felt a thrill of pride. The article concluded:

> *"He competes with two horses tomorrow. Can he do the double and become king of the 'C' Grade this year? Gibson has no doubts that he can carry the Irish flag to further glory. However, the latest addition to his team, Gentle Sea Breeze, is a young mare about which little is known and we must all wait and see. His confidence may be better placed in his grey, Lady Eleanor. One way or another, a second win is on the cards. Tomorrow may be another day for Irish eyes to smile."*

The article cheered him, building on a euphoria that had continued since the previous evening when he had returned triumphantly to the Liffey Yard. The staff had lined the driveway in playful but affectionate salute; there was genuineness about their pleasure. He was not short of volunteer helpers for his trip to Dublin the next day.

But what really excited Edgar was the knowledge that Volvo had been in touch – a message on his answering machine asking him to contact a Mr. Gustafson once the second day's competition was over. The faceless voice behind the machine ended by wishing him well in tomorrow's televised event. Edgar was now barely able to concentrate on his preparations – the singsong Swedish accent still running through his mind.

"Sponsorship! At last, sponsorship."

In the morning, Chelsea and Ellie were unloaded into a world that hummed with tension and excitement. Even the normally placid Ellie was alive with excitement. Chelsea more so; she fidgeted and panted, blowing noisily and pulling Michael, the lucky volunteer groom for the day, this way and that as he sought to calm her and walk her around the large practice area. Nothing would reduce Chelsea's tension as once again her antennae for the big occasion prompted her body to pump adrenalin. Fortunately, Edgar had timed their arrival knowing that this would happen, planning to harness the energy, as Chelsea was only the second horse to compete. Then, if she could have a clear round, he knew she would relax as they waited for the other eighteen horses to complete their rounds, giving Edgar plenty of time to keep her loose and alert for the inevitable jump off. He was certain that there would be six or more horses in the jump off. The cream of the British, Dutch and German young talent was there and, casting his eye over his rivals, he was aware that he was now amongst true class.

"A clear round for Caluso S and now, the next competitor, Edgar Gibson of Ireland riding Gentle Sea Breeze."

The loudspeaker announced their arrival into the ring. Wim Neuteboom and Caluso S barely had time to make their exit when Chelsea burst upon the scene kicking her hind legs backwards and bucking with pure and unbridled exuberance. The arena was almost full – some people laughed, instantly attracted by the display of openness and passion. Most of the crowd gasped with affinity for their Irish hope and a small burst of applause exploded from one corner. Almost as if in response, Chelsea ducked her head several times and Edgar pulled firmly back on the reins, desperately trying to bring her under control. Ideally, he would have cantered her once more around the ring but, as the bell rang, indicating that he could start jumping, he was already close to the first fence.

"Sod it," he thought, "let's just go for it."

The crowd gasped in amazement as, with a small adjustment of direction, he turned Chelsea towards the fence and urged her forward. She flew at the first obstacle, an upright standing almost four feet and bordered by flowers in large green pots, rattling the pole viciously with her front legs. It popped upwards and, miraculously, fell back into its cup. The crowd gasped again, then held their breath as Chelsea turned nimbly and, without slowing, drove towards the second, a double. She clipped the first pole with her front and the second pole with her rear hooves. Again both poles remained in the curved beds, but this time the crowd's sigh was a mixture of exhilaration and dismay. If she continued like this she would inevitably incur several faults.

As Chelsea approached the third, still eagerly thrusting forward, the television commentator murmured his disapproval: "…naïve and ridiculous, not a jump off ...".

Down, close to the ring in the first row of spectators, a single calm voice urged "Eaaasy, girl, eaaasy." It was spoken with a clear, hissing authority that carried clearly to Chelsea as she passed the stand. Instantly she recognised Eric, even in the buzz of excitement, and instinctively responded to the familiar tone and command, checking herself, adjusting her stride perfectly and clearing the straight planks with fluid ease. Edgar did not hear Eric's voice but, in harmony with Chelsea, he relaxed his contact and returned to his natural riding style, smooth and mechanically professional. In the same way that Chelsea had instinctively eased up to the loved and familiar voice, so the crowd now relaxed in response to Edgar's competence knowing that he was again in control. Six further fences were cleared effortlessly, including the final testing treble that had been set, intentionally, to test the competitors' concentration right up to the last moment. With one gasp, two gasps, and then a final resounding cheer, the crowd urged Chelsea over the treble and several of them, barely able to contain themselves, rose to their feet, clapping and waving in unrestrained joy. Chelsea's exuberance had won their hearts.

Whereas the television commentator described the scene in carefully modulated terms "... never seen such a response right at the start of an event ... normally the sort of reaction that greets the eventual winner ...", the event commentator's voice reflected the joy of the crowd and blared over the tannoy, "Another clear round, and in the most amazing manner, so now we have an Irishman in the jump off, joining Wim Neuteboom and, at this rate, goodness knows how many more. This could turn out to be one of the most memorable ..."

Edgar no longer listened. He was now outside the arena, in the collecting area. Kicking one leg backwards he slid smoothly off the blowing chestnut's back and hugged her neck. Michael slapped him on the shoulder and took the reins, allowing Edgar to continue with this uncommon display of affection and praise. Chelsea had won the hearts of everybody. She accepted the slaps and hugs with an air of contented indifference, but her ears flicked back and forth searching once again for the sound of Eric's gentle authoritative voice. She sensed his presence but, that day, other than hearing his comforting voice, the two would never come into direct contact. For fate had decreed a different outcome.

Michael fussed and calmed Chelsea, whilst Edgar rode again, this time with Ellie. He received a warm cheer as he entered the arena but, without Chelsea, the applause lacked its original intensity and, almost inevitably, the heroics could not be repeated. Ellie's four faults occurred at the first element of the testing final treble where Edgar sensed the approach was wrong and quickly asked for an extra stride. Her front legs caught the pole. To the sound of a communal groan of despair, it clattered to the ground. To her credit Ellie, with typical determination and experience, adjusted her own stride and cleared the last two elements. After Ellie, six more horses competed, giving Edgar time to return to Chelsea and prepare her for the most important moment of his life to date.

With seven clear rounds, Edgar knew that the competition was wide open. He knew each of his five rivals. Dieter Hamann, a young German whose equestrian skills were well known and who was already held in high regard in Europe, had been tipped to win from the outset. Now, as the only contestant to have two horses in the jump off, it appeared that the prediction was well founded. Like Edgar, the other four rivals were relative newcomers and yet he knew enough about them all to appreciate that everything was now in the lap of the gods.

Dieter Hamann rode first, ensuring another clear round by setting a steady and safe pace. Wim Neuteboom collected twelve faults and then three young British riders followed, each bettering the time of the one before; but, in striving to do so, they each incurred four faults. Once again, the testing treble was whittling the field down.

"So, once again, the treble does the damage. Now into the ring, Edgar Gibson on Gentle Sea Breeze, with a time of 40.6 to beat. If she repeats her effort in the first round, that target is well within reach. So, for Ireland – Edgar Gibson and Gentle Sea Breeze."

The volume of applause rose as the pair entered. But, knowing the importance of the occasion, a breathless silence quickly enveloped the arena and this time Chelsea's pace was controlled and determined.

As they trotted around, eyeing the fences and waiting for the bell, the total silence was broken by a single calm measured call of encouragement from within the crowd. "Go Chels – go, girl." Her small buck of recognition and enthusiasm coincided with the bell. Then, Chelsea broke into a canter and, in a long sweeping arc, rounded the end of the ring and glided across the starting line, triggering the timing mechanism.

The television commentary reflected the air of tension as viewers across Ireland sat in painful absorption and watched and listened; some even prayed. Maureen Gibson sat on the edge of her seat, twisting her pinny anxiously whilst Patrick placed one hand thoughtfully across his mouth, feeling it slick with perspiration. His other hand was bunched in a tight fist. Months of preparation were about to end, one way or another, within the next minute.

"Nicely over the first, now for the double, take it easy, one – that's it – and two. Ahh," the gasp echoed through homes across Ireland. Everybody heard the clack of hoof against wood. Breaths were only drawn again when the pole rolled back into its cup. "She's still clear and now the third, here's your chance to gain some time, cut in front of the gate, yes she's done that. But is the angle now too tight? No, she's clear – brilliant riding by Edgar Gibson. Straighten her up, that's it. Well done. Now drive for the next, steady, steady, and over she goes. Yes, no problem so far but she's over a second behind Dieter at this point. I can't see where she can pick it up unless she takes some chances. Over another, yes, still in touch. Good, now turn quickly for that dreaded treble and go for it!"

Edgar sensed he was behind the clock. He gave Chelsea and urgent nudge as he pulled her sharply round to face the final treble. Her back legs slipped briefly in the turn and she lost her approach to the first element. Edgar helped by urging her forward and, with a small check and a snort of determination, Chelsea powered at the fence and cleared it. But now her stride pattern was wrong. She needed to lengthen at the middle fence to save time. For a moment, Edgar was certain that she'd recovered the situation but the distance was just too far. Had she not slipped approaching the treble, her athleticism would have pulled it off. Now, as she tried to soar across the fence, her back legs came down fractionally too soon, dropping on either side of the pole. It twisted unevenly in its fall and caught her again. Both back legs collapsed against the impossible obstacle and Chelsea swerved sideways, falling heavily against the mock brick wall that comprised the third element of the treble.

"My God, she nearly did it!" The commentator lost his poise in despair. "What an effort but that's the end of Gentle Sea Breeze and Edgar Gibson's challenge. Wait now. Oh lord no! She's still down. The horse is still down. Gibson's up – he's all right, but … oh how we dread these moments. The horse is down. Let's pray she's just winded. People are gathering round. Even somebody from the crowd has joined in. See, the officials are asking him to leave – it looks like a young man, there with the red hair, between the two stewards. He seems to be in tears …

Chapter 4

Education and Discipline

Helen Anderson sipped an ice-cold gin and tonic as she finished reading the end-of-term report on her son and smiled, passing it to her husband.

"Mrs. Reid is right, she's summed him up well. What do you think, darling?"

Jim read the teacher's summary and chuckled, "Not very bright, but seems to try." The teacher's words were written in beautifully formed italics, reminding Jim of his own schooldays and the horrors of learning to write.

"It's a bit cruel and to the point. We'll tell Jimbo about the good bits, about trying hard and enjoying the football. I like the bit, "he deals with his handicap with characteristic good nature". But the sooner we get that scar dealt with, the better. In the years to come that will really be a burden."

Then, sadly proving the emptiness of his own words, Jim broke the news to his wife. "They want me down at the Jinja Dam. Two more years. Can you manage that?"

Helen had known this would happen. Overseas postings were renowned for their uncertain durations and the civil engineers working for the Arthur Garland Consultancy took it in their stride, that is, if they wanted a career. Nearly always, it was the wives who struggled, especially if a family and schooling was involved. The expression 'Take the number, then double it, and finally add some' was no longer a joke. The number of years served by engineers on each project was invariably more than double the number they originally signed up for.

Actually, Helen didn't mind as she knew many of the wives at Jinja and now quite enjoyed the lifestyle, the money and the status. But she raised the inevitable question: "Jinja has got no school. James will have to be boarded; isn't he a bit young?"

"Yes, but he'll cope and we can give him some great holidays when all this is over. You know, they've offered me an SRE position after this one; somewhere of my choice."

Helen knew that Senior Resident Engineers were highly prized at Arthur Garland and this was the making of her husband's career. Those of the calibre to be left in charge of construction sites, sometimes in remote places, would find the material rewards worthwhile. But Arthur Garland never mentioned the sacrifices, especially for young families. It came with the job.

"We'll put Jimbo into that good preparatory school in Nairobi. The one that the Jeffries' son is at. They say that it's strong on results, and also on discipline. That should set him up for a good academic start in life – maybe we'll hear less of 'trying' and more of 'succeeding'."

Helen nodded but a shiver of anxiety ran down her spine. "For just two years, Jim. Then we must get him back to the UK and have his face seen to." How easy it was to postpone difficult things. Helen accepted the logic of the situation but, once again, she did not listen to her inner voice – God's own way of communication with his children.

Steam hissed from the side of the train's engine and the eight boys leapt backwards, shrieking in mock terror, and ran back to the gaggle of parents who were chatting by the side of their carriage in forced conversation, desperately trying to keep their spirits up as they waited, longing for the train to leave to cut short the agony of this extended farewell. Railway stations are never good places in which to say goodbye. For the boys, the dread of being sent off to a school many hundreds of miles away was eased only by the exciting prospect of a train journey. Along with all the others, parents and children alike, James could not shake off the sadness of the occasion. The more he thought about it, the more it gnawed at his stomach and made his throat tighten, almost to the point of nausea. On the drive to Kampala Railway Station, tears had glistened in his eyes and he had hugged his mother. She had to bite her own lip to hide the quiver of emotion. Three months ago, the decision had been easier to make than the reality that she faced now.

Even Jim was unusually quiet, his normal cheerful confidence seemingly crushed by the occasion. It was difficult to put on a brave face, but he tried: "I envy you Jimbo. Think of the fun of being on a train. The rest of today, all night and most of tomorrow. You can play with new friends and remember – tomorrow you'll pass through the Great Rift Valley. It's world famous so watch out for the sights and write to tell me about any wild animals you see."

"Yes, Daddy, but I'll miss you and Mummy." The response had come in a tremulous quaver and, once again, the tears had welled into his eyes.

Now, as the boys joined the group of parents, a huge lady called Mrs. Bartlett, their guardian for the journey, emerged from the carriage and summoned them. Referring to a sheet of paper, she called out names and seat numbers. "James Anderson and Stephen Jeffries, you are 5A and 5B. You can fight over who has the top bunk tonight. Next, Peter Havranek and David Lewis, you take 6A and 6B …"

Minutes later, the carriages juddered, steam poured from the engine and, to metallic screeching and grating noises from the couplings, the Kampala to Nairobi train drew out of the station taking James to the strange and frightening world of a British boarding school.

"Goodbye James, goodbye darling." Helen waved at the sad face, head covered by a navy blue cap, and she watched her son drawing further and further away. The image of his scar was etched in her mind, cruelly taking on the form of a demented grin as his other features faded into the distance. Helen broke down and buried her head into Jim's chest. "Oh, the poor wee mite. What have we done, what have I done?"

When four boys get together on a steam train, is it possible to be downhearted for long? They behaved for the first twenty minutes of the thirty-six hour journey. That was whilst Mrs. Bartlett sat James down, with the three others in his compartment, and gave them instructions for the day, the dos and don'ts and whys and wherefores. None of what she said penetrated their consciousness although, by the intent look on their faces as she spoke, Mrs. Bartlett was certain that they had fully understood. As soon as she left, David Lewis suggested a full tour of the train.

"Let's pretend Mrs. Bartlett is an enemy agent. You're captured and tortured every time she sees you, so let's find all the hiding places."

And so they ran up and down the corridors, giggling with their own self importance, ducking under tables in the unoccupied restaurant car, leaning out of windows to wave at each other from either end of the train, and trying to work out whether they could ride on the running boards outside the doors of the carriages. At eight, David was almost two years older than James and had assumed heroic proportions in the youngster's eyes. Later, at school, he would learn that the boy was a troublemaker and, worse still, a bully. Meanwhile the four lads joined in the play and pranks with the abandon of newly freed spirits. The idea to stand on the outside of the train as it travelled was not entirely hair brained. Their speed on the narrow gauge railway never topped thirty miles per hour and, at times, they slowed to 10 mph when they started long, slow climbs up Uganda's massive escarpments. When this happened, cheerful Africans would run alongside the carriages, swinging on to the steps for free rides to and from neighbouring villages before jumping down at known safe spots. Thus, with the windows open, black faces would often appear, smiling cheerfully and chattering in different dialects of Swahili. To the boys, their way of travel was much more fun than sitting on boring seats and the temptation was too strong to resist.

The train driver was forced to ignore African joy riders – it was an accepted fact of these journeys which would otherwise have been interminable had they stopped to remove every illegal passenger, none of whom could be caught anyway. But the train slowed to a complete halt when the white boy was spotted, leaning fearlessly outwards, one hand on the windowsill and the other waving ostentatiously to his friends in a display of bravado.

It was David, who shot back into the compartment and hissed to his friends, "Nobody say a thing. If they don't know who it is, then they can't do anything."

He was almost right, but Mrs. Bartlett had been with the other four boys in their compartment so she knew that the culprit was one of the four in David's group.

"You, David Lewis, are the oldest. You were meant to keep an eye on the others, not lead them astray. Now who was it hanging outside the train?"

Facing a sullen and guilty silence, she accepted the inevitable. They were confined to their compartment until dinner time and were given an ominous threat: "Appropriate measures will be taken by the headmaster tomorrow."

The reality of their predicament was soon forgotten in anticipation of the overnight adventure. A friendly African steward clucked crossly at the boys for their earlier misdemeanour that was now taking on legendary proportions as gossip seeped up and down the entire train. Samueli had been working on this route for many years and had never seen the likes of it before – not from white passengers, at least. This would make good telling back in the village. He helped them to convert the padded bench seats into four bunk beds, and left them with a cheery wink: "Mbaya, mbaya sana." But the reprimand, "Bad, very bad", was lost in his beam of friendly conspiracy and the final wink reduced them all to uncontrollable giggles. The pranks and chatter continued into the small hours of the night but ended on a gloomy note when the exhausted boys discussed their impending fate.

"Have you ever been caned?" David whispered in glee. "Mr. Squires is bound to cane us. I get beaten every term for something. It's not hard to get into trouble at Kingston. I think he likes beating boys."

Suddenly the excitement of the journey drained from James and he realised how much he missed his mother. Exhausted and silently tearful he fell into a deep troubled sleep. The rhythmic pounding of the train and his fear of the new school with such a monstrous headmaster caused him to dream. Confused, pulsing dark images cloyed his mind – a giant bearded ogre carrying a huge club chased a leaden-footed boy and unremittingly beat him.

The new day deepened James' gloom. Somehow, to his young mind, the prospect of a night on the train had been hugely comforting and divided present from future like a wall. Now that wall had crumbled and only 'today' existed, a day in which he would be without his mother, where a beating was inevitable and where, apart from these two grim certainties, he was moving into a completely unknown world. He sat tiredly and read comics, missing the enforced stop at a watering station where David announced he could turn a copper Ugandan 'cent', with a hole in the middle of it, into a silver shilling, simply by laying it on the track in front one of the carriage wheels. "When the train moves over it, it melts it into silver," he announced to the awestruck Stephen. "So go on then, put your cent onto the track."

He showed little interest in the running, shouting Africans, ululating with excitement as the great long train trundled past their villages. They were now into Kenya, where stories of the Mau Mau still held many, blacks and whites alike, in fear. Unlike Uganda, Kenya was rumbling in anticipation of independence and many villagers shouted, "Uhuru!," the cry of "Freedom!" at the white faces peering back at them from the windows.

Worst of all, James barely noticed the majestic view of the East African Rift Valley, its steep sides falling into a shimmering broad expanse of Savannah where huge herds of wildebeest moved like a black cloak being drawn slowly across the massive brown shoulders of Africa. The train struggled along the steep sides of the valley, sometimes passing through long dark tunnels before emerging into painful sunlight. James slept as the afternoon sun changed from a burning yellow to deep orange and finally to the heart-stopping beauty of ever darkening red behind towering black cumulus clouds. He was shaken awake by Mrs. Bartlett in time to see the black clouds of foreboding.

Before she shook his shoulder, Mrs. Bartlett looked at the sad scarred face and thought to herself, "He's got so much ahead of him, poor thing. I'll make sure that I speak to Mr. Squires." Her innate decency was repelled by the headmaster's harsh regime, but she had a steely core and a sense of right and wrong. In many ways she was ahead of her time.

"Wake up, James, wake up. Good boy. Now pack your night bag and get ready. Nairobi's not far away."

James woke the next morning to the sound of a bell. He felt stunned and barely remembered the previous evening, arriving at the school in darkness, being given a sandwich and cocoa, and finally falling into bed and into a deep sleep with tears of confusion and homesickness still seeping from exhausted eyes. He struggled out of bed, noticing for the first time that he shared a dormitory with twenty other boys, all about his own age and all appearing to be just as confused as he was. A kindly lady in a blue uniform, Matron, clapped her hands in businesslike fashion and cajoled them to the bathroom. "Come along boys, rise and shine, smile don't whine."

And so James started his first day at boarding school. He was on the verge of tears, picking at his porridge for breakfast until told, "Eat up, all food must be eaten." Eventually, Mr. Squires rapped the head table and called for attention – he was a plump man with white hair and reddish/blue cheeks. James thought he would explode at any moment, like his father looked when he emerged from the swimming pool, gasping for air after doing two lengths under water.

Mr. Squires gripped his black gown by the lapels and puffed out his chest. "Right then boys, another term has started. Remember the rules and you won't go wrong. All together now, what are the rules?"

"Work hard, do as you're told and never tell a lie," the boys chorused back; all except James and the other new boys who had no idea what to say.

"That's good. Now I want to see all new boys in my study after assembly, and I want David Lewis to wait outside the study door now."

The ominous tone carried across the stunned hall and nobody spoke, not a word, not even whisper. All that could be heard was the sound of chairs scratching across the floor as boys stood up to leave. If you were asked to 'see me', all was well, but boys who were told to 'wait outside the study door' had only one grim prospect – that of a beating with Mr. Squires' thin cane. Nobody had ever been punished in this way on the first morning before so, that term, a frightening tone was set that affected the whole school. James could not concentrate at all, even when his class teacher, Miss Cherry, put her arm around his small bony shoulders and welcomed him with a hug and a kindly smile.

"Welcome to Kingston school, James. I want you to enjoy your year in my class and to always ask if you want any help at all. Now, off you go and sit beside Stephen."

James smiled nervously and sat beside his new friend, but his mind was swimming with emotion – sadness and homesickness, and a mixture of fear, of Mr. Squires, and relief that Miss Cherry was just the opposite. How was he to behave? Would he escape the dreaded summons to 'wait outside the study door'?

During his first term, James learnt to adjust to the confused messages that Kingston gave him. He enjoyed his lessons with Miss Cherry, although the spectre of Mr. Squires was ever present. James learnt that boisterous behaviour was likely to incur his wrath. Outside the class, he therefore withdrew into his shell and thus gave contrasting impressions to the staff. Some thought that he was sulky and introverted, but Miss Cherry knew better and always reminded them that the youngster was full of enthusiasm and fun.

Over the months, she coaxed him out of his shell and his performance blossomed. He was second overall in the class and was top in arithmetic and science. The latter fascinated him to the extent that he never failed to bubble with enthusiasm when Miss Cherry demonstrated practical examples of basic physics. One day she performed a piece of pure magic that thrilled James, making him jump up and down in his seat and clap his hands with amazement.

"OK boys, here's a peeled hard boiled egg. If I try to put it in the milk bottle, it won't go, not even if I push and squeeze. James, you have a go."

James placed the egg with the narrow, pointed end facing down into the neck of the bottle like a golf ball on a tee. He squeezed its sides but could not compress it enough to slide it through the opening.

"Thank you, James. Now, here is a candle. What should I do with it?"

The room remained silent and engrossed. "Any ideas?"

James' hand shot up. "You light it, Miss."

"Good, James, and then?"

But he could not think of a reply. Instead, his brow furrowed in thought. "Please Miss, show us, show us," he babbled, forgetting that this was a lesson, instead becoming lost in the fascination of the moment.

"Right, James, go back and sit down. Stay clear everyone and watch carefully."

Miss Cherry placed the candle in the milk bottle. It was only an inch long so she lit a long taper and, feeding it into the bottle, touched its flame to the wick. Then she took the egg and held it up to the class between thumb and forefinger. Looking at the faces, agog with fascination, she felt a pulse of pleasure and resolved to maximize the fun of the moment, for herself as much as for the boys. With her free hand she waved it dramatically around the egg and simply couldn't resist saying, "Abracadabra, shebiggle, sheboggle, please, Mr. Egg, go into the bottle." Then she placed it on the neck of the bottle and they all waited. To begin with, a brief mist of smoke filled the container, then the flame flickered as it burned up the remaining oxygen and struggled vainly to find more but the egg sealed the neck until, with a sudden rush, it was sucked into the resulting vacuum and popped, complete and unbroken into the bottle.

To gasps of amazement, she bowed to her class and did not reprimand James when he clapped vigorously. Again, picking him out from the others, she gave the thrilled youngster the bottle and a final set of instructions.

"Your job, James, is to get the candle out and clean the inside of the bottle. Remove all traces of smoke stains and wax. Then dry the inside and all we have left is an egg in a bottle, just like a ship in a bottle but harder to explain. It'll be our secret. Don't tell the other classes. Some may know already but it'll be fun to test them." She sunk her neck into her shoulders and gave them all a mischievous look, rolling her eyes in fun.

"And, shall we see if Mr. Squires knows the trick? Shall we try it out on him?" At this point the boys giggled with glee and the bell sounded for the end of class.

The year passed, full of ups and downs. This was reflected in his third end of term report, which Helen read with a growing concern. Fortunately, Miss Cherry had taken James for all classroom activities so the overall tenor of the report was one of success. In Painting, Arithmetic, Science, English, Scripture, Geography and very basic Latin and French, James was in the top four of the class. Miss Cherry's summary was heart-warming: "James is a charming boy and it has been a pleasure to have his company for the year. If I must pick up an area for improvement, it is that he should worry less about things but, equally, it is the responsibility of the school to help him here."

Helen did not fully appreciate the courage that it took for Miss Cherry to write those words. Nor did she know that the teacher had only been at Kingston for one year as well and, like James, had spent most of that year worrying about the aura of fear that pervaded the place. So, although Miss Cherry had agonized about writing those last words, she had resolved to include them as an indirect message to Mr. Squires, hoping that he would approach her about the issue and that they could then have an open discussion.

As it transpired, Mr. Squires' only reaction had been to add, under 'Headmaster's Comments', the curt words, "James seems to have done well in class, but he must learn to come out of his shell more, otherwise he will struggle over the course of next year."

During the long summer holiday Miss Cherry resigned and took up a position at the prestigious Delaware High School in Nairobi where she would eventually become a respected and loved head of English. Her only comment, on leaving Kingston, was to confide to a sympathetic Mrs. Bartlett, "I'm about the most junior person here. I did what I could, but if senior members of staff do not have the courage to address the issue, then I only have one choice. I love children too much. That's why I came into teaching – it's my calling."

The next year, James moved up a class, joining Mr. Arnold. The regime was completely different. Mr. Arnold wore a black gown that was always encrusted with chalk dust. Although not an unpleasant man, he never smiled and he expected boys to stand up when speaking in the classroom. All this contributed to an air of gloom and austerity that stifled James' ability to think freely. Thus it was that, whereas the classroom had once been a haven of relief, now there was nowhere to relax and he withdrew further into his shell, developing a heightened respect for authority and a realisation that certain ideas, and especially certain types of people, should never be challenged. Instead James simply avoided trouble, 'behaved himself' and survived a miserable year. He came eighteenth out of twenty-one, a decline that did not go unnoticed. Mr. Squires' 'Headmaster's Comments' at the end of the second year simply stated, "James must make a massive effort, and soon."

Helen insisted to Jim, "Look at him – he's changed, withdrawn and miserable. Have you heard him laugh recently? He never goes back to that place, Jim. I know they want you here for another year, but I'll take him back to UK and get him into a decent school. Then, I'll rejoin you, but not until I have peace of mind about James."

It was not a request, simply of statement of intent. Jim Anderson had never seen such independence and determination in his wife and he did not argue. He sighed with resignation and resolved to speak to Arthur Garland. This might have financial repercussions as it was generally accepted within the company that fees and expenses would only be paid for Kenyan boarding schools.

James was eight when he had his second operation. It should have been carried out sooner and Helen acknowledged the consultant surgeon's implied reprimand, accepting the blame and expressing genuine regret.

Professor Naughton looked sympathetically into her anxious face. "We'll do something about the nose, but he's going to carry that scar for the rest of his life. There have been great advances in plastic surgery since the war, mainly because of disfigurement from war injuries, especially burns, so we can do something there as well. James may want to come back when he's a young adult to try again but, for the time being, let's see what we can do. Please do not concern yourself, Mrs. Anderson, there will be a marked improvement when this is all over."

Four hours later a dopey eight-year-old lay weakly in the hospital bed washed with nausea. Helen saw his eyes flutter and stroked his forehead, above a swathe of dressings, and whispered consolatory words. As she waited for him to return to consciousness, she looked intently and with incredible love at the small bundle, utterly vulnerable and yet holding within the frail form a nugget of pure goodness. For the first time, she felt an affinity with God, a oneness with His source of love and gentle guidance. She knew what she had to do; her inner voice spoke with a certainty that she could not ignore. Helen did not attend church, finding that none of the recognised religions offered answers and more often than not imposed dogmas that seemed devoid of love. Instead they offered messages of a mighty Lord, one that should be held in awe, at whose feet one should tremble and before whom one should expect final judgment. Yet how could the God, who spoke to her now so gently and with such utter calm certainty, who had created the perfection of spirit that was her James, how could he be such a mighty and fearsome Lord? The love she now experienced acted like a medicine, a balm, full of soothing, precious peace and wonder that eased her own spirit just as she attempted to soothe James' discomfort. She began to experience an incredible purging as she gave of herself unconditionally, not out of duty or sacrifice, not as a result of guilt, utterly without motive. And finally, at the moment that her lips gently caressed his forehead, as the intensity of her feeling for James, her bond of love, became so great, so limitless in its purity, it seemed as though all the love in the Universe responded, enveloped her and swept through her, beautiful and full of grace, strengthening her resolve and giving her confidence and certainty.

"James, my darling, darling James. It's Mummy. I love you."

His tiny hand squeezed hers, once, twice, three times. Words were not needed. Each squeeze spoke, "I love you."

"You're tired, darling. I won't make it worse but I'm here, all the time, I'm here so don't speak now, just remember, I'm here and will be from now on. No more boarding school, just you and me, living together until Daddy comes home. That's enough for now, darling. I'm sitting close, all the time, sitting close and loving you so much, so very, very much." Her kiss caressed his forehead and a single tear fell from her eye and landed where her lips had just touched him, like a raindrop of love from the Universe.

Chapter 5

A Broken Spirit

The huge shed was dark and carried an air of dankness and decrepitude. Echoes were thrown back and forth across the cavernous gloom in an eerie mixture of reflected shouts and clatters. Chelsea fidgeted with anxiety as she waited to be schooled. Her body was tense, ready to react to any strange movement or noise, fearful of the massive human whose stentorian barks broke out across the arena in a crisp and heartless tone. She was tethered, her lead rope attached directly to an iron stanchion. So, as she jerked her head in fright, the rope became taught cruelly jarring her neck until she stopped resisting and accepted that there was no escape from the misery of the constraint. Before she had been left in the hands of Mike Feherty, she had always been tethered lightly, the lead rope attached to a loop of twine that would snap if she jerked too fiercely. And that had never happened because she had never been as panicky and frightened as she was nowadays. Over the past three months she had learned a new, more brutal means of restraint, and that resistance was futile. Only in moments of panic, like now, did she renew her battle with the rope.

Chelsea had experienced six months of pain. It was now becoming a part of her life, a strange and frightening period during which her trust in humans was gradually and inexorably melting away leaving a petulant and unpredictable animal. Ever since Edgar Gibson had sold her to Mike Feherty she had become wary of human motives. She was now in the hands of a horse dealer whose sole intention was to sell her on at the best possible price.

When she fell at the Dublin International Horse Show, she stayed down for several minutes, badly winded and momentarily unaware of her surroundings. Edgar Gibson was thrown clear of her sprawling body as she rolled once before crashing into the supports of the final element of that testing treble. Instinctively she remained still, recovering her wind, until she became aware of her ungainly and vulnerable position with people milling around. She recognised Eric's voice, somewhere distant, full of concern. Sensing the tension in the unnatural silence of the arena and, with panic growing amid agonising stabs of pain from damaged back muscles, she struggled to her feet, flinching with discomfort and starting in alarm at the sudden roar of relief and exultation that exploded from the crowd. Then she froze, standing in pain, and her head slowly eased downwards as she felt the stiffening of damaged muscles and the agony of movement. Her strength simply ebbed away like a punctured tyre and she stood, rooted to the spot.

From that moment, when she was led gently from the arena, limping slowly, a confused and frightened animal, the weeks of pain began. Initially, Edgar's concern was evident and in the days that followed the accident, he visited her daily as she stood miserably in her box. He stroked her constantly and fussed around, feeling helpless to relieve the obvious discomfort and confusion. Edgar's feelings of worry and affection were genuine, but he was not able to get through to the mare who now seemed to have lost heart and lacked the flash of spirit that, until then, had been her trademark. In those early days of recovery, Chelsea seemed to turn her energy inwards, concentrating on the healing but distancing herself from the world. Edgar could only hope that the spark would eventually return.

She was too badly injured to make the short trip to the vet for X-rays and scans, and so a mobile unit was brought to her. When the results came through, Edgar's spirits plummeted as he realised that a long haul lay ahead. Subsequently the vet visited several times, feeling her back, watching her still-stiff walk with growing concern and continuing to administer pain relief. Edgar's heart went out to Chelsea and he resolved to see the treatment through until, finally, the vet admitted that, as a show jumper, the mare's future was 'very uncertain'. "Don't expect her to compete at a high level again."

So once again, at his parent's home and, ironically, over a meal of steaming Irish stew, the decision was made.

"I just cannot afford to carry the burden of a horse that may never be fit for top competition again, Dad. She's a great animal and I could have done wonders with her. But, with the Volvo sponsorship, I have to come up with the goods and that means three top-class performers in time for next summer."

Patrick Gibson nodded sadly and accepted the inevitable. He had also thought deeply about the issue knowing that, by keeping Chelsea, the financial burden would be too great. Edgar's future now depended upon the sponsorship. This was not a hobby any more – top class show-jumping was a total commitment in every respect, including the need to make hard decisions. Even so, his heart cried out for the wonderful animal whose fate lay entirely in their hands.

"We must make sure that Chelsea goes to a good owner," Patrick urged, "and I'd love to think that Eric could take her. Let's give that possibility a go. I'll also advertise, just in case."

In the three months that Chelsea was under Edgar's care following her fall, Eric visited several times. On the first occasion, on the day after the accident, Chelsea whickered in quiet affection and relief at the loved and familiar presence. But she was in too much pain to show her usual pleasure at his company. Eric however, was affected deeply by the meeting. The first rush of relief that had surged joyously through him when he realised that she would survive had passed quickly when he then understood how badly the beloved mare was injured, and how much of her spirit had seemed to drain away. Faithfully he visited her, almost weekly, happy to see physical improvement each time but always leaving with a gnawing feeling of anxiety at her change of character. These days Chelsea stood quietly, sometimes her head resting on his shoulder, pressing painfully into his collarbone. In those moments, it seemed to Eric that he was helping to take her weight, easing the pain in the back. But, apart from the gentle, almost inaudible whickers, Chelsea showed little affection, just a dull relief at having his company.

Eric mentioned this to Edgar whose only reply was, "Believe me, Eric, she still loves you. What she's showing is much, much more than I get from her, and I am trying to regain her confidence. We'll give it time – she'll come round in due course."

Eric would have loved to accept the offer to buy Chelsea. But exams loomed and his financial circumstances were dire. He tried desperately to see how he could make it happen, contacting his parents, then Henry O'Sullivan and even Majella. Sympathy was clearly evident, but it was not a substitute for money. His parents respected him for making the effort but worried about this distraction from exams and finally, and very firmly, advised him to concentrate on his studies and not put his future career in jeopardy. They argued that he could always keep in touch with her progress. In that they were wrong. But financial pressures bear down on every person and colour their decisions. So it was understandable and Eric accepted the inevitable. He spoke to Edgar, a week after the offer was made, giving him his answer with a sheen of tears glistening in his eyes.

Patrick Gibson was prepared for this turn of events, but he was not prepared for what followed. No replies had come in from the advertisement and, in the meantime, Edgar had been offered a wonderful opportunity to purchase a jet black stallion, a top class Hanoverian called Titan who, ironically, had already been a class winner at the same Dublin Horse Show that had been Chelsea's downfall. Titan was perfect for Edgar, horse and human seemed made for each other, both competent handsome males full of arrogant self-confidence.

"I must go for it, Dad, I must. Titan's going to cost a packet but I'll never forgive myself if somebody else gets him. Even if we can only recover a quarter of his cost from selling Chelsea, I'm going to do it. I've already got a meeting with Mike Feherty. There's clearly no point in continuing to advertise – people will be well aware of her history by now."

Patrick's blood ran cold and his immediate thought was: "Over my dead body" but he kept his counsel and, later, thought the matter through in private. Feherty was a horse dealer. Most of his stock went across to the United Kingdom where there was a good demand for quality Irish bred horses. The chances were that Chelsea would eventually find herself with a good, caring owner. The British loved their animals and many horse owners doted on their charges. However, the short term looked bleak as Feherty only ever did what was necessary to make a sale. He was a forceful cold-hearted man, not at all the type who would show concern for Chelsea's welfare.

"Edgar, take care over this. When you meet Feherty, make it clear that Chelsea has a superb track record. Try to get the man to appreciate that she's worth a lot more if she's happy. Make sure he knows that, with Chelsea, only a gentle approach will succeed and anybody who gets her back to fitness, and can prove it, will be well placed to sell on her at a good price. We've simply got to make Feherty understand that he cannot apply his usual roughshod methods on this animal. I'd never forgive myself."

Edgar picked up the tone immediately. Normally his father never laid down the law like this so Edgar became alert, watching Patrick's face as he spoke, seeing the worried frown crease the forehead, but also observing the eyes – cold, unblinking and determined.

The warning was heeded and Edgar made every effort to make Feherty aware of the one condition of the sale. His last words to the dealer were spoken with feeling, born of guilt and shame: "Treat her well Mr. Feherty, I mean it. Any effort will be repaid when you sell her on. Otherwise she'll become unmanageable and you'll have lost your investment."

The tailgate of the transporter then clanged shut, ominously, like the doors of a prison, and the vehicle rumbled out of the yard, and Chelsea out of his life. For a fleeting moment, Edgar's heart went out to the game, courageous creature. Then he turned and his eyes fell on the magnificent, shining black stallion, alone in the paddock, imperious and masculine, watching mares in a distant field. Titan trotted the length of the field, his muscles rippling in the early winter sunlight and he let out a long confident 'look at me' neigh. At that moment, the contrast between the fit, athletic stallion and the departing demoralised mare was stark. Chelsea's injuries had barely healed and, although her back was now passed fit by the vet, her muscle tone was poor and much work was required to return her to jumping fitness. Would Mike Feherty be true to his word?

"It's done. Time to move on." Edgar spoke the words aloud to himself, trying to dismiss Chelsea from his life, to put aside his feelings of guilt, striving to be positive by thinking of Titan and all that he had to offer. At that moment he was unaware that one day, years in the future, he would once again meet Chelsea.

Mike Feherty was a huge man, perfectly fitting the expression 'a son of the earth'. He came from farming stock and looked the part. His large rough hands had tufts of black hair on the knuckles and were calloused with years of manual work. He had spent much of his life outdoors so his almost bald head and mean ruddy face were a wind-burned red colour, although Guinness stout and Bushmills Irish whiskey had played their part too. But it was his size that dominated his appearance. At six foot seven inches he towered above the stable staff and Mike Feherty knew that he could easily intimidate his fellow men using his physique and blustering character to impose his will on others – sometimes physically. He prided himself on his presence and, in the rough male world of Irish manual labour he had nurtured a reputation for toughness. Now, as a horse dealer, he continued to bully his way through life. Horse and man were expected to kow-tow to his will.

"Tim lad, put draw reins on Chelsea; it's time we got her back to the ways of the world."

Mike's assistant jumped to the instructions, and clumsily fitted the reins to Chelsea's girth and through the bit rings. Draw reins are used to school a ridden horse, encouraging it to work correctly and to control headstrong tendencies. Having just recovered from her accident, Chelsea's posture and muscle tone were poor and, at most, she might have coped with short sessions of gentle and knowledgeable schooling with draw reins. However, Mike now used the reins unsympathetically and the already frightened mare was subjected to half an hour of painful physical torture. From her poll, through her neck and down into her back, a constant throbbing discomfort plagued her during the session making her fight the entire process with an air of bewildered dismay.

This routine continued for several weeks during which time the antipathy between the brutish dealer, together with his downtrodden staff and the now cussed mare, increased day by day. Chelsea learned to hunch her neck, appearing to take a correct outline but really setting her neck muscles in a tight permanent sulky shrug that exaggerated her petulant appearance. She also learned how to obstruct the tacking up process, striking out with her front legs or simply turning her back on the stable lads. On one occasion she bit Tim's upper arm tearing away a slice of skin. It was not a nip but a vicious wholehearted bite, the first time Chelsea had ever been vindictive. Tim responded with three sharp slashes of his whip across her neck and back. This made Chelsea completely uncontrollable and the session was abandoned for the day. However, the following morning, Mike insisted that they persevere because he had already received instructions, from a Scottish dealer, that a prospective buyer was interested in purchasing a 'well-schooled jumping mare'.

Colin Nisbett was based in Stranraer, on the south-west coast of Scotland, and he had been approached by the customer to find a suitable show jumper for his daughter. Colin loathed Feherty but recognised that he was a useful source of horses so, from time to time, when he could not find a suitable animal, he would send the Irishman his potential buyers' requirements in the hope that Mike would be able to meet his needs. This was just such an occasion.

Mike was therefore anxious to return Chelsea to a standard that would, at least, approach his glowing description of her ability. So the schooling continued. As well as ridden sessions with Tim, Mike lunged the mare using poles on the ground to teach Chelsea to pick up her feet and use herself properly, forcing her to concentrate on her position and thereby maintain a correct outline. Used sympathetically, this technique could have worked and would certainly have helped Chelsea's back muscles to recover their tone. But the pole sessions were hard, no-nonsense affairs with Mike calling out irately and thwacking the ground noisily with his whip. So, for Chelsea, poles on the ground became associated with harshness and misery. Together with the artificial posture she had adopted in response to the draw reins, Chelsea had now learned that fear and confusion could only be countered with devious non-cooperation and even violence.

Sensing that her days with Mike were coming to an end, Chelsea timed her retaliation to perfection. In his final session, Mike decided to loose school the mare forcing her to walk and trot over a series of poles. He usually considered loose schooling to be something for soft-hearted exhibitionists. But now he was sick of Chelsea's unsettled behaviour on the lunge line and he was running out of ideas. In truth he would be glad to see the back of the increasingly difficult mare. So now he used the small jumping lane on one side of the school and stood, blocking the open side with his huge body, ready to guide her with his whip across the small obstacles. Without the constraints of tack, Chelsea sensed a new degree of freedom and continually turned sharply before the line of poles, avoiding them and trotting crossly into the open arena before Mike could stop her. Each time, Mike had to catch her and lead her once again to the run of poles. He was becoming increasingly irritated, swearing at the horse and pushing her harder to trot through the obstacles. When Chelsea broke off yet again, Mike dashed in front of her, arms waving in furious intimidation. Chelsea did not turn. Instead she surged forward, at full gallop, kicking her back legs wildly as she passed Mike. He had not expected this reaction and was too late to move aside. Her inside hoof struck his upper thigh with a full-blooded impact that sent the mountain of a man tumbling like a leaf in the wind, howling in high pitched anguish. The stable lads rushed to his side, full of outward concern. But when the ambulance drew out of the yard, several knowing smiles were exchanged. It had taken a horse to teach a lesson to a bully where no human had had the courage.

The next day, Colin Nisbet's huge transporter arrived at the yard and seven of Mike's best horses were loaded for the trip to Larne, over the Ulster border, and on across the North Channel to Stranraer. Colin always joined his yard manager for these trips, not trusting Mike's word since he had been misled on several occasions in the past. Now, he always checked his purchases carefully before they arrived in Scotland. Colin was a small, quiet, pinched Scottish borderer whose physical appearance and character traits were in complete contrast to his Irish counterpart. Whereas Mike was all size and bluster, Colin was short and withdrawn, with a typical Scottish reticence. He asked solicitously after Mike but was secretly delighted that the Irishman was absent. Not that he wished ill upon the man, but Colin smiled inwardly as his shrewd mind read between the lines of Tim's account of the previous day.

"Which horse kicked him?" he asked Tim.

Tim looked askance. "I didn't say he was kicked at all," he replied in a pleasant Irish lilt. "More barged like," and then he paused and added, "by accident, of course."

"Of course, and which horse was it?"

"Just one of our new batch just in, sir, not from your lot." But Tim's eyes could not help falling on Chelsea who was waiting to be loaded.

"Oh aye, laddie. Well, give Mike my regards." Colin then winked at the startled Tim who did not know whether to be taken aback more by the unusually cheerful response from the dour Scot or whether it was because he had given the game away. "Dinnae fash, laddie, I'll take the chestnut anyway."

Colin left Tim's side and ambled across to Chelsea. She looked fit enough, but there was a sadness in her eyes and she watched him suspiciously, turning her head away from his extended hand. "OK, lass, life will get better from now on."

Colin was not a rider of horses, but he had an uncanny ability to size them up correctly and saw, in her early return to physical fitness, a wonderful potential. But he clucked sadly to himself, wondering exactly what might have happened to her, and why she had ended up in Feherty's hands. It was conjecture on his part, but guessing what life was like under Mike Feherty was not difficult. "I'll work on her a bit more before passing her on to the MacAllans." He thought about the prospective buyer and the daughter. "Alison's a lovely lass, she'll maybe do the rest." With a final pat he concluded, "It's a gentler touch that's needed from now on."

Two days later, Chelsea emerged from Colin's stable block into bright spring sunlight. The trip across to Scotland had been uneventful. An overnight stopover in Larne had been followed by a calm crossing during which the horses had stayed in the transporter. Larne to Stranraer is the shortest sea distance between Ulster and the Scottish mainland so the horses had been perfectly comfortable.

As Chelsea was led out, Alison MacAllan gasped with pleasure. She was an attractive sixteen-year-old girl, mad keen on riding. Like all teenagers, she dreamed of great things, of riding winners in races and especially of winning in famous show-jumping competitions around the world. In truth, she was simply a relatively competent rider for whom a hobby had become a temporary infatuation. But John MacAllan was happy to indulge his daughter's whims which he regarded as constructive and character building. He had plenty of money and was a generous, loving father. So why not? Alison had outgrown her pony and had begged her parents to let her have a horse, "a real horse, one that has experience of jumping". With Alison he had visited Colin Nisbet, discussed the issue and had been promised that enquiries would be made. True to his word, Colin had called him back within the fortnight and now father and daughter stood in the dealer's yard viewing the results.

Colin liked Alison. He was a staunch Presbyterian, wary of the way the world was going and disapproving of 'modern youth'. At sixteen, you were still meant to be a child, pursuing wholesome childish activity, enjoying the security of parental care and free of the evils that society would soon unleash. That perception of life was suitably matched by what he saw in John and Alison. Here was one sixteen-year-old who was not going to run off with the first boy she met, start a family out of wedlock and present society with the bill.

He smiled at the girl's obvious excitement. "Remember, Alison, this is just a visit to view your horse. You can look at some others too if you prefer, but if it's Chelsea you want, I'd like to keep her for a few weeks, just to make sure all's well and she's in tip top form for when you get her. Then, when we're all certain, your dad can pay for her and she'll be yours to keep."

John stroked his daughter's long, silky hair and picked up the thread of the conversation. "Fair enough, Mr. Nisbet, here's a cheque for the deposit. The balance when we collect her – OK?"

And so the deal was closed leaving a contented father, an excited child and a relieved dealer, who placed much value on his own business ethics and reputation. He would now work Chelsea for a month and try to remove the scars of her time with Michael Feherty. In that, he would only be partially successful.

A month later, Chelsea was once again in the hands of a new owner. Yet again, she emerged from a horse carrier, this time a well used two-horse trailer, and anxiously viewed her surroundings. She was in the gently rolling hills of the Scottish border country, still partly covered in late spring snow. Alison scuttled around, proudly showing her horse to the rest of the family and, with innocent self-importance, ensuring that it was she who took control of Chelsea's accommodation arrangements. The long Easter week end lay ahead and she could barely contain her excitement at the prospect of four full days of proper riding and, as she announced somewhat grandly over dinner that night, "getting-to-know-you time".

Sadly, that Easter weekend was a disappointment. Chelsea's good looks and 'nice way of going' had been artificially produced by the two dealers. In reality, Chelsea still distrusted humans and, with her returning strength, she had become even more headstrong and difficult to manage. Her instincts told her that Alison was a weak character, easily frightened, so the mare reacted in the only way she knew – by taking control of the sessions, occasionally showing encouraging signs of her past ability but otherwise seeming to be difficult and uncooperative.

It quickly became clear that the new partnership was not working. Alison's morale plummeted and she ended many of her sessions in tears. John realised that their expectations had exceeded their ability to produce results and that the naïve, if well intended, project should be brought to a timely end. Through contacts, he knew of an equestrian centre near to Aberdeen, two hundred miles to the north, whose owner had been commissioned to find horses for some of her clients. The horses would probably be kept on the yard, as working liveries, and John felt sure that Chelsea would be well cared for in an experienced environment with a new owner, whoever that should be. Alison's tears were not of grief, more of regret – a sign that the decent, good-natured girl, with compassion and intelligence, had suddenly matured into a practical, pragmatic young lady.

"You know, Dad, it's not Chelsea's fault. I thought I could handle anything and didn't realise that horses are far more complex than we think. Somebody will know how to get the best out of Chelsea. At least she's had two happy restful months here. I've loved her to bits and I know she likes me, even if she insists on being the boss."

Affection and admiration washed through John as he saw in his daughter, for the first time, insight and maturity. He hugged her, holding her tight and promising to find her another, easier animal.

Lisa Graham stood in the grounds of Balmoral Castle, blew out a single long excited breath and looked upwards into the cold, bleak spring skies above the snow-capped peak of Lochnagar. The mountain accepted her admiration with the same lofty indifference with which it had accepted adulation for centuries. Feelings of awe and fear, of wonder and of gratitude were, to this massive sentinel towering above the valley of Royal Deeside, but as nothing compared to the steadfastness of infinite time. Unchanged in form through the eons the mountain had simply clothed itself in seasonal garb, white and stark through the long winter months, sometimes black in silhouette, sometimes kilted in heathery browns and blues in the summer sunshine. But always its profile had remained unchanged. This guardian of permanence rose above the surrounding Mounth hills and dismissed Lisa's puny presence.

But Lisa too was a character with granite-like determination. As she stood before nature's might, she resolved to do something that would change her life. And, like the mountain, she was unperturbed as she thought of her childhood and what had brought her to this moment, some forty years later.

"Forty years too late." The thought was snuffed out immediately. Lisa never allowed regrets to cloud her positive and cheerful nature. "No, wrong. It's never too late to fulfil a dream." And she allowed her mind to go back in time …

She was at primary school, being given a day off to go to the Royal Highland Show, near her home in Edinburgh. Her parents were of farming stock and regarded the visit as 'educational'. Lisa remembered how much she had enjoyed seeing the judging, walking round the various exhibits, meeting people she knew and, by far the best, watching show-jumping in the Main Ring. She loved show-jumping but could not explain what it was that made it so fascinating. How can you explain the love of something? You can only feel it, feel its power and attraction and simply know, just know, that it is what you want to see and experience and, above all – do. Her parents, however, were firm in their ideas. Instead, the piano lessons continued. But Lisa never stopped thinking about the jumping and even managed to practise without a horse. She would tie a skipping rope between two trees on the back lawn and then do her best to canter up to the 'fence', collect her horse-self a few strides out, launch forth, clear the jump and then canter on. She would also play this game when out on walks – cantering up to imaginary objects and then jumping, soaring with graceful ease over cracks on the pavement as they became water jumps, or leaping high over small branches and logs as they transformed into uprights and spreads. Sometimes there were even combinations. Nothing was impossible in the imagination of a child.

But Lisa never lived only in her imagination. She learned to ride by reading most of the Pullein Thomson books, immersing herself in the 'horsey' tales so beloved of pony-mad youngsters. So, at least in theory, she taught herself how to walk, trot, canter, turn and halt. She even began to understand the basics of tack and grooming. Very occasionally, just once or twice, she got the chance to ride a real pony – mainly when she went to Edinburgh Zoo with visiting friends and cousins. There the Children's Zoo offered pony rides. Sometimes, too, she was lifted onto one of her grandfather's Clydesdales, by then retired from work on the farm, and experienced the heady thrill of bareback riding, her spindly legs poking awkwardly outwards over the broad back of these massive, gentle animals.

Eventually, Lisa outgrew those summer sessions of 'let's pretend', but she continued to love watching show-jumping at every opportunity, both live and on television and, of course, she enjoyed reading more adult 'horsey' books. Later, at university, she enjoyed athletics as well as academic study and music. Tall and leggy, she was encouraged to try high jumping but this never became her strong point. Her technique was hopeless – she always found it impossible not to canter up to the jump head on – an approach that limited her success and took much explaining to her team-mates! "But horses do it head on" did not seem to others to be a good reason for humans to emulate the equine technique.

"Stick to the four hundred yards, Lisa," Jim Murray, the university athletics coach, was always encouraging. "And think any number of horsey thoughts while you run it!"

Then Lisa thought of her marriage to Andrew, spending several years abroad and, for a while, living in South Africa amid the grandeur of the Drakensberg Mountains and their awe-inspiring amphitheatre. Trekking had been a popular pastime and riding up the steep slopes seemed to make so much more sense than walking. Most of the local resort hotels had ponies – tough little Basuto ponies that had never read the Pullein Thomson books and generally ignored her attempts to determine pace and control. But they were wonderfully sure-footed over rough and, at times, precipitous terrain. They were mean creatures, not above nipping, and not nearly as friendly as the shaggy and amiable Highlands back home in her beloved Scotland. Nonetheless, the Basutos were a start to her adult equine education and transported Lisa into some of the most spectacular scenery in the world.

Lisa and Andrew's return to the United Kingdom were challenging years, forcing them to live in the hectic South of England, away from Africa's raw vastness. A rat race of existence – not living, just existing, building her career, buying a house and turning her mind to the hard slog of survival – had all put riding on the back burner once again.

And finally, Lisa sighed with deep satisfaction as she remembered their return to sanity and back home to Scotland. There, in the beauty of the Grampian Mountains, they built a house in a small and friendly Deeside village and re-established some lost priorities. "People over things," as Andrew kept reminding her…

So here she was, on this cold and windy spring day, paying homage to Lochnagar and re-planning her already happy life. In fact re-planning was too strong – it was more a refinement, a move towards perfection, but what would Andrew think? Today, on the spur of the moment, Lisa had decided to forget work for an afternoon and to go to Balmoral for her first ride in years. Between March and August, the Queen's ponies were available for trekking – anyone could ride the plump little animals that had recently been brought out of winter sloth for six months of work and a return to fitness in time for the Royal Family's autumn stay at the castle. Lisa had felt confident that she would cope. And now she knew that she had been right!

She was given a lovely quiet Highland mare and enjoyed an idyllic afternoon, walking and trotting in reasonable harmony and coordination through woods of pine and silver birch, by the tumbling river, swollen with melt water, and finally back in front of the famous castle. At the end of the ride, Lisa's smile seemed to extend round to the back of her head. She knew that tomorrow she would have some very sore muscles! But it had been wonderful. And she was hooked. When could she do this again? How could she improve her riding and get really fit so she wouldn't be quite so sore? Her Majesty and that lovely pony had much to answer for.

Lisa shook herself from her reverie, feeling elated and also certain about the future. But her homage to Lochnagar, brief as was, had chilled her to the bone. Heavy, icy winds seemed to drop from the ragged white peak and were now cutting through her clothing, a reminder that winter was not yet prepared to offer tenancy of the glens to spring. The car journey home took less than ten minutes, not enough time to warm up, but sufficient to plan her line of action. With hands cupped around a steaming mug of tea, Lisa felt warmth returning to her fingers, took a sip and reached for the Yellow Pages. Was there anywhere nearby where she could take riding lessons? Would they think she was daft – a forty-five-year-old wanting to learn to ride? Never mind, she'd do it anyway and yes, there were stables just a few miles away. Still feeling a bit foolish, she rang the number.

"Hello, is that Kinord Equestrian Centre? Do you teach adults to ride?" Lisa's tone was brusque with embarrassment.

The voice at the other end of the phone responded, crisply efficient. "Oh yes. As a matter of fact, we have quite a number of adult beginners."

Lisa explained her circumstances, how she'd done a little trekking, years ago, but had never had any lessons. And she was delighted to hear a positive response; the niggling feeling of foolishness dissipated quickly.

Jean Walker was also delighted. She liked the sound of Lisa's friendly, determined voice. Just the sort of customer her equestrian centre needed.

"I suggest you book a couple of lunge lessons and see how you go from there. Come up and have a look around too, if you would like."

The visit was booked for the following day. The yard was perfect – quite small but with good facilities, friendly faces and, most important of all, friendly, seemingly well-kept horses. The first lesson was booked there and then. Suddenly Lisa was a six-year-old again! She was so excited. In the newsagents the following day, she browsed through the horsey publications and a child's pony magazine caught her eye. The cover advertised an article 'Lunge Lessons Made Easy' – just what she needed. Never mind that it that was meant for small girls – after all, wasn't she one again anyway?

The lunge lessons were great fun. Lisa was introduced to Barney, a beautiful large schoolmaster. Her immediate first impression was that, since that early experience with her grandfather's Clydesdales, she'd actually only ever ridden ponies. So now, having struggled inelegantly into the saddle, she found it strange, sitting so high up, but comforting to have a substantial neck and head in front of her – and, of course, a lovely coarse mane to grab hold of in emergencies! But what a long way up! They moved off into their circle – just as described in the Pony magazine – starting at walk with simple exercises to loosen up and find a sense of balance. Then, on to trot, where Lisa discovered the difference between theory and practice. To begin with she was joggled along rather than truly rising and sitting in time with the horse. But quite quickly, Lisa's natural skill allowed her to relax sufficiently and to trot around with hands on her head, on her shoulders and even out to the side. By the end of the first half hour she had also managed, without stirrups, to walk and even to trot with rather less confidence, hanging grimly onto the mane! Barney had seen it all before – a wise and experienced school horse – so he did not mind the indignity as his mane was gripped tightly, pulled this way and that with the rhythm of the trot. All too soon the lesson was over, and Lisa was delighted as she walked her trusty steed back to his loose box – or was it Barney who ushered Lisa along with his steady gait?

The next lessons followed a similar pattern and Lisa's confidence grew – her riding becoming ever more natural and relaxed. Trotting, especially, was going well – she simply listened to the horse's hoof beats and rose and sat to their familiar rhythm. Soon she was deemed ready for her first hack, which was booked with great excitement.

When the day arrived, Lisa was a little alarmed to find that the only other person hacking out was a very experienced albeit rather rusty rider. Lisa hoped she wouldn't hold back her companion, although the lady was friendly and didn't mind at all. In fact, Lisa's natural friendliness and enthusiasm meant more to her companion than the niceties of perfect horsemanship. Their ride leader was also kind and easy-going so the group immediately gelled and relaxed with pleasure at the prospect of an amiable and trouble-free hack. The small party walked into the forest amid free-flowing chatter. Lisa rode her gentle mare, Lady, with confidence and a song in her heart.

After a spell of walking and trotting, the ride leader suggested a short canter: "Only if you feel up to it. I'm aware that this is new ground for you, Lisa, but I've been watching you carefully and I'm confident that you'll be secure. Anyway, Lady will look after you."

Lisa was delighted to know that others had so much confidence. "I feel the same, but I was content to let the experts decide. Let's try a short burst."

Hanging on to the pommel, she felt the mare push off, following the lead horse in an oft-repeated routine. Lisa was ungainly, bouncing from side to side in time with the wonderful rocking movement, but it felt exhilarating and the motion was so gentle that even the sensation of speed did not concern to her. In fact, it was an amazing feeling that ended all too soon. After what felt like only a few strides, Lady came back to trot. Lisa soon learned that this quiet mare always came back to trot when she felt her rider becoming unsteady! Encouraged to try again, Lisa urged Lady forwards and, for a few more strides, the pair found a companionable rhythm and Lisa caught the riding bug with a thrill of utter pleasure. It seemed like no time had passed, but the hour was suddenly up and they were back at the yard. Most customers would normally dismount and say their farewells. But not Lisa – she insisted on removing the tack and helping with the usual end of hack chores. From that day on, Lisa always watched and learned, practising her horse care, making mistakes and loving the entire process. Forty years after her initial childhood resolve, she now strove with determination to fulfil her every aspiration. A new era had begun. Before leaving the yard that evening, Lisa booked the next hack.

And thus a pattern soon became established. Lisa always rode at the weekend and, whenever she found herself working at home, she would coordinate her days so that early morning or late evening rides became a routine. The hacks grew in length from one to two hours, sometimes even longer, as she became fitter and more confident. She soon passed Lady's canter test and managed to keep the friendly mare going with the others. Soon she also graduated to other, more challenging horses, although her attachment to the lovely gentle hacking schoolmistress never wavered and Lady remained her firm favourite.

Lisa learned quickly on these hacks. She learned how to stay put when she lost a stirrup cantering round a corner. She understood how to handle horses when they took off, how to cope with unscheduled dismounts – 'falling off' in common parlance. Mercifully these few falls only resulted in her being winded and bruised. And she learned about stable management when she got back from the hacks. Soon she was completely familiar with the nature of the horse. Her bond with Lady especially, but also with many other of Kinord's herd, often outshone that of the staff who could not compete with Lisa's love of the animals. But it was not love alone – Lisa had a granite resolve to regain the ground lost over those forty years and she became a sponge, absorbing facts and tips, and learning, always learning. She also became a source of constant attention, outpouring her energy and love to each and every one of the herd of wonderful animals at the yard. She began to get to grips with the jargon too. Soon she became so familiar with all the regular two-hour routes, and gained the confidence of the staff, so that she was often given the choice of route, especially during the following winter when customer numbers fell away on weekdays and more often than not, the riding party consisted of Lisa alone with the ride leader.

The changing seasons were always a source of joy for Lisa as each brought its own particular beauty. Riding out made her even more aware of this and she loved to watch the trees change from the shimmering fresh greens of spring, through the bountiful growth and shades of summer before taking on their autumn colours, offering their moment of red and auburn glory before fading into bare, often snow covered, winter starkness. Nor had Lisa ever been in a position before to fully appreciate the wonder of wildlife partly, she supposed, because humans were considered to be less of a threat when accompanied by a horse and partly because, being seated so high up, she enjoyed a grandstand view. She soon became used to seeing the resident herons, hearing the buzzards overhead and spotting deer.

During that winter, Lisa also learned how to ride on ice – carefully, and with no stirrups, in case the horse should slip and she needed to fall clear quickly. She also experienced the joy of wonderful silent canters through powdery snow, trying to avoid the snowballs tossed up from the hooves of the horse in front! In the early spring, her newly found skills were tested on a five-day trail ride but now Lisa was a match for anybody and even Jean Walker, leading the ride, always turned first to the gutsy and buoyant enthusiast for help and for moral support. By this time too, Lisa had acquired all the correct gear – jodhpurs, hat with silk, boots, chaps and gloves. And she had been subscribing, for almost a year, to a multitude of horsey magazines, keeping herself up to date with anything and everything associated with her new and fulfilling world.

In April, the Kinord yard buzzed with news – two new horses had arrived. For two weeks, Lara and Chelsea were quarantined in a steading, remote from the main stables. During the day they were allowed to graze in a small paddock and they became friends, out of necessity. But, as soon as the mares were allowed to join the Kinord herd, Chelsea and Lady immediately gravitated to each other and became inseparable. Chelsea was tense and excitable, bursting with spring energy and a newfound fitness. She was therefore difficult to handle, especially as her trust in humans had been tested for too long. What she needed was stability – an owner who was prepared to invest time and patience in rebuilding what had once shone out like a bright and clear star but was now a dull flickering glow. It was not surprising therefore that Lady's placid good nature provided comfort and companionship to Chelsea. Also, both horses were chestnut mares. But, whereas Chelsea's coat glistened and shimmered with fiery redness, Lady's was a duller, almost dusty-brown colour. Their coats mirrored their characters. In the mornings, Lady would gently sniff her companion, welcoming Chelsea to the field. Chelsea, on the other hand would squeal in marish excitement and rear back from Lady in dramatic pleasure. Then they would settle, grazing close to each other and sometimes standing nose to tail, swishing their tails across each other's heads and shoulders to keep the flies at bay.

Both Lara and Chelsea were destined to become the property of new owners, regular users of the Kinord Equestrian Centre. The intention was to base the horses at the yard as working liveries. Lara's owners were a pleasant and caring middle-aged couple with good riding experience. So Lara settled quickly into the daily regime of working with visitors, mainly on hacks and occasionally in the school, and regularly working with her new owners to whom all the riding facilities and trails had been made available. Jane Matheson was to be Chelsea's owner, under similar conditions. However, Chelsea was proving to be a handful. She had become almost impossible to catch in the field. When she was eventually brought in for work, she unseated several inexperienced riders and it became clear that she could only be used by very experienced visitors, or ride leaders, and only on good days. She never became used to the schooling arena, which unsettled her as soon as she entered and always caused her to misbehave, bucking or rearing in agitation. She loathed pole work, refusing to jump even the smallest obstacles and stolidly refusing to step over grids.

Jane very quickly realised that Chelsea was not for her and the sale fell through. But when, shortly after her success on the five day trail ride, Lisa remarked that she'd consider a horse of her own within the next year or so, her casual remark did not go unnoticed. Jean saw in Lisa a true affinity with horses and, above all, a steely determination to master her newfound hobby. It was clear to Jean that Lisa was the sort of person who would strive ceaselessly, doing all that was necessary to achieve a goal that she considered important. Would Lisa's relative inexperience be too great a burden and would Lisa balk at the challenge that would inevitably lie ahead? On both counts, the answer was clear to Jean. And she was correct.

"Yes, I'm interested. Really interested," Lisa replied, almost before Jean stopped speaking. "But let me look at Chelsea first and see if we take to each other."

Lisa walked into the stables and saw Chelsea at the far end, alone in her box, dozing with her back to the door. She opened the top half of the door, leaned comfortably on the lower half and just watched, saying nothing. Chelsea sensed her presence and turned to look into Lisa's eyes but, otherwise, did not move.

Lisa waited for a few moments more and then said, "You look so sad, Chelsea, and so old, but your face is kind." She knew Chelsea was only seven years old. "What's happened to you, girl? Something bad has happened, that's for sure. There's a story behind those eyes."

Lisa did not ask Chelsea to come to her. There were no clucks, offered hands or enticement. Slowly and stiffly, the beautiful chestnut turned and stood, looking carefully at the human, keeping just out of reach. Lisa watched Chelsea. Chelsea watched Lisa. Their eyes probed each other in a comfortable and completely unchallenging meeting. And Chelsea saw and sensed peace and love mixed with certainty and permanence. Here was an unchanging human. It seemed to Chelsea that Lisa was utterly trustworthy – good and bad would be met with the same steadfast resolve. Unlike Alison MacAllan, or Jane, or even Majella, there was no glimmer of uncertainty, no lack of confidence – only a peaceful sureness of purpose. But unlike the confidence of Edgar, Lisa seemed to glow with calmness and love. Chelsea sensed the gentleness and strength that she had seen in Eric and she took a pace forward and laid her velvet muzzle lightly in Lisa's hand. Then Lisa moved for the first time in five minutes. With her free hand she stroked between the dark, trusting eyes and kissed the crescent, cementing a bond that would last a lifetime.

"Now all we have to do is impress Andrew. But we'll manage that, between us – you and me, Chelsea."

That night, Lisa told Andrew of her aspirations. The news was only a surprise in the speed with which events were moving, for Lisa had been speaking for just a few days about buying her own horse. Andrew had seldom had any contact with horses but he loved all animals. The next day, as he prepared to meet Chelsea, Lisa was delighted to see him slip a packet of Polo mints into his pocket. They set off nervously for this very important meeting. At the yard, Chelsea was once again waiting in her box. They walked over to the gate and she immediately turned to greet Lisa. She nodded to Lisa and then, as if the conspiracy had been fully rehearsed, she walked straight up to Andrew and nuzzled her nose into his neck. It was as simple as that. He too was hooked! Chelsea had another fan.

So, although she wasn't an obvious choice for a first horse – difficult, petulant, apparently not that well schooled, and highly strung – Lisa knew that she was the perfect choice. Andrew also loved her. With her mind made up, Lisa moved into action and within a short space of time Chelsea was duly vetted, insured and paid for. Lisa had a horse that was to change her life forever. And Chelsea had found a soul-mate. It was time for her spirit to mend, for her to blossom.

Chapter 6

Moulding the Clay

"His nose is going to be quite normal."

Helen sighed with relief at the consultant's comforting words. Her eyes were red with worry and tiredness. Now they glistened with tears of anguish as she was unable to suppress her dismay at the sight of James' bruised and swollen face. She had sat by James' bedside for two weeks, watching his gradual return to strength and carefully balancing the games, the story telling and chatter with moments of quietness and rest. Her instincts had always been correct and it was Helen, rather than the nurses in the hospital's private wing, who dictated the schedule for each day. She had slept in an adjacent room, in fitful bursts – always semi-awake listening for signs of distress. The lightest of whimpers would cause her to jerk to consciousness, even from the depths of exhausted sleep.

It had been necessary for James to have a second, minor operation, after the first week.

"Please don't concern yourself, Mrs. Anderson. Sometimes this is necessary, but it is perfectly routine."

The technical explanation was lost on her. Always she sought the bottom line, looking carefully into the consultant's eyes for signs of false optimism. Each time she was met with a level, sincere gaze. The same pale blue eyes that now returned, with confidence and sympathetic concern, this mother's looks of desperation also caused student doctors to quail with indecision in the teaching wards of the famous London hospital. But only when they deserved it. Professor Sir Ian Naughton was a legend – brilliant, genuine and fearsome. But he was also steeped in humanity and never failed to serve his fellow man, empathising with patients and their relatives, nursing staff and doctors. His simple philosophy was to never assume that his now lofty status should ever permit him to forget where he had once been in life – an impoverished and dedicated student, living in near squalor and taking night jobs to pay his way through medical studies at Edinburgh University. Helen had seen him several times over the past fortnight, not just when he visited James and spoke directly with her. She had also seen him working with his staff, making quiet, authoritative decisions, drawing from people looks of admiration, even awe. And Helen would never forget the moment – perhaps she alone had seen it – when he put his arm around the shoulder of a distraught nursing auxiliary, took the bed pan from the girl, gently placed his crisp, clean handkerchief into her hand and spoke to her for several minutes in hushed and comforting tones that Helen could not hear.

Later, Violetta, the West Indian auxiliary confided in Helen, speaking emotionally in a gently lilting Caribbean accent: "Man, what a man! How did he know that Mr. Townend had been giving me racist grief, refusing to be touched by a nigger?"

"He probably didn't, Violetta. Mr. Townend is in a private room so nobody could have heard. That's probably why he felt he could abuse you and get away with it. But Sir Ian must have seen you were upset. Can I ask you, Violetta, what did he say to you?"

"Oh, he was great, just great. Said that my beauty and care shone through in all that I did. Even said I was one of the best nursing auxiliaries he'd ever seen, and some other stuff that made me feel like I was queen of the ward. Me, the lowest of the low! I tell you, Mrs. Anderson, no man has spoken to me like that before, not even my husband." Her teeth shone in a huge uplifting smile. "I tell you, I love the man. Don't misunderstand me. He turned the day round for me – total misery to pure joy. Yes, indeed, misery to joy." Violetta had the habit of repeating her own favourite phrases, as if she was constantly composing the lyrics to a new song.

Helen smiled. "Don't worry, I know what your saying. Oh, and Violetta, he's right, you know. You are the best. Forget Townend. Thank you for all that you do for James – you're certainly his favourite. He keeps telling me that black people are the nicest. He wants to work in Africa when he grows up."

"Well, I never," Violetta chortled as she walked out of the room. "It certainly takes bad to bring out good. Bad to bring out good. Yes indeed, bad to bring out good."

Helen would never forget the incident. She trusted Professor Naughton completely. Even though James looked bruised and puffy, her spirits rallied. "And what about the scar?"

"He'll carry that for life, but it will fade. Believe me, it'll fade to a faint line. He may want further surgery, but he will most certainly be a handsome young man. With the nose fixed, and with those wonderful brown eyes, he'll be quite a catch for the ladies. He may even want to leave things as they are – let him decide on further surgery when he's a young man."

Helen's drained features lit up with relief and pleasure. She could not resist hugging Professor, Sir Ian Naughton, medical legend and to many in this hospital – a God.

"Thank you, not just for your skill, but also for your humanity. We'll always be grateful that we came here. Thanks also for letting me stay close by all the time, and for asking the nurses to go with my judgment on James' routine. I know a few eyebrows were raised."

"Ah yes, that. The rules were bent a bit there. But it was to everybody's benefit, not least James'. Your instincts were always right so no harm was done, only good. Anyway, that's the way hospitals will go in the years to come so why not be the pioneers, eh?"

Two days later, James was discharged amid smiles of genuine affection from all the staff. Helen bought a huge box of chocolates as a 'thank you' to all the nurses, who took turns to hug his tiny frame. Finally, James threw his arms around Violetta's ample waistline and handed the beaming auxiliary a small posy of flowers. The deep purple of violets sat proudly amid a carpet of miniature white daisies. Violetta read the card. The words touched her deeply. 'Your dark beauty was there for me all the time. Thank you and love, James'.

Tears of appreciation welled into her eyes. "Well. I never. What a strange and beautiful combination. Thank you Helen, and a big thank you, James – my favourite patient, my gentle, pure James. I'll never forget this. Dark beauty and gentle purity. Yes indeed, dark beauty and gentle purity."

James and Helen enjoyed a wonderful, uplifting and recuperative holiday on a popular resort island off the Clyde coast. During the 1960s Millport thrived, providing simple resort comforts to the many working families in the west of Scotland who sought their annual fortnight of rest and entertainment. To James, this was a new world. He was used to the wide spaces of Uganda, the permanent warmth of equatorial sunshine and the black faces of Africans. Here, the days were grey and cool, the tiny island positively throbbed with the movement of people and all the faces were white or, at most, a sunburned red. James felt quite out of place.

He was alarmed to be mocked by children, not because of his disfigurement which was healing well and now gave him the appearance of a somewhat cavalier adventurer, whose battle wounds could be worn proudly, but because he had a 'posh' accent. The rougher Glasgow accents that prevailed in high season Millport were noticeably different to James' manicured tones. But the mocking was good natured and James didn't mind, giving as good as he got, telling his tormentors that he would much rather be 'posh' and have been brought up in Africa than have to live in a cold and crowded island. None of which he really meant, because he loved every minute of Millport.

He and Helen shared a room in a simple seafront hotel with kind staff who never seemed to stop laughing. Glasgow humour travelled well and James was never far from merriment. They hired bicycles and spent a glorious day riding the twelve miles around the island's coastal roads, sitting on a secluded sandy beach and enjoying a picnic of cucumber and tomato sandwiches and a jam sponge cake that was crunchy with a multitude of gritty windblown sand particles. Treats that were quite normal to Scottish holidaymakers were regarded by James as unheard of luxuries – like ice cream cones, sherbet fountains, lollipops and penny chews.

"Mum, I feel sick" became his daily mantra. And Helen did not mind. Life was too good to worry about a fortnight of treats and overindulgence.

One glorious sunny day, they took a trip in a converted lifeboat to a lighthouse that sat on its own small island, protecting the Clyde estuary. They disembarked onto the island but ten minutes later, the skipper suddenly called out to his passengers, warning them that the great liner, Queen Mary, was sailing out of the Clyde and that he would have to take their small craft back out to sea for a short while. Would anybody like to join him? James volunteered and was thrilled to discover the reason for this urgent course of action. As the massive liner sailed by, half a mile away, it sent huge bow waves across the sea, turning its gently rolling surface into mountainous peaks and valleys. Up and down they bobbed, riding the giant waves in wonderful surges and swoops, until the turmoil abated and the boat returned safely to its mooring.

"Now you ken why I had to go out again, laddie," the skipper winked at James, "else we'd have been swamped and crushed against the jetty."

The seas around Millport were crystal clear. On many days, James and Helen hired a rowing boat and rowed into the bay, watching the seabed shelving away beneath them. But always it remained clear enough to see to the bottom. They watched the seaweed change from gently waving tendrils in the shallows to a still, barely shimmering magic forest in the deeper waters. James had spent much of his time playing in swimming pools in Kampala. He therefore swam like a fish and loved diving fearlessly off the boat into the chilly waters. Helen's alarm soon fell away as she saw his white, eel-like body surging effortlessly in the buoyant seawater. She even joined him one day, edging slowly, feet first over the side of the boat until her waist was submerged and then, with a shriek of terror and shock from the cold, she let go.

The fortnight ended too quickly. Jim Anderson joined them for the last few days and, as a family, they discussed James' schooling.

"Jimbo, Mummy will stay with you for the next year. We've found you a nice school, near Bristol, where Auntie Jean lives. Mummy and you will stay with Auntie and you can be a dayboy at the school, unless you want to become a boarder in which case we'll make another plan. Daddy has got to stay in Uganda for some time yet, but I will try to visit you for Christmas."

"OK, Dad." James felt sad, his spirits dulled, overcome by the depressing realisation that life was returning to normal.

Redfield Academy was a minor preparatory school. During the first half of the century it had flourished, riding on the back of British colonialism and, in particular, offering a boarding education to children of Britons working in India. After the war that market had died away and now, during the 1960s – the era of MacMillan's 'Winds of Change' – the world was indeed changing as the other colonies began to dismantle and independence was passed to a series of fledgling countries, one after the other. In a brilliantly coordinated and peaceful transition, the Union flag was lowered respectfully around the world and was replaced by new symbols of nationhood. And the ripples affected the mother country in many ways.

And so the days when Redfield could pick and choose its children had long passed. Now it was delighted to accept any child; social standing or academic or sporting prowess, were no longer regarded as qualifying factors for admission. In fact parents now tended to interview the school, rather than the other way around. This necessary evil unsettled the headmaster who was an old fashioned conservative, coming to the end of his working life and unable to accept the new ways of the world. Some people might have described him as an old buffer, stuck in a time warp. But he was a kindly man, and for that reason alone Helen had agreed that James should be admitted. The image of Mr. Squires' cruelty would never leave her. Instead, and thankfully, Dr. Julian Walters exuded an old world charm and a ruffled, slightly eccentric air that was really quite endearing.

During his interview with Helen and Jim, he kept referring to 'my boys' as if they were a family. Helen soon discovered that 'my boys' was also Dr. Walters' means of describing former pupils. "My boy, Arnold Dickinson, is a member of the Government, you know. I always knew he'd head for great things."

Helen kept her counsel. Arnold Dickinson had been a junior minister in the Foreign Office a few years earlier and had visited Uganda, annoying everybody with his ill informed pomposity. Jim found it harder to keep quiet. As Dr. Walters stood to arrange the tea trolley to his liking, wheeling it from the door of his study closer to their cosy circle around his desk, Jim whispered, "If Dickinson had learned the difference between a colony and a protectorate, he'd have understood that Uganda was managing its own transition to independence very well. He's a pompous fool."

"Hush, Jim." Helen looked up as the headmaster settled down again in his chair and began to pour tea. "How interesting, Dr. Walters. I'm sure James will be happy here. Tell me, do you use corporal punishment?"

"Yes, as a last resort, but I regard it as a sign of failure. However, I let each master decide for himself. Now, Mrs. Anderson, milk, sugar? One lump, excellent, splendid. Help yourself to a sandwich."

The interview ended well and James was duly enrolled. Helen's one proviso was to ask Dr. Walters to pass on to James' teachers her respectful opinion that corporal punishment would be regarded as a sign of irredeemable failure; "on their part, you understand; James is a delightful boy". She left it at that.

Jim smiled at the flustered figure of Julian Walters, tripping over the tea trolley in his haste to usher them politely to the door, murmuring effusive agreement. "Quite so, quite so." However, he now looked at Helen with a new respect. She was no longer the accepting and docile wife who had started her married life so nervously in a strange land. And he liked what he saw, loving her all the more for her determination, and her commitment to James' welfare.

Now, the youngster was thrown into the world of an English preparatory school. James' gentle and friendly nature attracted many companions, but it also became a magnet for those who saw in these traits a sign of weakness. Every school has its bullies. Dr. Walters faithfully passed Helen's message on to James' teachers, all of whom were males. Times were indeed changing – never before had parents imposed their own conditions and a stir of comment rippled through the common room. The reaction divided exactly along lines of age with the younger generation of teachers all accepting the instruction with good grace and even a trace of relief. Two of the 'old brigade', however, bristled at the impertinence and clucked about a decline in standards that would eventually have its consequences. Nonetheless, in a short space of time they were all drawn to James with his innate good manners and his constant desire to please. So, as a matter of contention, the issue became an irrelevance. Julian Walters was relieved, realising that change need not involve painful upheaval, and he was also delighted to notice that the tendency of some to use gratuitous physical punishment was slowly declining in the face of Helen Anderson's firm convictions. The new philosophy for discipline was extending to other boys. Indeed, the 'consequences' were being felt in a most gratifying manner and Julian Walters sensed that an air of relaxed cheerfulness had begun to permeate the school. At the end of James' first term, Julian Walters read the masters' reports on all the boys with careful interest and he was delighted to observe a general trend towards increasing standards of class work. The very proof that he was seeking. "Amazing, truly amazing," he confided to his wife.

"I only wish that I had followed my own instincts on the matter many years ago."

James fell into the way of the school with cheerfulness and a determination to do well. His life to date had taught him the importance of obedience and the ethic of hard work so he was not a problem pupil. In fact he was a decent and kind boy but in his attempt to conform and to please others he lacked imagination and self-confidence. The scars of his early upbringing were having an effect that was far deeper than the physical scar that now ran as a thin white line across his face. James had learned for too long that, to avoid disapproval, he should conform to the demands of his superiors. This did not mean that he was without spirit. He genuinely believed that the correct way was the cooperative way. Nonetheless, in his small frame, there burned a flame of determination and courage that he showed in his approach to his fellow pupils.

In his second year at Redfield, he developed a circle of friends, mainly new boys to the school who, like himself, had joined within the past twelve months and with whom he now had a close affinity. During the previous year, a group of older boys had bullied the newcomers, partly through their age and size but also because they regarded themselves as old hands whose experience should be accorded respect. They were all boarders and enjoyed picking on younger new boys, terrorizing them into acts of obeisance, like making them do their cleaning duties or contribute sweets to their stocks. James' gentleness had made him an obvious target in his early weeks at the school. But now, a year later, and with the moral support of his friends, James decided to put an end to the bullying. He knew that he could not stand up to the older boys in a group so he waited for an appropriate moment to take them on one at a time, if necessary. As it turned out, Joe Cook was the first.

The opportunity arose at the end of one day when the boarders were making their way to their houses and the day boys drifted towards their bicycles or waiting parents in cars. It was at that time of day when, within five minutes, the main school block changed from a bustling babble of noise to an empty and silent shell. James met Joe in the deserted corridor leading to the main exit. Nobody else was in sight and the empty silence seemed so ominous, reminding both boys that they were the last two to leave the building.

Joe's eyes stared coldly at James; a sneer cracked the corners of his mouth. "Bye, bye, baby James. Time to go home to Mummy."

"You're such an idiot, Cook. Don't you know how silly you look trying to be all tough with your friends when really you're a coward? Why don't you prove how tough you are? Go on, I dare you."

James' insides fluttered with fear but he was determined to see it through this time, especially with the image of his best friend, Robert, clearly in his mind. Yesterday, Robert had been picked on and had been left in tears of anger and humiliation, crawling on all fours in front of his tormentors, including Joe, as they forced him to apologise for not having any sweets for the 'Redfield Rogues'.

James raised his fists in the orthodox boxing stance. He was taking boxing lessons at the school and now adopted the techniques he had learned, knowing no other way to fight seriously.

"If you want to be a Redfield Rogue, then you'd better prove you're not all hot air, Cook. Go on, I dare you." His high-pitched voice trembled. James hoped that the quaver would not be noticed. His mind was filled with dread and he felt the first pangs of fear and regret. Now everything seemed like a dream, a foolhardy, silly nightmare of his own making.

Joe was stunned. In front of him stood a squirt, three inches shorter that himself, stick-like arms raised ridiculously in front of a startled white face. But, even so, Joe balked and froze. There was a determined hunch to the shoulders and a ferocity about James that rattled the older boy. He couldn't believe it!

"You've had it, Anderson. You're marked. We'll get you now."

Joe did not realise how close James was to breaking off. James' tiny frame had turned to jelly. But the words now stung him, helping him to dig into his well of courage and remember that there was no going back.

"That's just it, Cook. You can only do it with your friends. OK, I don't care any more. Maybe you will get me tomorrow, but now you're all alone. How do you feel about that?"

Joe recognised the reality of the moment – that he was indeed alone and scared. The small gutsy figure that stood between him and the door had touched a nerve and he knew that he was a coward. Alone and isolated, he wanted none of this so he turned and ran back towards his classroom, shutting the door and bursting into tears of shame. The door opened and Joe turned in alarm, expecting the worst. James' face peered into the room. This time it was full of concern and, amazingly, showed neither triumph nor disdain.

"What do you want?" Joe snivelled.

"Just to be friends and to let you know how horrid it was of you and the Rogues to think that it is tough and clever to make the younger boys feel miserable. Let's forget it though and start again."

Joe remained silent, sulking and awash with shame. So James left quietly and said nothing about the incident to his mother that evening. Instead, he went to his room and replayed the incident time and again in his mind, sometimes feeling a burst of pride that he had stood up for himself, then feeling a cold dread at the prospect of the next day. What would the Rogues do? Should he apologise? Should he take in extra sweets? The thoughts and negatives tumbled around his worried mind, but through it all his self-esteem seemed to burst through, proud like an African lion, telling him to be brave. So the next day he set off on his bicycle for Redfield, alive with a sort of fatalistic resolution, with no fear, just a determination to see the day through.

He arrived early and was pleased to meet Robert in the playground, waiting for him as usual. The sight of his friend made his spirits soar and confirmed ever more strongly that his actions yesterday were justified. He had not just defended himself, but also his best friend who looked up at him now through thick spectacles that magnified his eyes into goggling orbs of relief and pleasure.

"Hello James, I'm glad you're here early, before any of the Rogues turn up."

"Hi, Robert. I've got to tell you something amazing." And so James recounted the whole story and asked for support. "We're either in for it good and proper, or we may be lucky. Shall we stick together?"

It was barely possible, but Robert's eyes widened even more. Huge blue circles popped out of his head under the thick lenses. "OK, Gosh!" was all he could muster. Then, after a thought-filled pause, "Maybe we'll get Harry to join us before the Rogues arrive. Wow!"

They sat beside Harry in morning assembly and tried to convey to him, in a short space of time, exactly what was happening. Harry, good faithful Harry, was game from the outset. He was the largest and the most sporty, of the three of them. Academically weak, he was nonetheless the most affable of lads and his slightly dull wits were more than compensated for by his faithfulness and good nature. Also, his physical presence meant that he tended not to be picked on by the Rogues. In other words he would be the best of allies and suddenly the tight unit felt able to face up to anything. It was a wonderful feeling, a mixture of nerves and exhilaration, combined with the strength of friendship.

James caught sight of Joe Cook as they left assembly, but the older boy averted his gaze and looked shamefaced, his eyes dropping downwards. Was that a good or a bad sign? Was something afoot and was Joe trying to avoid giving the game away? Only time would tell. During the mid-morning break the two groups met, inevitably, in the playground.

"This is it, the Three Musketeers against the Redfield Rogues. Here goes." Harry murmured in excitement and James' heart went out to his friend. Robert remained half a pace behind them, his tousled fair hair blowing in the breeze across anxious eyes. But he gamely remained with the other two even though his legs were all wobbly and his mouth was so dry that his tongue seemed to be too big. He hoped he would not have to speak.

Peter Phelps was leader of the Rogues, a year older than his colleagues but in the same class as them because of his slow wits and laziness. He was the first to speak.

"How's creepy crawly today?" They all looked at poor Robert who quailed in dread at being picked on first. "Are his knees all sore from crawling and grovelling?"

"No, they're not," James squeaked, defiantly, "but how is Joe feeling today?"

This took everybody aback and James realised that Joe had yet not mentioned yesterday's set to. In fact, he would probably never mention it to the Rogues. Joe's eyes looked into James', the appeal for secrecy heavy and desperate.

"What do you mean?" Peter was suddenly confused, taken aback by the diversion and the heavy significance of the exchange, although it meant nothing to him.

"Oh, nothing really. Just that Joe and I decided yesterday that it's silly to bully and to fight, and that we'd rather be friends. That right, Joe?"

"Yeah," Joe glanced nervously at Peter.

Instead of being three against three, the balance of the groups had changed subtly such that the Three Musketeers were now faced by only two Rogues – age and size did not tell quite so much. Then Joe changed the situation completely.

"Peter, I don't like fighting. It's wrong to pick on younger boys." With that he walked across to James and put a hand on the smaller boy's shoulder. "I prefer friendship and to be liked. You don't like me; I'm just useful to you."

Nobody could believe it! Peter's jaw dropped. He turned and walked away, followed by the only other remaining Rogue who now seemed uncertain. For a moment he remained rooted to the spot before, almost reluctantly, following his leader. Gentle, bespectacled Robert felt a wash of relief and suddenly feeling returned to his legs. Faithful Harry muttered in exhilaration, "Yes" and then shouted across to the departing pair, "Just leave us alone!"

And courageous James' heart went out to Joe. "Thanks Joe," he said quietly.

James was grateful and astonished. Was this the same boy who had tormented him for so long? Joe was no longer a coward; in fact he'd been the bravest of them all, as if he'd wanted to prove that his failure yesterday was not his true self. Although they never became close friends, the year's age difference was too great for that, they always remained respectful and smiled and chatted when an opportunity occurred. Joe blossomed and eventually became school captain, the year before James did. The Redfield Rogues broke up immediately and, in any case, Peter Phelps left the next year when it became clear that he would never pass his Common Entrance examination for a public school.

Three years later, James passed his Common Entrance for Manorfield Academy, a highly respected public school close to Bristol. Manorfield was not one of the major public schools, but it had an excellent reputation and, in all respects, it suited James and his parents. Jim Anderson had been promoted to Senior Resident Engineer and had requested a plum posting to South Africa where he was to head Arthur Garland's work on a prestigious pumped storage scheme. Helen had honoured her promise to James and had stayed for four years in Bristol whilst her son completed his preparatory schooling at Redfield. But now the twelve-year-old assured his mother that he would be happy to board at Manorfield and take full advantage of the sporting and other extracurricular activities for which the school was renowned.

As James walked into Wishaw House on his first day, a familiar sensation fluttered inside him – nerves and apprehension were now feelings that had become common friends to the sensitive youngster. And yet he was determined not to show any failings. After all, he was now in a senior school where such weaknesses would surely never be tolerated. Also, he knew that Robert was also joining Manorfield that term and he was thrilled to know that they had been allocated to the same House. He looked forward so much to seeing his best friend after eight weeks of summer holiday. Robert was such a genuine friend, with earnest eyes that shone with pleasure whenever he met James. They had become inseparable at Redfield and yet were such different characters. James now enjoyed sport, especially rugby and cricket, and his stick-like frame was beginning to fill out as a result of healthy continuous exercise and natural development. He did not really enjoy boxing but felt an obligation to continue with it because everybody seemed to approve and, in actual fact, he was really quite good at it! Robert, by contrast, had all the appearance of a miniature boffin. His thick National Health spectacles straddled a large forehead and magnified his friendly and intelligent eyes. But physically, Robert was small and uncoordinated. He tried his best at sport and, amid a high degree of activity and effort, he actually achieved nothing remarkable other than to earn the liking of the masters and other boys.

James walked into his new study and saw his friend kneeling in front of an open suitcase amid a welter of chaos, unpacking books and magazines. Two apples rolled across the floor towards James who stooped to pick them up and, with a smile of pleasure, said, "Hi, Robert."

Robert's eyes bulged with delight and he returned the smile. "Hi, James. Look at all the food Mum's given me. Enough for weeks and weeks. I'll share with you."

And there it was. Eight weeks of separation were ignored as the youngsters fell into immediate conversation. Robert's generosity was typical and was immediately repaid by James who offered him a toffee, hot and sticky from his pocket, which Robert struggled to unwrap properly. Eventually he gave up trying to pry loose a single sliver of paper and popped the sweet into his mouth with the tiny piece of wrapper still clinging ferociously to its crinkled sides. The toffee bulged his cheek and he sucked and chewed studiously. Then a dribble ran down his chin as he spluttered with enthusiasm.

"Did you see 'Goldfinger' during the hols? I did. Great! He got sucked out of the plane when it was decompressing. It was amazing, James Bond and Goldfinger had a fight in a jet and a gun went off and blew a window out ..!", and so the amiable chatter continued until the door of the study opened and Mr. Alec Fraser, their housemaster, peered in.

"Hello, boys. Settling in well I see. Nice to hear cheerful banter."

James and Robert stood up respectfully. The flood of chatter stopped. Alec Fraser was a kindly Scot who had interviewed both boys, on separate occasions with their parents, and had made an immediate positive impression on James. Although he looked like a schoolmaster – thinning grey hair and half-moon spectacles were typical 'schoolmasterish' features – Alec's eyes gleamed with humour and mischievous good nature. His barely perceptible Scottish accent carried with it an air of fatherly concern. There was no doubting his affinity to children. His pleasure at meeting James, and his ability to talk with the boy with relaxed ease, had been the main reason why James had agreed to board at Manorfield. James recognised and respected Alec Fraser's sincerity and values. Also, Alec had spoken so enthusiastically about the sporting opportunities at Manorfield that James thrilled at the prospect that lay ahead.

"Hello sir. Robert and I were unpacking. Is that OK?"

"Of course, James. This is your study. The two of you can set it up the way you want. I just popped in to say that I've seen your parents on their way and your mother is very concerned about returning to Africa and leaving you here. So I promised to make sure you had settled in well and to wish you a very happy time at Manorfield. Remember, if there's anything that's troubling you, anything at all, have no fear about speaking to me."

"Yes, sir." In the excitement of meeting Robert, James had momentarily forgotten the gnawing disquiet about leaving his parents. It wasn't as bad as saying goodbye on the platform of Kampala station, but the emptiness and flutter returned in a sudden wash of despair. Alec saw James' face and shoulders droop perceptibly and he felt for the boy. He'd seen it so often in the past.

"Chin up, James. Here's a promise. In a day or two, you'll be in the swing of life here and you'll be enjoying it. Come and see me if I'm wrong and let me know what's not working and I'll put things right. AND I'll take myself to task for misleading you in the first place. That's a promise. OK?"

James smiled with relief although he did miss his mother and couldn't imagine himself being happy in a day or two. Still, he couldn't complain about the way things were turning out so he forced a cheerful "Thanks, sir," and turned to Robert. "Robert's here with me so we'll be OK. He's said I can go home with him at half term and sometimes at the week-end."

"That's very good of you, Robert." Alec's eyes fell on the bespectacled boy. "And the same applies to you. Just see me if you have any worries. It's not easy to start with and you will also be missing your parents. Oh, by the way, boys, supper in half an hour. Don't be late. You'll meet the other boys from Wishaw and make some new friends. Don't eat too much before then." His eyes dropped to the stock of food that Robert had begun to stack onto shelves in the study. "Leave some space for books too!"

With a friendly wink, Alec slipped quietly away smiling with understanding and perception. He knew that James would be fine in a day or two. He had put him in a study with Robert knowing quite well that the benefits for each boy would be mutual. It was also perfectly clear that James would very soon take Robert under his wing!

As predicted, James and Robert soon forgot their homesickness. They were placed in the same classes in most subjects, mainly because their academic levels were similar – both boys had passed the entrance examination with little to spare and were starting their secondary education literally from the bottom! Robert's boffin-like appearance was not supported by intellectual brilliance and James, as ever, tried hard with his studies but really only excelled at sport. The pair became inseparable and very quickly established a routine that allowed them to share a single satchel to carry one set of books to their common classes. As it was Robert's satchel, James carried it, to the interest and amusement of their fellow pupils. A world of lessons, games, hobbies and homework kept them fully occupied and the days passed quickly.

The values of Manorfield comprised a constructive mixture of benign tolerance underpinned by an expectation of good manners and obedience. Thus, James' innate respect for authority ensured that all his teachers liked him and his basic decency and desire to accommodate others made him a popular, if unremarkable, child. James continued to accept that the status quo should not to be challenged, that his elders and teachers were endowed with a wisdom that could only be correct at all times and that it would be wrong to put himself before the needs of others. In a school environment, particularly within an English public school, this philosophy allowed him to flourish. In the years to come, he would eventually begin to understand how much better it would have been if the school had encouraged him to develop a greater degree of independence of mind. However the public school system had survived for over a hundred years on the basis of its traditional and conservative values; it had produced generations of patriotic Britons who had helped their country prevail during two world wars and a multitude of lesser conflicts, who had willingly served in far flung countries during the heady era of colonialism and who continued to feed the country's famous universities and work institutions that still operated on the basis of an increasingly redundant class system. At least with regard to the latter, Manorfield had already seen the direction in which society was moving and, unlike many of the more famous and traditional public schools, it had begun to teach the need to maintain an open and classless approach to the real world that awaited its students.

The terms passed quickly. James excelled at rugby during the winter terms, and cricket during the summer. He therefore loved these terms and relished the feeling that he was contributing to his house and school whenever he represented them in teams. At thirteen, James was a short and chunky boy and so played as a hooker in the front row of the scrum. Early attempts to encourage him to play at scrum half were short lived as he could never resist joining in the melee of loose scrimmages, leaving the vital position of scrum half empty.

His first year games master tried in vain to develop his halfback potential. "Anderson, keep clear of the scrums boy. Stay back and wait for the ball. It'll come to you. You're needed to feed the fly half."

"Yes, sir!" James shouted back enthusiastically until his exuberance once again overcame him and he dived back into the pile of bodies, adding his weight to forward thrusts or pulling fiercely at opponents' arms and legs trying to loosen and release the ball.

Alec Fraser watched the training sessions with particular interest. He could see James' potential as a scrum half and understood why the coach was so keen to develop him in that position. There was no doubt that his darting runs around the scrums were effective and that his direct and fearless tackling in the open was a hugely valuable asset. But he also saw the boy's pleasure in scrummaging, his love of the hard physical rough and tumble of the less flamboyant world of set pieces and forward thrusts, and his determination to win the ball for his team. It was important to have in a team those who were prepared to take knocks, unseen and often unrecognised.

Alec also understood that James would achieve more on the field if he was in his element, so he spoke to the coach.

"If he wants to get involved in the scrum, let him. Give it a go and see how he gets on for a while. If it doesn't work out, we'll put him back at scrum half. But look at the way he gets stuck in. He's an ideal hooker – squat and tough and always right there in the centre of the action."

And it worked! James was in his element. Supported by two sturdy team-mates in the front row, he enjoyed packing in low at set pieces. He loved the challenge of striking and winning the ball, especially against the head, and hearing the shouts of congratulations from his team mates as he emerged last of all from scrums to see the fruits of his effort, when his strike turned defence into attack, or when pushing forward in attack, he helped his team to maintain possession and force the opposition onto the back foot. He also loved the loose play, hoping that the action would break down infield so that he could lead the surging forwards, be first to the point of breakdown and then join in, heaving and thrusting to regain possession.

James soon became a recognised hooker, the best of his year. Manorfield Colts were due to play a neighbouring secondary school. The 'Colts' comprised second year boys, mostly aged fourteen and some even fifteen years old. In choosing his team, the school rugby coach needed to fill this important, but unpopular position. The first choice boy was at home with flu. So he spoke to Alec Fraser about the possibility of promoting James from the 'Yearlings'.

"He's still a youngster, only just thirteen years old. Do you think he'll handle himself or are we being too optimistic?"

Alec thought carefully. "If it was a match within the school, I'd be happy. Anderson wouldn't let you down. He certainly is the best hooker in set pieces. But this is between schools and the Portishead boys are a tough lot. As Comprehensive lads they like to put one across Manorfield, especially as we're regarded as softies and snobs. One or two years is a massive difference at that age and James might be out of his depth. But the lad is fit and very determined to do well. I suggest we pick him and keep Smith as a reserve. If Anderson struggles, we'll pull him off. But let me speak to him and see what his reaction is."

That evening, Alec spoke to James.

"Yes, sir, I'll do it."

The reply did not surprise Alec, but he put his hand up.

"Listen, James, this is not something you have to do. I want you to enjoy your rugby and, in a year or two, see you represent the school at the higher levels. The chance will come again in the future. Don't feel obliged to say yes."

"But I want to, sir, I really do."

James sat in the changing room with the Colts team, waiting to be called out to the pitch. He felt out of his depth in the company of the older boys; in fact he hardly knew any of them to talk to. He'd spent the past three days in a fever of excitement, looking forward to the rugby match and sharing his joy with Robert. But James had thought only of the coming game. He had not considered the build up. The preparations had been tense and sombre and, right now, everything seemed so daunting. James was used to cheerful banter with his friends; now he was a stranger within a group that knew each other well. He watched the other boys change into their rugby strip, navy blue shorts and white shirts with navy blue hoops, and he saw the developed bodies of teenagers whereas his own physique looked so immature and weedy. Her heard gruff, masculine tones whereas his own voice squeaked nervously and suddenly seemed so shrill that he dared not say a word. And he squirmed with self-consciousness when the coach entered the changing room and began the team talk.

"Remember, lads, this is Portishead. They think you're toffee-nosed public school pansies and will be an easy touch. Let's show them that they are wrong and that last year's result was a freak. This time we're at home and they're on our patch. Just play your usual game, give it your all and above all enjoy yourselves. This time we'll win. Now remember, we've got Anderson here as a stand-in hooker. He's good but he's young so give him your support."

All eyes turned to James, who smiled weakly. Nobody smiled back and his heart thumped ever more heavily. He looked to the ground.

"James, remember the signals. Black and Mathers will help you during the game."

The two props scowled fiercely, simply typical adolescent boys trying to be tough, to emulate their adult idols and to pump up their egos. But to James, the atmosphere was cold and unfriendly and he took it to heart. The excitement drained from him so he failed to hear any more of the coach's words.

"Right lads, let's go. Skipper, you lead the way."

The captain, handsome and athletic, picked up the match ball and led them out to the field. The Colts were the only Manorfield team playing at home that Saturday so they had been given the honour of playing on the School First XV's pitch. A small crowd of boys lined one side of the large field and cheered them out, mainly in the excited and high pitched tones of youngsters. Few of the elder boys would deign to watch the Colts. However, several masters and their wives sat on benches and applauded politely. James caught sight of Alec Fraser, sitting with his wife near to the centre line.

Alec called out, "Come on the Colts. Play well, Anderson."

James half raised his arm in recognition before letting it drop self-consciously to his side. Instead, he jumped up and down, pulling his knees to his chest and swinging his arms left and right to loosen up. Then he joined his team-mates in a huddle, straining to put his arms around the shoulders of his taller colleagues. In a daze, he heard nothing that the captain said, but he slowly began to feel a return of excitement as he sensed the buzz of motivation within the group. Then, just before the circle broke apart to take their positions on the field, the captain urged, "Finally, team, everybody give Anderson a pat of encouragement as you go. We won't win if we don't gain possession. He's a key to set piece possession. Play like a lion, James."

Suddenly, the heavy dread was lifted and James head spun with the pure joy of relief and acceptance as a series of friendly touches flipped across his small shoulders and he heard encouraging mutters from his team-mates. He ran to his position, with the rest of the pack, ready to receive the opening salvo from Portishead, who had won the toss and elected to kick off.

As the whistle sounded for the start of the match, James heard the shrill sound of Robert's voice, close by on the touchline. "Go, James, go."

The Portishead fly half launched the ball cleverly, high into the air, giving his forwards time to meet it at its point of landing. Inevitably, the ball floated towards James' tiny figure. He was surrounded by his fellow pack members but the ball fell slowly and unerringly towards him. He fixed his eyes on it with utter determination so he could only sense the approaching strides of the Portishead pack bearing down on him and hear the shout of exhortation from their leader: "Get him."

James did not flinch. He caught the ball cleanly and, for just a moment, he froze waiting for the support of his own pack and the well-rehearsed, combined forward thrust. But the opposing lock arrived first, pumped full of adrenalin and over-enthusiasm. The larger boy leapt at James' shoulders in an attempt to smother him and prevent release of the ball. Instinctively, James ducked and his diminutive physique came to his advantage. He slid below the arms of the onrushing player and was suddenly free, in open space. Instinct took over and he ran towards a gap, surprising the opponents who had expected him to allow his own pack to form a loose scrum and consolidate. Instead James broke away over the gain line and, to a huge cheer from the home crowd, he thrust forward winning ten, fifteen, twenty yards, taking the play into the opposition half. Just as the Portishead backs were about to close him down, he kicked forward, blindly, in desperation. The ball caught his instep and dipped fiercely. What was intended as a punt deep into the opponent's territory, now turned into a delightfully placed grubber kick which skidded and bounced wildly infield, viciously bobbling past the outstretched arms of the Portishead full back who turned in despair as the Colts fly half sprinted past him and scooped the ball up to run over the try line unopposed. Gasps of disbelief and pleasure hissed from the small crowd and then, as one, they cheered and clapped the astounding opening try.

Alec Fraser was delighted for James. "Beginner's luck, you wee blighter," he muttered to himself in pleasure. The instinctive duck and the lucky miskick had not gone unnoticed by Alec's keen eyes. "But you gave it a go and got your reward. Well done laddy, well done."

Edna, his wife, looked at him in surprise. "What's that, Alec dear?"

"Sorry, nothing. Just muttering to myself." He stood up clapping his hands high in the air. Then he called out to the stunned youngster "Well done Anderson, well done. Good quick thinking."

James once again took up his position, in his own half waiting for the easy conversion kick and the restart of the game. He glanced self-consciously at Alec Fraser before spitting dramatically, once on each hand, and crouching down with a fierce intensity. The game started again, this time a deeper kick that was fielded by the Colts' scrum half, who darted towards the safety of his own pack and grounded the ball, which was immediately smothered in a welter of young bodies.

The referee pointed to the Manorfield side and said, "Ball dead, scrum down – possession to the hoops." The first set piece scrum!

James gritted his teeth and reached up to the broad shoulders of his props, Black and Mathers. He looked so small and vulnerable, but he felt a thrill of self-confidence after the amazing start to the game and scowled at the opposing hooker before the front rows dipped and thudded into each other. His opponent was a sturdy fifteen-year-old. They were bound, head locked beside head, and the Portishead hooker rubbed his bristly jaw fiercely against James' smooth cheeks. Once again James experienced a feeling of dread, only momentary, as he was reminded of his immaturity.

His opponent was proud of his two-day growth and was using it to dominate the youngster, literally rubbing James' soft face in it!

"Coming in Colts, coming in … NOW!" The Manorfield scrum half called out his warning at the moment of release and the ball was fed cleanly into the scrum. James struck quickly and was pleasantly surprised at the ease with which he won ball. Possession was retained as James' right foot knocked the ball smoothly back to the Manorfield second row. A perfect strike. The ball was heeled quickly to the No. 8 who allowed release to the scrum half and the Manorfield momentum was maintained. They ran the ball across the backs and gained thirty yards before play broke down and a second scrum was awarded.

"Scrum down … to the hoops." The referee once again gave Manorfield the put-in and the scrum reformed. Yet again James felt the rasping intrusion of his opponent's jaw. Yet again, he concentrated and struck cleanly, gaining possession, but this time he felt a searing pain in his shin. The Portishead hooker had realised that James' speed of strike could not be matched, so he allowed James to win his own ball, instead aiming a vicious kick at his right leg. It was a boorish and unsporting tactic, easy to hide from the referee in the melee of a scrum. James hobbled from the pack, tears of pain and frustration in his eyes.

The match continued, ebbing back and forth across the swathe of the grassy pitch. Every time Manorfield were awarded a scrum, James would strike cleanly, winning possession, but he would become the target of his opponent's well time stabs. At half time, Manorfield were leading 5-0, the early converted try being the only score. Portishead had slowly begun to impose their physical presence on the Colts, who had spent much of the first half in defence. During the half time break, James hobbled to the touchline and asked his housemaster for help.

"My leg's cut, sir. Can I have a bandage?"

Alec was astounded when he saw the bruised and cut shin. Nobody had noticed the cowardly actions of the Portishead hooker, but this could not have been caused by a single accident. Alec Fraser's sharp mind understood clearly what was happening.

"James, do you want to come off for the second half. This is not right."

"No, sir"

"Then, we'll bandage you up right now and give you plenty of padding. Brave lad, don't get downhearted. I'll have a word with the referee. If this goes on into the second half, let me know and we'll bring you off, but don't worry, the ref will watch the scrums carefully from now on."

As no shin protectors could be found (this was not a game of football), James' leg was bound thickly with a long bandage and he trotted back to his team-mates.

"The lads got guts, Edna. He's so keen to play the match out, but this isn't sport any more. I hope Mr. Wilmshurst catches the culprit."

Peter Wilmshurst was appalled to hear about the first half tactics of the Portishead hooker. Just before the half time break came to an end he summoned their coach, together with the sullen No. 2, and laid down the law.

"I haven't seen it happen and I can't prove it, but I've seen the result and it's disgusting. Do you understand? We'll have no more of this nonsense. No second chances or warnings. If I catch you trying that tactic again, you're off, and that will only be the start of something you'll regret for a long time lad. This is sport, not a war."

James enjoyed the second half. He felt bruised, but exhilarated, as he held his own against his opponent. In a tense, pulsating match, he won every strike with the head and even managed to win two against the head as the frustrated Portishead No. 2 began to lose heart.

The year before, the Colts had been thrashed 45-3 in a high scoring open match. This year, deep into injury time, Manorfield held tenaciously on to an 8-6 lead in a tight match dominated by kicks to touch and set scrums. As a rugby spectacle it was a dull affair. Nonetheless the drama of the situation held the onlookers in mesmerised awe. Gradually the numbers in the crowd were swelled as passing teachers and boys caught sight of the scoreboard and realised that an upset was on the books. Everybody seemed to be drawn by the drama, even those with no interest in rugby.

Manorfield were wilting under an onslaught from the larger and more physical Portishead team. In the dying moments, the match seemed lost as the lightning-fast Portishead wing back struck loose and surged down the touchline, breaking two despairing tackles from the Colts defence. Finally, and miraculously, the Colts full back tapped his ankles and the winger stumbled just short of the Manorfield line. James hurled himself on the falling opponent, preventing him from rising and, instead, a loose scrum formed but the ball was not released. Peter Wilmshurst whistled for a set scrum. Who would be given the put-in? The Portishead winger had knocked the ball forward in the tackle. It seemed clear to those nearby but had the referee seen the knock-on and would he award the scrum to Manorfield? Everything hinged on this decision.

"Scrum down, red ball."

A gasp of dismay rose from the Manorfield team. Portishead had gained the put-in, and the advantage now swung dramatically to the visiting team. Only five yards from their line, the Colts could only hope that their exhausted defence could hold out against the inevitable loss of possession at the impending scrum. Portishead now had a perfect attacking opportunity, with options left and right, and they would certainly use the crashing weight of their star fly half. Any score would mean a defeat for the brave Colts. There would be no time for a restart.

The Colts captain ran up to James and put his arm around the youngster. He also called the two prop forwards and breathlessly made the final exhortation.

"Listen. They'll be expecting an eight-man push from us. Mathers and Black, you set up with James as if that's what we're going for. But James, don't join the thrust, go for the strike against the head. The chances are slim, but go for it. I won't blame you if you fail. Just remember that if you win possession for us, all we have to do is hoof the ball out of play and the ref will blow time up. Get your own back on their hooker and win us the match. Go lads, go!" He slapped James' back and the youngster thrilled to the trust and his complete acceptance as one of the team.

The three bound together, felt the second row join them and then the two packs locked for the final time. James feinted as if to set up for the eight man push but, just as the Portishead scrum half fed the ball into the scrum, he swung himself forward from a crouching thrust to an upright stance and flashed his right foot at the ball, stealing in front of the labouring strike of his opponent. Then, using the outside of his foot, he dragged the ball from the Portishead front row with a determined sideways pull.

"Yes!"

James heard the shout of jubilation from his skipper. At fly half position, the captain had a perfect view of the scrum and thrilled at the vital clean strike. The first part of his strategy had paid off. Now they had to use the hard won possession. He shouted to his forwards.

"Hold steady, scrum hold steady. Keep control, keep control."

The ball was fed back, through the second row and was held at the feet of the back row forward. "Hold it, hold it." The No. 8 obeyed, forcing the Portishead scrum to remain bound until the ball was released.

"Now, now, release."

The scrum half whipped the ball from the feet of the back row and passed it perfectly to his skipper, who caught it and, just before the surging Portishead backs could nail him, he hoofed the ball safely into touch.

Peter Wilmshurst blew the whistle; three long blasts, signalling the end of the titanic encounter. A massive cheer erupted from the spectators. Young boys leapt in the air, older ones applauded without restraint and the more dignified adults beamed and clapped in delight. Alec Fraser stood up and applauded the two teams as they walked off the pitch, sportingly giving each other three cheers. Even the Portishead lads offered their cheers with respect and gusto! He was delighted to see James' two prop forwards hoist the youngster briefly onto their weary shoulders.

"Well done, boys, great stuff!" Alec called across to the exhilarated threesome. He was a dedicated teacher and mentor and it was at times like this that he felt a surge of well-being knowing that he was experiencing the true rewards for his patience and energy. The glow on James' face repaid the many hours of toil and behind the scenes effort, thinking and planning how to bring the best out of his boys. Last year, after Manorfield's heavy defeat at the hands of Portishead, Alec had felt pride at the team's dignity in their moment of despair. He had personally thanked the boys for their courage and for the manner in which they had applauded their victors with grace and good nature. Alec remembered how he had spoken later to the demoralised Colts about "Loss without losing." "Remember boys," he had said, "competing is about doing the best you can and having no regrets if you lose. If you can all say that you did your best, then you have won. That may seem hard to appreciate right now, but it is a truth and wisdom that you will learn more about as life goes on. But remember that the same applies in victory and, believe me, victory will come to you all just as often as defeat. It is equally possible to win without winning. So never cheat and always act with honour."

Today, uncannily and yet inevitably, he had witnessed the other side of the coin and his heart went out to the team, most of whom were newcomers to the Colts. But a handful of the team had played last year and had remembered his advice, providing living proof of those words right now in the way they shook hands with their opponents and congratulated them as fellow participants in the game of rugby.

Alec mused to himself as he relished this moment of pleasure.

"Uncanny the way the world responds to your thoughts and repays you for what you give out. There's something more to it all than just luck or coincidence."

In his third year at Manorfield, James was asked by 'Cass' Cassell to join the 'Never Again Club'. Cass was an elderly teacher, a bachelor whose sole purpose in life was to nurture and develop Manorfield's pupils. He was a legend. No other master, living or dead, had served longer. The world contained people like Cass in the same way that huge rock formations contained tiny crystals of diamond, hidden from view in a mass of bedrock. Occasionally they would be unearthed, dull and covered in grime until spotted, glistening amid a mass of ordinariness. Only then could they be polished and cut into sparkling perfection. Cass had been spotted forty five years ago by a former headmaster who needed a helper to take the Manorfield Scouts on their annual camp – somebody to organise games for the boys, to supervise tent erection, fire building and latrine digging. Peter Cassell had been a youthful assistant groundsman, helping to maintain the school's pitches and facilities. But he had caught the old headmaster's eye with his enthusiasm and his desire to help the boys, some not much younger than himself, in their sports training.

Cass had never had the good fortune to receive more than a basic education. Yet in the past forty-five years, he had gradually taken over some of the teaching duties, taking the younger boys for History and Geography, both subjects that he had taught himself. Through personal study he had become a mine of information and then, with enthusiasm and an irrepressible sense of fun, he had translated his knowledge into stimulating and enjoyable lessons. Thus, Cass had become an institution, loved and respected by all who passed through Manorfield's impressive portals. Even the Board of Governors had accepted him after initially frowning upon this unqualified teacher. They had arranged for Cass's lessons to be monitored and were staggered by the outcome, clucking in disbelief before bravely bucking the traditions of the education system and finding devious ways to increase his workload. Even the most crusty and rule-bound had been forced to agree that they had found their diamond.

At the end of the war, when Cass returned to his beloved school after completing four years of military service with the infantry, he had started the 'Never Again Club'. During the war, he had met many young men whose lives had been filled with drudgery – young men who never had the benefit of an education such as Manorfield provided and who were destined to return to that same drudgery in peacetime. And so, to Cass, 'Never Again' meant that he would never again take for granted his good fortune in finding Manorfield nor would he ever allow the school's pupils to take for granted their privileged start in life. However, the boys who joined the club had soon taken 'Never Again' at face value. As its reputation grew over the years, those who were its honoured members became convinced that they were being asked to do things that were so challenging and fearsome that they would never wish to repeat the experience! They were happy to perpetuate the myth.

"James, now that you are sixteen, you qualify for the 'Never Again' Club. I only ask boys who will make the most of what we do, who enjoy physical activity and who are prepared to take on unusual challenges. Are you game?"

"Yes sir."

Yet again James would have found it difficult to say no but, on this occasion, he was enthused with a feeling of intrigue and pleasure at being asked to join this strange club. All he knew was that the members would sometimes disappear for weekends and would return filthy and exhilarated. Sometimes they may be seen dangling at the end of ropes in precarious locations, or emerging from potholes in the Cheddar Gorge. Cass chose his boys well. None had ever refused a challenge and always there was an air of fun and buoyancy that carried over several days after their meetings, stimulating excited chatter and oft-repeated tales of amazing and intriguing goings on. At any one time there were only ever four boys in the Club.

James' first experience came a few weeks later. Cass waited for a glorious May weekend before springing the surprise on him, together with the three other members. The sun beat down from a cloudless sky and the forecast for the next day, Sunday, was for no change.

"Don't go anywhere tomorrow, boys. Be outside my house at 8.00 am sharp. Wear casual clothes and good strong climbing boots. Ask the kitchens to prepare a picnic for eight people."

"Why eight, sir? Who's coming as well?"

"Never you mind. By the way, find out what you can about Borstals."

James always took instructions from adults very seriously. That night he asked his housemaster if he had any suggestions for reading. "About Borstals, sir."

Alec Fraser chuckled, knowing why the request was being made. He'd spoken to Cass earlier in the day and had been forewarned.

"Try a novel, James – 'The Loneliness of the Long Distance Runner' – we've got it in the library. It's a good read. I'll say no more."

So James spent the evening skimming through the famous story and wondered what the next day would hold. Would they be going for a long run, or would they be meeting boys from an approved school? It had to be one of the two.

"Meet Joe, Art and Billy, lads." Cass introduced the four public schoolboys to three sullen teenagers who simply scowled and muttered aggressively. Instantly, the atmosphere chilled as adolescents from entirely different backgrounds sized each other up.

"They're from Polston. I've got special permission to let them join us in today's activity. So come on lads, you're the hosts – talk to each other, and be prepared to share in the fun!"

Cass slipped away, intentionally leaving the boys to their own devices. He pretended to scout the side of the Avon Gorge, looking for a suitable spot for abseiling. But he kept the seven youngsters in his sight, watching with interest to see what would develop. James made the first move. He crossed to Billy and put out his hand in friendship.

"Hi, I'm James, pleased to meet you."

Billy eyed him suspiciously, then glanced across at Cass and, knowing he was being watched, took James' hand and held it in a challenging grip.

"Billy Nichols. You been in a fight then?" He nodded his head and raised his eyes, indicating the thin white scar that was still clearly visible across James' face. "How long ago did you get that?"

"I was born with a disfigurement. That's just an old scar from an operation. So what?"

"So you're a stuck up public school s***head whose never been in a fight then. Bet you've never seen it tough either?"

James' heart sank. He wanted to be friendly, but this was difficult to respond to and he felt a rush of panic, until he remembered his set-to with the 'Redfield Rogues'. A surge of determination helped to fill him with confidence and displace his agitation. He took a deep breath.

"I've maybe not had it tough, chum, but I've seen it tough OK. You try living in Africa before you think you've got it bad. Kids out there on the streets, starving to death with no legs who still know how to be friendly. They're tougher than you'll ever be with your roof over your head and your three meals a day. Don't try to compare tough with me. Tough's stupid. Friendship's what matters. You want to be friends or just waste the day? Makes no odds to me."

"Didn't ask to be here. Didn't ask to mix with you lot," Billy shot back.

"Suit yourself, chum. Have a miserable day if you want. I'm off to have fun."

James turned to Cass, flushed with anger and boiling with frustration at his own inability to communicate with somebody so different to himself. He cringed at the sound of his own accent and the clumsy way that he'd tried to coarsen his speech to accommodate the other's style. But it hadn't worked and now he felt humiliated, utterly despondent.

"Don't give up James. You tried to accept Billy as an equal, but it's harder for him. Be friendly – it's your nature, but also be proud of your background. Let Billy see what's good about your type. By the way, he's got no parents. Fell into bad ways because there was nobody to guide him or love him. But he's got a heart of gold. Loves animals too."

That was all Cass had time to say before the other boys joined them, wordlessly. The atmosphere still crackled with the tension of hostile silence. Even Cass wondered if he had made a mistake.

"Right, lads. Abseiling. Who's done it before and who wants to be shown how?" Cass dug his heel into the gravelly topsoil and pointed to the Avon River three hundred feet below them. "One way or another we're going to go from here to there straight down this cliff face."

"No way!" Billy peered over the precipice. The river was so far down, it glistened, but only dully like a foul muddy mirror. The tide was out and there was no sign of flow, just murky shades of brown from stagnant mud on the banks and the sliver of water, hundreds of feet beneath them, easing its way beneath the Clifton suspension bridge. It seemed to Billy that a bottomless pit of cloying slime awaited him and he imagined himself falling into its evil, sucking clutches. The prospect appalled the youth who had never before been introduced to abseiling.

"I'll help you, Billy. I've abseiled before so here's the deal. We team up and I make sure you're safe and enjoy the thrill; then you can tell me about life on the tough side of the street." Once again, James cringed at his awful attempt at conversation, but he was amazed at the response.

"OK. Can't let you ponces think we've got no guts. It's a deal. When we get down there in one piece, I'll show you a few things." Billy eyed his friends coldly, daring them to chicken out of the challenge.

James showed Billy how to attach himself to the ropes. At first, they practised over a small bank until Billy felt confidence in the straps and support of the ropes. Then James encouraged the teenager with quiet words and gentle urges of congratulation whilst he leaned backwards over the yawning drop and eased himself slowly down the cliff face.

"That's it, that's it. Great. Try a little faster when you get the feel of it. Nothing can go wrong."

Billy's terror gradually subsided. Nobody had ever encouraged him in such a positive way. His fear, hidden by a determination not to refuse the challenge and lose face, slowly gave way to true exhilaration, a new and wonderful experience. It was a visceral feeling that took him, in one and the same moment, to the edge of fear and pleasure. And with each foot that he descended his confidence grew.

"Well done. Well done!" James really meant it. He'd been thrilled to see the change in Billy, how the rigor of horror gave way to a bright-eyed gleam of pleasure. "Try swinging out and dropping a few feet. That's the best bit. Wow, you've done it! And again, more this time."

As he reached the ledge by the cave, Billy whooped with joy, his rolling Bristol accent exaggerating the tremor of pleasure.

"F*** me, that's something unreal that is. Whehey!"

"Hang on there, Billy, uncouple yourself; it's my turn. I'm coming now."

Then James leaned backwards and launched his body away from the cliff face, dropping ten feet at a time before the pendulum motion swung his feet back into contact with the rock face. Like an agile floating monkey, James plunged and swooped his way down to Billy in only a few seconds. Billy gasped with admiration and grinned at his newfound friend. Now they sat beside each other in the small cave. It could not be seen from the top of the gorge, but Cass had known about it and was now using it as a rest point, part way down the cliff face.

"F***ing show off." Billy punched James' shoulder and scowled conspiratorially to show no hard feelings.

They sat together for a several minutes, waiting for the others to arrive, and chatted inanely about the experience, how it was just like the SAS and how there was nothing to it. They planned what they would do with this newfound skill and James spoke of the East African Rift Valley, and Billy of prison walls that could be scaled. "Not been there like," he qualified himself immediately, guilty with the sudden revelation of his past. "Just know about it from talk you know." But James' face only showed fascination. He'd become utterly enthralled by Billy's chatter and vivid stark honesty of character. The Polston lad immediately relaxed and returned James' smile. "We're no different, you and me."

"I know," said James, not realising the wisdom of what he was about to say. It just came out, naturally, as just another part of their open and absorbing interaction. "What's outside is full of difference. What's inside is full of no difference." Sitting side by side on a ledge high above the Avon River, James remembered that other moment, years before, as he had sat on a pavement edge with the mutilated, mucus-encrusted black waif. Momentarily James once again had the pure unsullied mind of a five-year-old. He put his arm onto Billy's shoulder.

"Hey, Billy, will you be my friend?"

Chapter 7

Learning to Trust

During their first summer together, Lisa planned for Chelsea to be at working livery. Her intention was simply to enjoy Chelsea's company, getting to know her and developing a rapport whilst, at the same time, continuing to improve her own riding skills. By now she was confident that she understood the basics of horse care and, for more complex or unforeseen aspects of horse management, she was quite happy to rely on the support of the Kinord staff. Lisa's work was still taking her away from home so, this way, Chelsea would continue to be given work and some schooling when she wasn't around. The Kinord staff were also keen to have Chelsea on this basis and Lisa felt confident that they would take care of the horse in her absence. Thus working livery seemed the ideal option.

But she had not reckoned on Chelsea's thoughts on the matter, nor the extent to which those thoughts would influence her own life! Remembering her recent harsh schooling, Chelsea made it perfectly clear that working livery was unacceptable. So she ran away with or ejected any rider she didn't like, particularly those who used force or hectoring tones that reminded her of Mike Feherty. When she was working away from home, Lisa began to dread her phone calls with the yard. What would Chelsea have done next and what drama would be waiting to be reported? Those who rode Chelsea were all experienced and, on the whole, seemed to be kind and patient, but it became clear that they were dividing into two categories – those, a very few, who adored the mare and asked if they could ride her again and those, the majority, who never wanted to see her again. This both puzzled and deeply touched Lisa because, although she was not yet experienced, Chelsea sensed her love and never took advantage of her. Together, they simply enjoyed being out and about.

Already Chelsea was whispering to Lisa, explaining that she did not like the present arrangements and that Lisa was away far more than she ought to be! Inspired by these views, Lisa resolved to find a way of being at home more often. The rewards were all too enticing. She loved the routine of those wonderful summer days – up with the first daylight and riding by 6.00 am, meeting deer and their young, watching buzzards hunt for breakfast, listening to the excited chatter of blackbirds and the calming response of wood pigeons and, most of all, simply enjoying one another's company. Lisa had always had a tendency towards workaholism, loving her job and her customers and being proud of her small business. But Chelsea was whispering that there was more to life. So Lisa responded, recognising and relishing the benefits of an all-absorbing passion. Like many others, she enjoyed the staples of gardening, cooking, reading and walking, all of which could be turned on and off in deference to work. Chelsea, on the other hand, was a much more powerful distraction. She had to be cared for and exercised but, above all, she had become a friend whom Lisa missed if she didn't see every day. Chelsea made Lisa stop, think, and simply *be*.

Something else made her stop and think – having a horse for the first time was rather like having a new baby. Everyone wanted to give Lisa advice, and mostly it was contradictory. She soon discovered that, in the case of horses, there were three main schools of thought:

'Traditionalists' derived their views from the army and hunting – horses should be dominated otherwise they would take advantage of their riders.

The 'Racing' mentality – these people were often harsh but tended to make some allowance for individuals, especially those who were winners. However, a horse that did not perform would be given little sympathy or love.

And finally, 'Horse-centred' people such as Monty Roberts, who were able to see things from the horse's viewpoint and would try to understand 'Equus', the language of horses, and would both listen to and communicate in that language. Lisa's extensive reading and her practical experience were teaching her that this approach, although requiring much patience and dedication, was immensely rewarding, particularly for those for whom a horse was more than simply an object of work or play.

Lisa's granite resolve was tested but never wavered so, although Chelsea was not the easiest horse for a relative newcomer to riding, something deep within the mare understood that Lisa's rawness of skill was not a sign of weakness. Instead, it was compensated for by love and dedication, both of which combined to make manifest a gentle firmness. Jean Walker was of the traditionalist school of thought and constantly reminded Lisa to "Take no nonsense" and "Make her get on with it". In other areas of life, Lisa was not interested in throwing her weight around. As a consultant she tended not to have any direct authority over people and, instead, used her influence quietly. Thus, in just the same way that she never imposed her will upon her clients, so with Chelsea she took the same approach. Calm certainty of purpose, coupled with gentleness and love, achieved so much more! And whenever the siren calls of traditionalism that surrounded Lisa at Kinord told her that Chelsea would soon take advantage of her, she stood by her instincts to be kind but firm, remembering the famous 'Birtwick Balls' served up by the kindly groom in 'Black Beauty': "kindness and patience, firmness and gentleness all wrapped up in common sense and fed daily".

It felt so much more natural to ask Chelsea to do something, to understand her fears and praise her when she obliged, rather than scold her for being petulant and spooky. After all, who had made her that way in the first place? Lisa accepted, not simply as a challenge but also as a wonderful prospect of fun-filled rewarding sessions to come, that it would be necessary to take time to earn Chelsea's trust. As a consequence, this approach was vindicated sooner than Lisa expected. Chelsea responded best when Lisa was calm and confident and very quickly became happy to let Lisa be the leader. With Alison and Jane, both of whom were hesitant, Chelsea had become bothered and alarmed; so then she had taken charge and her negative traits of panic and petulance had come to the fore. Similarly, to show Chelsea anger, especially when she was already afraid, would terrify her even more. Her memories of Mike Feherty would never fade!

At first, the successes came in small ways. Lisa noticed that, in the first few weeks, if any small thing alarmed Chelsea early on in the day, she would spend the rest of the day in a lather of anxiety, expecting monsters round every tree and corner. Gradually, after a little time, she became much calmer and scary things caused less alarm and were quickly put behind her – she'd stop spooking at every strange object, or walking round the outside bend on the forest tracks to see what was coming! Simply, a quiet word of encouragement and a pat for being brave worked wonders. Chelsea shed her fears and once again began to trust humans, or at least one human, in the same way as she had done with Eric many years before when the gas cylinder had exploded. Amazingly, Lisa too became even more unflappable. One of her clients remarked upon this calmness and added that it was one of the reasons why they valued her presence in their office! Well done, Chelsea! The effect that each was having on the other was remarkable.

Lisa made another discovery very early on – Chelsea's brakes were non-existent! It wasn't that she bolted – just that she tended not to stop. When she arrived at Kinord Lisa discovered that Chelsea had been ridden in a very strong bit. Presumably this was to try to restrain her and make her more controllable. She also wore a martingale, a device that certainly has a proper place in helping to control a horse's head but, in Chelsea's case, it had been fastened tightly to stop her tossing her head. This was both incorrect and unkind. With advice from a kindly and knowledgeable friend who agreed with Lisa's approach, they chose a much kinder bit, dispensed with the martingale and made a few other adjustments to her tack. Lisa discarded contraptions that mechanically re-engineered a horse's posture and behaviour in the same way that methods of compulsion and discipline in schools and the workplace were being reappraised by society. In both circumstances, not everybody agreed.

Lisa was much inspired by Monty Robert's book 'The Man Who Listens to Horses', which had been published not long before she met Chelsea. In the book, Monty describes his experience with a horse called 'My Blue Heaven' who also would not stop. Monty taught the horse to love stopping more than keeping going and before long My Blue Heaven was winning competitions. Although Lisa's riding skills were no match for Monty's, she was determined to follow the same principles. First, they started at walk. When Lisa asked Chelsea to halt and the mare responded, she got a pat and was lavished with praise. Gradually they worked up through the paces – walk, trot and, greatest test of all, canter. It took time before Lisa could really trust the brakes but they got there in the end and eventually the reward came – Chelsea learned to stop simply in response to Lisa's voice.

Chelsea learned to love stopping more than going on. This reminded Lisa of her own successful approach to losing weight – by learning to love the feeling of slight hunger rather than always satisfying the urge to fill up at every meal. Simply by praising Chelsea whenever she stopped, Lisa taught her companion to enjoy the rewards – sometimes a Polo mint would be slipped into her mouth, or a piece of carrot which Lisa always put in her pocket before taking Chelsea out on a hack, or sometimes she would simply lean forward in her saddle and pat the side of the mare's neck, murmuring appreciatively in the ever-listening ears which, like radar dishes, would twist and flick in a constant scan of her surroundings and her mistress' instructions.

Kinord offered a superb variety of hacks. Tracks wound through wooded valleys, across open fields and up into heather and bracken covered hills and mountains. There was always a choice of routes that included opportunities to canter and gallop but the most exciting one of all was called The Windrush. The most experienced riders favoured this steep track because it offered a long, straight uphill pull over a soft peaty earth track with few stones or boulders. Instinctively, all the Kinord horses knew that when they were turned up The Windrush they could expect to break into canter. For this reason, ride leaders seldom used The Windrush when taking out novices or nervous folk who did not want to lose control of their mounts. But, occasionally, there would be sufficient demand for such a challenge and the leaders would delight in the opportunity to experience the thrill of a full-blooded gallop.

Towards the end of Lisa's first summer with Chelsea, she decided that her own skill and confidence levels were now sufficient to join a party of more experienced riders hacking out with Kinord's head girl. Gail was in her early twenties and had been riding all her life. She was filled with the confidence of youth and was unable to fully appreciate how others could be beset with uncertainty and apprehension. She was lightly built, but her muscles were toned by years of riding so her legs straddled the sides of horses in a confident and powerful grip that gave her a sense of security and balance that was by now instinctive. But Gail could not relate to those whose strength and fitness levels, whether through age or lack of riding experience, were not perfect. Lisa had seen Gail lead hacks before and had wondered at the girl's suitability to take responsibility for such events. The girl had no patience and would chivvy other riders, clucking crossly when they failed to keep up, or showed tiredness or any form of weakness. Under the guise of 'ensuring everybody's well-being', she led in a bossy and imperious manner and her normally pretty face could instantly become set in a look of sulky disapproval or, worse still, haughty derision. Today, Gail was delighted. All the riders had indicated that they could canter and one of the party was her old school friend, Della, an excellent rider with whom she'd enjoyed many exciting times.

"You can all canter so I'll take you up The Windrush. Keep behind me and nobody try to overtake. I'll set the pace. OK?"

Without waiting for a reply, Gail turned to Della and a giggle of excitement carried across to the mounted party. Lisa felt a stirring of alarm. Gail was planning the hack around her own pleasure. But being able to canter was very different from being competent to negotiate the cavalry charge that inevitably ensued when the horses got a scent of The Windrush and felt the challenge of each other's presence.

"Gail, are you sure everybody's up for this?"

Lisa eyed the three remaining members of the group and saw the alarm in the face of a tall middle-aged man. He sat comfortably and confidently in the saddle and had obviously ridden before, but his eyes betrayed an anxiety.

Gail looked scornfully at Lisa. "You've all said you can canter, so we'll canter. I'll keep a safe pace. Lisa, you go at the back if you're worried. Keep well away from the pack and, if you want, you can walk up The Windrush. Right everyone, me first, then Della, then the remaining four pick up a single file in any order."

With that, Gail nudged Bruno's sides and her gelding led the party out of the yard and onto the forest tracks. Lisa waited for the others to follow and then spoke quietly to the man.

"Hello, I'm Lisa Graham. Have you ridden here before? I don't remember seeing you."

"Once or twice, a year ago. I used to ride quite a bit but I've not done much since I began working in Holland so I sold my horse. This is a 'getting back to riding' session so I'm a bit nervous, but I should be OK. My name's Peter by the way."

"Tell you what, Peter, you go last and I'll go just in front of you. That way we can keep each other company if we don't want to take The Windrush full tilt."

Lisa's concern began to fade as she now knew that Peter was more experienced than she initially thought. Nonetheless, she could not completely shake off her disquiet. Peter was riding Benjy, a lovely young gelding but with a reputation for flightiness and excitability. The two chatted amiably as they wandered through the forest and, in no time, Lisa felt Chelsea fidget with excitement, sensing that the turn off to The Windrush was approaching. Lisa turned in her saddle and saw Benjy jogging and pulling, but Peter seemed to be in control.

Fifty yards ahead, Gail stopped and turned Bruno around to face the party and wait for them to close ranks. She smiled at Della in anticipation of the thrill that lay ahead.

"Right everybody, I'll turn left at the next fork and will walk for twenty yards, then I'll break into an easy canter. Is everybody ready? Right, off we go."

Peter muttered, "As ready as I'll ever be," and shortened his grip on the reins, taking a handful of Benjy's wiry mane. Lisa smiled back at him before turning to face the front, feeling a damp clamminess in her hands as she too shortened her grip.

"Walking, just walking, Chels; that's my girl."

Chelsea responded immediately to her nudge and Lisa once again felt the horse tighten with excitement. Up ahead, Gail and Della had taken the turn up The Windrush and had broken into a canter, both rising expertly in their stirrups and leaning forward in perfect balance going with the explosive movement of their mounts. One after the other, the trailing horses broke into canter and Chelsea followed instinctively, her competitive urge now taking over as she closed the gap on the horse ahead. Lisa heard Peter shout, "Wheyhey!" as Benjy too took up the challenge. All six horses were in full flight and Lisa thrilled to the experience, sensing the rush of trees on either side. But she looked ahead, avoiding any downward glance at the ground, now surging beneath Chelsea's powerful legs. It was wonderful – the sound of pounding hooves and the onrush of wind blowing manes backwards and caressing the excited eager faces of the riders. Chelsea loved it and responded to the atmosphere which was now palpable with an intensity and tension.

Ahead, Gail and Della urged their horses forward and the canter became an uncontrollable racing gallop as the horses responded to their own challenges with each other and ignored the riders. Gail whooped with pleasure and gave Bruno free rein. Behind, the other horses responded and each rider felt a distinct surge of acceleration. Lisa had never been so fast before. Even in the thrill of the moment she wondered with amazement at Chelsea's power and pulled backwards on the reins, testing her response and gaining a small degree of control. Chelsea checked very slightly then, sensing no further pull, she once again drove herself towards the horse ahead, easily making up the ground. Without room to pass on the narrow track, she was forced to maintain her position.

In the rear, Peter felt a gradual loss of control. His grip on Benjy's mane tightened as he felt the gelding pick up the pace of the others. He heard Benjy's breathing, gasps of air perfectly synchronised with the rhythm of the gallop. Peter's legs had weakened over months of sedentary office-based living and he very soon realised how quickly he was tiring and losing stability in the saddle. Unlike the girls ahead, he sat deep in the saddle, trying to ride with the rocking motion. However, with his grip on the mane, he was still leaning forward so he was unbalanced when Benjy stumbled briefly over a small rain-washed rut in the path. Peter held on grimly and only just regained his position but now felt a complete loss of confidence combined with tiredness. He shouted, "Whoa, Benjy, whoa."

The gelding was out of control, completely absorbed by the race and only recognising, in Peter's frantic cries, sounds of greater excitement and exhortation. So he surged forward ever more purposefully towards Chelsea's galloping form. Peter had almost reached that moment when despair gives way to acceptance. He was now certain that he would fall and felt a clarity of thought that surprised him as he wondered whether he would hit a tree when he rolled.

Ahead, Lisa heard his cries of despair and sensed what was happening but with Chelsea in full flight she also felt the same loss of control and was certain that she could do nothing. However, she eased the reins back, quietly without any sudden jerking, and used her voice in a long slow calming tone: "Whoah-ho, whoah-ho, Chelsea. Steady now, steady."

Amazingly, Chelsea responded, one ear flicking back to listen to the commands of her beloved mistress. Instinctively, without further thought, the faithful mare eased back from the gallop to a controlled canter and then to an immediate trot before settling back to a brief walk.

"Well done, Chelsea!" Lisa felt like shouting for joy but kept her voice low and calm. "Steady now, and Whoa."

They came to a halt. Behind, Benjy had been unable to pass Chelsea on the narrow track and he too had fallen back to a walk, before stopping close to the mare's sweating quarters, breathing heavily with disappointed excitement. Lisa felt her throat tighten with pride and love. A tear glistened in one eye. She felt a surge of emotion, gratitude mixed with love. Chelsea, her wonderful, faithful Chelsea, had listened and obeyed, had repaid her for all the time spent patiently working at stopping and had done it under circumstances in which very few horses would have responded. In the middle of her excitement, Chelsea had ignored the chase and had stopped! It was truly amazing. Lisa leaned forward across the mare's withers and, with one arm now on either side of Chelsea's neck, she hugged and patted the darling animal.

"Thank you, Chels. Thank you so much." Lisa spoke aloud but quietly, and the words were choked with emotion so she dared not look up at Peter's smiling face. Instead she hid her tear-filled eyes down the far side of Chelsea's neck as Peter, in turn, thanked her.

"Sorry to ruin your gallop, Lisa, but I was in trouble – just about to fall. You probably saved me from serious injury. Thanks so much."

At last, after a noticeable pause, Lisa felt able to speak without appearing emotional and stupid.

"Peter, it's my pleasure. In fact you've made my year. Galloping I can do any time. Today, I've been rewarded by Chelsea's learning and respect for me. I'll never forget ..." Once again her voice choked and she hid her face against the neck of the best horse in the world. Lisa was unaware that, even with her limited riding experience, she had achieved more than Majella: she had, through listening and love, gained the mare's confidence and respect, and a willingness to obey even in the midst of a full, competitive gallop.

One month later, Lisa joined a group of ladies for a three-day expedition through the Grampian and Cairngorm mountains. This was Chelsea's first experience of expedition riding so Lisa was a little anxious, but her natural optimism and respect for Chelsea's abilities came to the fore and she concluded that they would both enjoy the challenge, which required stamina rather than skill. As it transpired, Lisa need not have had any doubts – Chelsea took to the experience with what was becoming a typical joie de vivre, an enthusiasm for anything that entailed being out and about with her caring and intelligent mistress.

On the first day, she cantered up a mountain – her choice of pace – and confidently crossed rough, plank bridges. However, it became clear that neither Lisa nor Chelsea had a head for heights so they soon struck a deal. Chelsea would carry Lisa up hills and Lisa would dismount and lead her down if the slopes were too steep. So good was Chelsea to lead in hand that, when they were forced to negotiate a fast flowing burn at the bottom of a rough track, Lisa didn't bother to mount again; she was confident that she could pick and leap her way across the glistening granite boulders that cluttered the watercourse, using them as stepping stones, allowing Chelsea a long rein. The unconcerned mare was content to tread her own path carefully over the uneven rocky bed of the stream. An instinctive confidence in each other's ability and support had grown so Lisa was certain that Chelsea would stay with her and not pull her into the water.

On the second day out, Chelsea's willingness to trust and stay with Lisa became essential. Their path had been washed away by summer storms and they were forced to make a long diversion by following a narrow deer track instead, before finding their own way down a steep hillside and back onto the main track far below them. Brushing through a patch of blaeberries they struck off straight down what Lisa considered to be a 'wall of death'. Lisa dismounted and kicked her heels into the soft peaty earth to cut out steps and prevent an uncontrollable downward slither. Chelsea looked at her, her eyes bright with affection and intelligence as if to say, "It's OK, I'm right with you." It was a look that Lisa would learn to love and recognise, especially when things became tricky.

All the way down the hill, Chelsea slipped and slithered in perfect step with Lisa. Had the mare hesitated or rushed ahead, she would have pulled Lisa off her feet. Instead she ducked her head with typical alert intelligence and watched her mistress, taking the same careful line as her in a studied and perfectly coordinated descent. When they reached the main track again, Lisa gave Chelsea a huge hug, and a Polo mint, whilst helping herself to a dram of Lochnagar Malt from a small silver hip flask. It had been a difficult moment.

With her arms around the proud mare's neck, Lisa whispered into an ever-attentive ear, "Chelsea, you're a star."

The horse dipped her neck with a mixture of what Lisa could only describe in contradictory terms: "You madam, you; stop showing such delighted nonchalance. You know well enough that that was a hairy moment."

Chelsea merely turned her head away in response and examined a distant kestrel with an air of cool aplomb. With another pat, Lisa stood on the upside of the slope and remounted, dragging her weary bones into the saddle whilst Chelsea stood patiently, accommodating the clumsy process with understanding. Eventually, she could maintain her nonchalant poise no longer and her ears switched back and forth, responding to Lisa's continued words of praise. With a huge harrumph, she began to walk again, slowly to allow the other riders, and lesser horses, to catch up.

Later in the day, Lisa was delighted to discover yet another trait, this time Chelsea's canny ability to assess the going. They approached a large, very boggy area. It was particularly bad because of the heavy summer storms, so a small detour track had been marked for walkers. This was not suitable for the horses so Jean Walker, the ride leader, acted as pathfinder and struggled across the bog on her mount. Seeing Jean's difficulties, the others immediately decided that it would be better to dismount and let the other horses pick their own way, one by one, across the treacherous ground unhampered by extra weight. The experienced expedition ponies were used to this and plunged and ploughed their way through the bog, up to their knees in cloying peat-browned mud. Chelsea's turn came last and Lisa released her whilst she took the walkers' track.

Someone remarked, "Poor Chelsea! She won't have a clue what to do."

'Poor Chelsea' raised her beautiful Thoroughbred head and imperiously surveyed the quagmire. Then her Irish Draught instincts took over and she picked a delicate path through the bog, well wide of the direct route taken by the ponies. She emerged to meet Lisa with barely muddy fetlocks. Lisa smiled delightedly and turned to wink at the 'Doubting Thomas'.

"No wonder Irish Draughts are highly regarded as the safest of horses over all hunting grounds." She left it at that.

From that day on Lisa would trust Chelsea completely, over any ground conditions and, whenever she was in any doubt, she would simply give her the reins. "Pick your own way lass." Chelsea never let her mistress down.

They continued to enjoy the late summer together in between their respective 'work' efforts. Inevitably, Chelsea received her quota of scratches, kicks and bites from sharing a field with other mares, especially when they came into season and their antics got out of hand. However, Lisa's knowledge of equine first aid improved with each incident. From the start, Chelsea seemed to understand that Lisa was helping her, even if treatment involved discomfort. The mare never tried to bite or kick, although she would occasionally flinch. On one occasion, she had discharge running from an eye and Lisa was given a tube of cream with instructions to 'tie her up and get someone to hold her head whilst you squeeze some into the eye'. Lisa could find nobody to help so she tethered Chelsea to a loop of twine and took a deep breath, approaching the horse with calm concern. Chelsea just stood, blinking with bemusement as the tube was placed gently in the corner of the eye and the salve was squeezed soothingly onto its surface. She seemed to be saying, "I don't know what you're playing at, Mum, but if you think it's necessary, then OK by me."

On another occasion, Chelsea developed an abscess under one of her front shoes. After removing the shoe and poulticing the hoof, to remove the deep infection, Lisa followed the vet's instructions and kept Chelsea indoors washing out her hoof twice a day and applying Stockholm tar to keep it clean. Although she was a naturally energetic and impatient horse, Chelsea soon accepted this new routine and could be relied on to stand with her hoof on a towel to keep it away from her bedding whilst it dried off. Lisa's affection and appreciation grew ever stronger one day when she had to leave Chelsea unattended, to wash out the bucket, and returned to find the mare standing exactly where instructed. Always, Chelsea's eyes carried a message for Lisa; on these occasions she would look forlornly into Lisa's eyes and whisper, "If you say so, Mum, but I'd rather be out grazing with my friends in the field."

Lisa was delighted and surprised at the strength of the bond that was developing between them. At first, even when she was away for a week at a time, Chelsea nonetheless knew instinctively that she belonged to Lisa. Often, Lisa would time her arrival at the yard to coincide with Chelsea's return from working hacks. As soon as she saw her mistress, Chelsea would walk straight up to her and stop. Lisa was deeply touched by this, feeling that it was more than she deserved after days of abandonment. She also grew to understand just how sensitive Chelsea had become to how she was feeling. One weekend, Lisa came home with a heavy cold. She felt weak but also in need of gentle fresh air, perhaps just a quiet hour out with Chelsea, nothing more. From the moment that Lisa went to collect her from the field, Chelsea sensed that her mistress was not herself. Often she would play hard to get, but not that day. Instead, she came straight up to Lisa and walked in with her very quietly.

"Had she been a person, I swear she'd have taken my arm!" Lisa reported to Andrew that evening as she sipped a medicinal toddy. "Then I tacked her up and we set off at a gentle walk. She was my transport and carried me round like a passenger. I didn't have to make an effort. I had intended only to do the short loop but in the end we stayed out for two hours, much longer than I expected, and it was just the tonic I needed. We did no more than walk and trot but when I tired, she came back to walk unasked. When we got to the tracks where we often canter, she gathered herself ready to go if I'd wanted but when I told her I was just too weak, she continued to walk with such good grace. What a star! I gave her an especially big hug when we got back to the yard."

Lisa learned much from Chelsea, especially about the bond that was developing between them. But she was also beginning to understand more about the bonds that form between horses – and how little humans take account of this as horses are bought and sold and friendships and attachments are broken up. After another wonderful ride Lisa turned Chelsea out into her field. Autumn was turning to winter and Chelsea was wrapped up warmly in her New Zealand rug. As usual, when she turned the horse loose, Lisa leaned on the gate watching Chelsea for a few moments and simply relishing the moments of peace and quiet. On some days, Chelsea would literally 'hightail' off to her friends; on others, her head would quickly drop down to the serious business of grazing. Today, a roll was a high priority. She began her usual energetic roll, going over completely from one side to the other. Then, to Lisa's horror, when Chelsea rose she saw that the spider strap fastening on the rug had snapped and that the New Zealand had slipped over her quarters. Grabbing a lead rope Lisa walked quickly up the field, calling out to Chelsea that she was coming to help. At that moment, the other mares in the field decided that it was time for a madcap gallop. Lisa's heart filled her mouth with dread as she envisaged Chelsea giving chase, tripping on the trailing rug and breaking her legs. Amazingly, Chelsea did not move. Her friend Lady, with whom she was now inseparable, sensed that something was wrong and ignored the high jinks that surrounded them both, staying by Chelsea's side. Lisa was privileged to watch the incredible sight of the two mares standing quietly in the middle of otherwise riotous cavorting. Both mares turned to Lisa, almost in relief, and stayed still whilst she snapped on the lead rope, unfastened the rug and lead Chelsea back to the yard to find another one. As soon as Lisa and her friend were close to the gate, well out of harm's way, Lady gave a furious buck and joined in the fun. Lisa mentioned the incident to Jean who informed her that Lady, this special friend, had spent many years sharing fields with a succession of rescue horses and ponies. She treated many of them with the same motherly kindness that she had shown Chelsea.

"Humans have as much to learn from horses as we have to teach them, Jean. For every bad case, there's a good one, sometimes an exceptional one. Lady reminds me of Mother Theresa – always looking out for the bird with the broken wing."

"That's more or less the case, Lisa. Except Lady also has the knack of knowing which other horses are worthy of help. She doesn't do it for any one, so Chelsea must be giving Lady the right messages as well. I can't see what's special about Chelsea – to me she's a typical, difficult chestnut mare. We'll never know the full extent of a horse's makeup."

Lisa was saddened by those last words. Clearly Chelsea was not behaving well with Jean, and yet with herself, the mare was obedient and trusting. Traditionalist views were once again clashing with her own enlightened approach. But she kept her counsel. Jean had a business to run whereas Lisa was indulging in a hobby, more than that, a passion. But should there be any difference in their approaches?

It was not surprising that Lisa felt that Chelsea was a kind and honest horse. And yet, those same siren voices at the yard continued to call out to the contrary. The matter was put beyond doubt at the end of Chelsea's first year at Kinord. She had muscled up beautifully and needed a new saddle, one that suited her new shape. When she had arrived at the yard, she had come with the small saddle that Alison MacAllan had used, ideal for young horses and the slight frame of the teenage girl. But it was too small for Lisa and the increasingly chunky Chelsea! For a while, Lisa borrowed a saddle that suited them both whilst she worked Chelsea, learned more about riding and researched the market. At first Lisa decided to test a very smart and flexible American saddle. She thought that it would be suitable because its manufacturer claimed that it automatically adjusted to the shape of the horse. However, Chelsea didn't like it. As soon as Lisa tacked her up and began to ride in the school she noticed that Chelsea was no longer her usual free moving self. At first she thought that the saddle was making her own riding ineffective and that this was constraining Chelsea, so she asked her teacher to ride for a while and see if that made a difference. Chelsea simply became increasingly unhappy. Janet, the teacher, then produced her own dressage saddle. It was too small for Lisa but Janet thought that it might fit Chelsea. Janet replaced the saddle and remounted. What followed amazed Lisa. Initially Chelsea was unsure about the new sensation; she was suspicious and inelegant, but after a short while, when the strangeness faded, the intelligent horse decided that all was well and began to perform beautifully. Lisa observed this honesty and willingness to try with admiration, and she resolved to always give her beloved mare the benefit of the doubt, a crucial decision that would be tested in the near future. Lisa had a clear message – if Chelsea was not going well, she was most probably not shirking but, instead, was trying to tell Lisa that something was wrong. Chelsea was an honest horse, but it was now becoming clear why others regarded her as difficult. The traditionalist school of thought was less able to accept that there would be occasions when underlying problems disguised a horse's obedience and good nature. The lessons of horse management were never ending.

Gail never understood Lisa's philosophy. Her personality was such that she could never allow any person, or horse, to take advantage of her. Her own lack of assertiveness manifested itself in an overbearing and impatient manner that Chelsea immediately sensed and balked at. With the approach of winter, Lisa decided to arrange for Chelsea's coat to be clipped so that her chest and stomach, down to her shoulders and haunches, would not become damp with lingering sweat chilling her after strenuous sessions in the bitterly cold air. This was quite normal and many of the horses were clipped in the late autumn, producing smart 'go-fast' stripes across their middle portions in a broad swathe between the bottom of the saddle and the upper parts of their limbs. Gail regarded herself as an expert and undertook to clip Chelsea along with Lady and Benjy.

Chelsea was appalled at the buzz of the electric clippers. Her ears lay flat against her head in fear and alarm and she backed away from the whining device. Both Benjy and Lady had resigned themselves to the experience, being familiar with it and recognising what was about to happen. But Chelsea had only been clipped once before, using very quiet clippers that only tickled her tender spots between her legs and her body. Now she was terrified and refused to let Gail close in on her whilst the clippers buzzed and vibrated.

"Stupid animal, let's twitch her," Gail blustered, and began to tighten the rope around the horse's upper lip in an attempt to release calming endorphins into her system. To be certain that she could not kick out, another girl pulled one of her front legs backwards, holding it firmly upwards, at the level of her waist. With Chelsea secured and undignified, they gradually began to clip her, starting at her shoulders and working backwards along her side and beneath her chest and stomach. Chelsea stood, rooted to the spot but her body quivered with tension and, even with the effect of the twitch, her eyes rolled sideways, revealing their whites in a picture of terrified fury, reminding Lisa of artists' impressions of battle scenes involving cavalry and artillery.

Lisa watched with growing concern. This was her first experience of clipping, and Lady and Benjy had seemed unperturbed. So she did not interfere, knowing that the procedure was painless, but thinking that twitching looked unpleasant and was so undignified. Yet she hated the fact that Chelsea was in turmoil, wondering what was going on as the buzz and vibration of the clippers invaded her body. The mare jerked her head away from the noise whenever Gail tried to clip her lower neck and started in fearful reaction to the device as it approached the soft fleshy area between her hind legs and her stomach.

"Stupid animal. Keep still." Gail was unsympathetic as she forced the pace, wanting to complete the procedure as quickly as possible and certainly before she lost her temper. She pushed the clipper fiercely across this most sensitive spot and Chelsea responded in a rush of fear. Even on three legs, she barged the girls aside and skittered backwards making Gail drop the clippers.

"That's enough, you stupid horse!" Gail lashed out with her foot and kicked Chelsea viciously in the ribs.

"Stop!" Lisa gasped in horror. The word hissed quietly from her but it cut through the rumpus with chilling ferocity. They all froze. "Never, ever do that again." This time the words were spoken with quiet authority. "I'll take over from now on."

Lisa opened the door to the box and walked straight up to her beloved mare, stroking and comforting the distraught animal who immediately began to calm down in response to the familiar loving tones.

"We'll leave it at that Chels. You'll look a bit odd with still a bit to go, but we've done enough for this year. Don't worry, lass, that's it, all over now."

Lisa's main work contract was due to finish the following April and she resolved to ensure that any future contracts that she undertook would be carried out either locally or, preferably, based from home whenever possible. She also resolved to ease back from full time commitments – quite an undertaking for a hitherto self-confessed workaholic. But now she realised that there really was more to life than work and she was ready and willing to make fundamental changes. Such was Chelsea's influence!

In the meantime, winter was upon them. Chelsea continued to enjoy her hacks with Lisa and did not mind the bad weather – including snow. Most horses will try to protect their faces from heavy rain and snow, turning their heads or even spinning around to put their backs to the wind. Chelsea, however, was prepared to walk straight into any weather if her beloved mistress asked her to. Fresh, powdery snow is no hazard for horses and Lisa loved especially the magical sensation of cantering through fresh snow on a pure winter morning in complete silence. The same instincts that had enabled Chelsea to assess the boggy ground in the summer were now used in snow and ice. Lisa never stopped wondering how Chelsea knew which icy puddles would break beneath her hooves and which would bear their weight. But she accepted with complete trust the mare's instincts and allowed her to deal with icy stretches on her own. Chelsea sensed the intensity of the bond that had developed between them and repaid the trust, gathering herself in perfect balance and carefully carrying her mistress. Whenever she stopped, Lisa respected the mare's assessment, knowing that the going would be too slippery to ride, and she would dismount and lead her. Sometimes Chelsea stopped when her hooves became balled up with snow and Lisa would hop down to clean them out with a pick. Over the weeks, these small moments of respect and understanding built up a rapport that would last a lifetime; it was through the tiny acts of kindness that true character was revealed and a relationship fully cemented.

During that winter, Lisa took her first opportunity to jump. Knowing that Chelsea was simply too powerful for her – she cleared fences with such soaring enthusiasm that even some of the expert riders at the yard felt they were having flying lessons rather than jumping – Lisa resolved to learn on the more sedate school horses. Her first lesson was taken on a beautiful, kind, grey mare who understood what to do without any help from Lisa. The jump was no more eighteen inches but when Lisa turned into it for the first time, she knew exactly what it was going to feel like. It was uncanny – she'd done this in her mind hundreds of times before as a young girl and now, at last, it was happening for real. They soared over the low hurdle and, just as on her first hack at Balmoral, the smile on her face stretched gleefully around the back of her head. Or so it seemed! In that moment, Lisa confirmed her belief in the power of the mind and the imagination. So, when it was too icy to hack out with Chelsea, Lisa pursued her quest for mastery by taking jumping lessons and gradually progressed to small combinations and slightly higher fences. Her jumping was raw and clumsy but she always knew what to do, even if she could not always execute the jumps as well as she envisioned them, and she always thoroughly enjoyed the experience and continued to build up her repertoire of skills.

And so winter passed and the stark lifeless beauty of the Highlands began to soften with the signs of spring. April arrived and at last Lisa's work contract came to an end. Her spirits bubbled with pleasure at the prospect of a free summer with endless days of riding. She was also full of new ideas, having read Monty Roberts' book several times over and having realised that she shared his values. First among these, she resolved to practise 'join up' and loose schooling. So, each morning, she rose early and drove to Kinord in plenty of time to use the outdoor school before it became busy with lessons. The early start did not concern Lisa who felt a rush of pure joy to be out of doors on these early summer mornings after a winter of confinement in an office. Chelsea quickly responded and was soon walking beside her, trotting when Lisa jogged and cantering when she skipped. Chelsea followed Lisa with intelligence and enthusiasm, listening to the verbal instructions and relating them to the physical movements. If Lisa stood on the spot and turned away, Chelsea responded and came round with her. It soon became a wonderful, magical game that they both enjoyed. Lisa's confidence grew and she soon taught Chelsea to move away and work loose in a circle around her. This required some precision on Lisa's part as she needed to look at Chelsea in just the right way and on the right spot on her quarters to keep her on the circle and not to go racing off to the other end of the school. Soon she was walking trotting and cantering around Lisa working off her voice, but their favourite moment was always when Lisa dropped her head and Chelsea knew then that she was free to come and stand by her mistress and receive praise and affection.

Lisa was amazed at the strength of bond that 'join up' created. One afternoon, the two continued the loose schooling in a partially covered arena near to a small sawmill when a large lorry arrived to deliver its load of gravel. The clatter of the gravel slithering off the truck took Chelsea by surprise and she started in alarm, making to break away before realising that Lisa was unperturbed. To Lisa's joy and amazement, although she lifted her head in consternation, Chelsea simply stepped nearer to her, keeping Lisa between her and the noise, and stood quite still. Lisa spoke quietly to

Chelsea, murmuring praise, telling her how brave she was, and rubbing her head as she always did when they stood side by side.

As a consultant, Lisa helped to coach leaders of organisations. During that spring, free of the pressures of work, she had cause to reflect how Chelsea was herself an interesting experiment in the application of leadership. If Lisa remained calm and positive, Chelsea would follow her anywhere. She would never tolerate any form of bullying or force. Occasionally she needed time to simply think about things before deciding for herself whether what she was being asked to do was, indeed, sensible. When Lisa wanted to teach her something new, clear, consistent instruction was needed. When she seemed not to understand, Lisa tried to put herself in Chelsea's place and consider the situation from her point of view. It reminded her that we all see the world from our own, different perspectives. Just like the people in her project teams, Chelsea responded very well to kind words, praise and encouragement. Although Lisa had always trusted her own instincts Chelsea helped to remind her that these were normally accurate. But above all, Lisa came to realise that gentleness prevailed over brute force and was, in truth, a great strength.

There was no doubt in her mind that Chelsea had made her a better leader. Having become used to observing body language – a horse's main form of communication – Lisa had become better at reading the unspoken messages that people often give. She also found that people responded to 'join up'. It was possible to 'send people away' and to make them feel uncomfortable when they behaved inappropriately. Equally, it was easy to make them feel comfortable in her presence when they were doing the right things.

"I find I have to be careful not to appear manipulative in applying this but with a bit of thought, it works quite well. I'm still practising!" she told Andrew after a business meeting that had gone particularly well.

During their second idyllic summer together, Lisa allowed Chelsea to experience cross-country competition. Again, Lisa sensibly realised that her own skill was not yet a match for Chelsea whose power and athleticism had returned fully for the first time since her fall in Dublin. Instead, Lisa was delighted to share Chelsea with a competent and caring young man whose own horse had retired due to age and injury. As Tony was soon to go to university, he decided to postpone his search for a replacement. But he loved Chelsea and, as was so typical with the sensitive mare, she picked up his feelings so, with her renewed trust in human beings, she quickly returned the affection. So Tony occasionally 'borrowed' her for his last summer of pony club activities. They went well together on the flat and also enjoyed show-jumping. Chelsea's love for jumping was always apparent and inspired great confidence in her new rider.

Lisa was intrigued to watch their first attempt together at cross-country. She was unaware of Chelsea's experiences with Majella, although she suspected that Chelsea had hunted, some time in the past. So she watched with interest. Tony was very experienced and decided to practise on a short course of jumps in a field near the yard. To warm up they popped over a small hedge a few times, then a huge fallen log. Chelsea was thrilled at the prospect of tackling natural objects once again and seemed to beam with pleasure, her ears alert and forward. Then they approached a combination fence – a small step down a bank, a jump across a shallow ditch and a step up the other side. The first attempt was ungainly as Chelsea sized up the uneven ground. She needed to be urged firmly through each element, but when they came around again, Lisa could see her intent look as she planned her approaches. The second time was more fluent. On the third circuit, however, she knew exactly what to do. Her concentration was intense, although the smile never diminished, and Lisa could almost see her mind at work. "Down, over and out." Chelsea knew exactly where to put her feet and managed perfectly before finishing with an exuberant flourish by cantering on to the final obstacle, a small water jump, swooping over it effortlessly.

Flushed with excitement, Tony tried again choosing another practice combination – a more severe test. This comprised two upright rustic fences with a 'bounce' between them. Show-jumping courses did not usually place fences so close together – normally they were set up with at least one full canter stride between the combinations – so neither Tony nor Lisa knew what Chelsea would do. Their concern was that she might approach it as one large spread fence and try to take it on in a single leap. Tony approached the obstacle at a steady pace, allowing Chelsea time to think ahead and see the two elements. She jumped the first one, hesitated as she realised there was no room for a stride and then, moving forward with her natural momentum, she nudged the second element with her chest. She did not refuse. Undaunted, she took a huge cat leap and cleared the second rustic fence almost from a standing start. Tony was jolted from his seat, and was then thrown forward on landing. His young body reacted immediately, holding firmly to Chelsea's mane and neck as they landed safely on the far side but the reins and stirrups flailed loosely. Other horses were grazing in the field.

With natural equine inquisitiveness they had wandered up to watch proceedings. What followed was another remarkable insight into Chelsea's character. When Chelsea made her ungainly leap out of the bounce fence, the others sensed her unease and turned together, instinctively cantering away back down the field. Already startled by the strange jump, Chelsea flinched in response to their reaction. Neither Lisa nor Tony would have blamed her for following the herd instinct and racing down the field with the others. But she stopped as soon as she recovered her balance and stood perfectly still, allowing Tony to gather himself. Then the pair ended their session by returning to the warm up fences to give them both a confident finish. That summer Tony and Chelsea continued to enjoy cross-country events. In the autumn they would close the year triumphantly by winning a local hunter pace competition.

Chelsea was happy that summer. Much as she enjoyed her sessions with Tony, she remained a one-person horse, becoming ever more dedicated to her new owner. Many of the Kinord staff commented on this, saying how much calmer and more friendly the mare had become since her arrival at the yard and especially since she had ceased her spell in working livery. No longer was she subjected to the vagaries of different riders with their varied skill levels and dispositions. Instead, Lisa took control of her daily schedule and only allowed a very few expert and, more importantly, sympathetic riders to use her equine friend. Amazingly, Lisa also felt that she had become a more gentle person herself, at ease with life and even more tolerant of her fellow humans. Lisa was learning from Chelsea!

Autumn and winter passed and their routine became well established. Occasionally if Lisa had to be away for a few days, she arranged for someone at the yard to ride Chelsea – very occasionally as the lead horse on a hack but, preferably, alone in the schooling arena. Chelsea's confidence returned; she settled and was happy to accept the small group of familiar riders. But Lisa was her firm favourite. When it was she who tacked Chelsea up, the mare would whicker with pleasure and open her mouth cooperatively, ready to receive the bit. Rides with Lisa were full of fun and chatter; Lisa was oblivious to the strange looks of passers-by as she burbled inanely to her horse and Chelsea became an eager and sympathetic listener, her ears rotating in response to her mistress' voice. She accepted with characteristic aplomb the constant pats and strokes of praise and she also became attuned to Lisa's sharper tones, recognising at once that she had misbehaved, or needed to concentrate, but she never started in fear because Lisa's voice always carried an underlying timbre of love.

During the same winter, Lisa saw a further example of Chelsea's strong attachment to her – this time on an occasion when she might, very understandably, have preferred to align herself with a fellow horse. Lisa led Chelsea in from the field one evening along with her best friend, Lady. Since the drama with the loose rug, Lisa had often stopped to watch the horses together in the field, never far from one another and often standing together by the hay ring looking like a pair of city girls chatting over a drink at the end of a busy day in the office, flirting with the world!

The road down from the field was icy, coated in a hard frost that had lain since the previous night. They picked their way carefully down to the stable block, Lisa in the middle with a horse on either side. Something spooked Lady. Lisa was unsure what caused the moment of panic but it was unusual for the normally calm animal to react so dramatically. Suddenly, Lady danced at the end of her lead rope, reared onto her back legs and tried to back away from the hidden demon. Lisa glanced anxiously at Chelsea. If she followed her friend's lead Lisa was certain that she'd be unable to keep her balance on the ice. But she need not have worried for Chelsea simply gave her 'that look' again, one of calm support, head down in a set and determined posture, as if to say, "Don't worry about me. I'm OK."

"Good girl," Lisa whispered. "Just stand quiet."

Lady quietened down sufficiently to regain her footing, but she was still alarmed.

"Walk on."

Chelsea responded instantly and their combined forward momentum persuaded Lady to follow, albeit at a rather nervous jog. When they reached the stable Lisa quickly looped Chelsea's lead rope loosely through a ring on the outside wall, knowing that the mare would not attempt to break away. Taking no chances with Lady, especially as she was still unsure of what had caused the fright, Lisa guided the agitated horse into her box and quickly returned to get Chelsea. Lisa smiled when she saw that Chelsea had moved over just far enough to look into the stable, obviously wanting to watch Lisa and check that all was well. With a hug and a pat, Lisa pulled the rope from the ring and led Chelsea to her own box, deeply touched that the faithful mare had chosen to follow her rather than her friend Lady.

Chelsea's uncanny skill at judging people manifested itself one cold winter's day. Generally, she completely ignored strangers to the stable block. Very often visitors would stop by her box, their eyes drawn by her well-muscled body and glorious copper sheen. Many would try to pat her, or stroke the lovely velvet nose, only to be rebuffed by the turning of her head. Those who persisted, and who were not considered worthy of her presence would be further insulted. Chelsea would simply turn her back, munch studiously on hay and occasionally break wind impertinently in their direction. But not always. She was particularly fond of children and Lisa quickly learned that she could be left safely in the charge of the smallest child – many volunteered – whilst Lisa made last minute preparations for a ride. On these occasions Lisa kept an amused but watchful eye as she was never quite sure exactly who was looking after whom!

One afternoon, because of the biting cold, Lisa brought Chelsea into her box for a pre-ride groom. She busied herself giving her a brush up when a family appeared outside the stable, peering in uncertainly as they looked for a member of staff.

Helpfully, Lisa enquired, "Can I do anything?" recognising that they were not prospective riders and may have stopped simply for directions. She found a delightful family, parents and grandparents with two very disabled children. One, a little girl of about five or six years of age, was confined to a small wheelchair. Her slightly older brother was able to walk.

"Are there any horses in?" enquired the father.

"Only mine," Lisa replied, rather dreading his next question.

"Could we come in to see it?"

"Yes, of course." Lisa did not want to disappoint them but anticipated that, when Chelsea saw the wheelchair and heard the little girl who was now squealing with delight, she would retreat to the back of her box. At least the girl would be able to peer through the metal grill of the doors to Chelsea's box.

Chelsea amazed and delighted Lisa. As the grandparents, mother and daughter arrived at her box, she unhesitatingly approached them and lowered her head gently to greet the girl through the metal tubes of the lower half of the door. With no power of speech the girl could only screech and squeal with delight and wave her hands in front of the huge head in front of her, straining through the bars towards the liquid brown eyes that glistened with wisdom and empathy. Chelsea would not have tolerated such behaviour from a normal person, but now she clearly understood that the tiny human was simply expressing delight in the only way she knew. So she did not rear back but, sensing the utter lack of threat, continued to nuzzle the child with interest and a type of motherly protectiveness. Lisa recognised the preciousness of the moment and removed a Polo mint from her pocket, by now certain that Chelsea could be trusted to take it gently. She placed it into the girl's hand, slowly unbending the tiny gnarled fingers, so that she could at least offer Chelsea the mint on a partially open palm. Chelsea understood that the exposed fingers were delicate and nuzzled her way to the mint, taking it from the small bent hand with lips as soft as an angel's touch.

At first the girl's brother had hung back, fearful of the huge beast. Now he decided to be brave and slipped quietly in beside Lisa, touching her leg to attract her attention.

"Hello. Would you like to give Chelsea a Polo mint?"

Silently, he raised his hand and a mint was placed in the palm. Then he offered it to Chelsea but in a frightened and nervous way so that the gift was presented and then withdrawn in fright as soon as he felt the first touch of the whiskers. Without concern, and realising that she was not being teased, Chelsea simply moved in time with the motion of the small hand until she could gently take the mint. The boy laughed with glee – no longer afraid now, just enjoying the tickling.

A lump came to Lisa's throat. Chelsea had made the afternoon for both children, especially the small girl who could only speak with her eyes. They gleamed with delight, shining with messages of love for horses and wonder at this particular animal, huge and yet so gentle. Chelsea had sensed that the children meant no harm and simply yearned for her own brand of love and affection, knowing that real humans lay beneath the somewhat disturbed behaviour.

During the worst of the snowy weather, Lisa continued to take lessons, working particularly hard at her jumping but only on the quieter schooling horses. Eventually she felt ready to try a small jump with Chelsea. Like Majella, Lisa sensed Chelsea's power and knew the potential danger of jumping with such a talented athlete. Lisa was now ready for the challenge, however, having built up her own strength and level of skill through hours of lessons and diligent practise. Now she was rewarded – jumping with Chelsea was an indescribable thrill compared to the sedate animals she'd used previously. Chelsea simply trotted up to the jump, took one canter stride and popped over. She had more impulsion, even in trot, than most horses had in canter and there was no doubt that Chelsea really did jump for joy, thrilling to the experience, which she could now share with her beloved mistress. Taking any jump with Chelsea was an exciting moment – Lisa loved to feel her energy and enthusiasm – even though she was occasionally thrown from the saddle, sometimes ending on the soft, yielding bark-covered floor of the indoor school. Whenever this happened, her dear Chelsea would always stop immediately, planting all four feet where they were, so that her mistress could not be trampled, and would then wait patiently until Lisa was back on her feet and had regained her grip on the reins.

Sadly, their jumping came to an untimely end. Lisa had begun to notice as they rode out on hacks that Chelsea was not always going forward with her usual enthusiasm and, occasionally, she would jog rather than trot. This was very unlike Chelsea so Lisa sought advice from the 'experts' at the yard.

"Oh, just kick her and tell her to get on with it. She's just being lazy."

Lisa ignored the advice, remembering the experience with the unsuitable saddle.

"No, I don't think so," she responded. "If Chelsea is being lazy, then it's for a reason."

She continued to keep a concerned eye on Chelsea for a further two weeks, without any sign of improvement, although neither did the situation seem to get any worse. She then asked one of the Kinord instructors, who Lisa liked and respected, to ride the mare and to give her opinion. Chelsea bucked whilst being asked to canter in the school and the instructor suggested that it was 'a stiff buck, not a naughty buck'.

Despite being told that she was worrying too much and wasting her money, Lisa felt that it was time to call in the vet. Not for the first time was Lisa glad that she had listened to Chelsea and not to the siren voices. The vet diagnosed spavins in her hocks – an arthritic condition that in a relatively young, nine-year-old horse was a sign that her earlier years of jumping had taken their toll. He also suggested that Chelsea was adopting a posture that favoured her painful legs and that she was thus aggravating an old back injury.

The vet concluded, "She's probably been over-jumped in the past, when she was young, and has probably had a fall too."

Neither he nor Lisa knew how uncannily accurate this assessment was – Chelsea's jumping days in Ireland were, indeed, returning to plague her. What a pity that Edgar had pushed her so much, striving to fulfil his own ambitions, and then failing to nurse her back from injury, instead passing her on to a dealer who had used draw reins to artificially force a return to correct posture and, in so doing, cause further damage. Seeds that had been sown years before were now beginning to take root and yet, not for a single moment, did Lisa regret her purchase.

Later that day she gave Andrew a full account of the vet's findings and concluded, "It's not the end of the world. Spavins cause the hock joints to fuse and, in time, this is not likely to be a major problem unless we have very high aspirations. I certainly don't. She's been given some anti-inflammatory powders and we have to follow a careful regime of exercises to strengthen the muscles that will protect her from further problems. So it's no more schoolwork, at least for a while – riding in circles will be too stressful for her hocks. Instead we've got to do lots of walking followed, after a few weeks, by a bit of trotting and so on until we gradually build her up."

Lisa accepted with good grace that she could only 'control the controllable' and resolved not to fall into the 'if only' trap. So she set about the new regime with an unquashable spirit and energy. As if following her mistress' lead, Chelsea sensed that her interests were being looked after and cooperated immediately. She soon got used to the idea that they should walk everywhere. Then, when they did move up to trot for a few minutes at a time, they both found the experience rewarding and even quite exciting!

But bringing a horse back to health requires more than a sympathetic and focused exercise regime. It also needed an environment of care and attention that Kinord was unable to provide. As well as being a traditionalist in her views on horse management, Jean Walker was a businesswoman for whom profitability was paramount. She was firm in her belief that the yard should be run with efficiency aimed solely at providing riding facilities for visitors. This was her main source of revenue. Horses and ponies had to be made available, at any cost, to meet the demands of her customers. Thus the animals were often worked too hard. Although Lisa had removed Chelsea from working livery, and no longer had to worry about how much Chelsea was worked, or who was riding her, she nonetheless had to accept that the yard would not change its ways to accommodate the few livery-only clients that Jean tolerated. Although they paid more than working livery owners, the arrangement was one of condescension rather than wholehearted support. Working animals were Jean's main concern.

Through the winter, things therefore became more difficult at the yard. As market forces tightened their grip and demand fell away, supplies for the horses often ran low. Straw beds were sometimes very thin and hay was not always as plentiful as it should have been, nor was the quality as good. After Christmas, Lisa found herself being forced to visit twice a day to look after Chelsea personally. Now that she had her hock problem Lisa fretted about her general well being. She especially wanted Chelsea to have a good thick bed of dry straw so that, when she lay down, she would not slip when she tried to rise. Lisa knew her stiffness would make this more likely. So she took charge of the daily mucking out and laying of new bedding. None of the staff objected. In fact they seemed delighted to have another pair of hands to help reduce the daily burden of chores. Lisa was also pleased, knowing that she could give Chelsea a deeper bed. Her main concern was on the days that she could not attend. Then she would return anxiously from her business trips hoping that the extra layer of bedding had not diminished too much. Often she found a compacted and inadequately turned-over bed, rank with the smell of urine. Faithfully, Lisa would remove the soiled straw, bank the sides of the box with the remaining, usable, bedding and allow the box to air for as long as possible before rebuilding the bed with as much fresh straw as she could find. As its revenue continued to dwindle through the winter, the standards of the Kinord Equestrian Centre fell away leaving Lisa worried and ever more thoughtful about the wisdom of keeping her beloved mare in the environment of a working yard.

Like humans, Chelsea was also happier when she knew what to expect day to day. Gradually, the normal routine at the yard changed and care became a matter of convenience, rather than a response to the needs of the horses. Like a stressed human, Chelsea lost weight and, sadly, began to behave badly reverting to her less acceptable traits. She refused to be caught, knowing that the attraction of a warm box and a good feed at the end of the cold winter days could no longer be guaranteed. She also became grumpy and uncooperative, on occasions even with Lisa who always did her best to offer fun and comfort. The staff at the yard began to talk of her as 'difficult'. Some even regarded her as 'dangerous' and refused to make an effort, tossing her evening feed onto the ground and leaving her in the field at night to 'learn her lesson' in the aching cold.

This was the last straw. It was time to look for a new home. Lisa started to make enquiries, but she also needed to be sure that this would be a final, permanent move, one that guaranteed care and attention, especially when Lisa was away on business. Fortunately, the Universe responded to her intentions and she was soon able to find a new home. In February, as the miserable winter still held them in its bitter grip, she gave notice of her intention to move Chelsea to a private livery yard on the outskirts of Aberdeen, forty miles away. The owner's stated objective was to provide 5-star care for horses. Lisa had satisfied herself fully that this was the case.

Chapter 8

A Young Man Emerges

James was full of good intentions but was often beset with self-doubt. When he knew what was expected of him, he gave his all, both delighting in praise but also feeling crushed and demoralised if he failed or was criticised. He noticed how some boys, a very few, seemed not to care about what the teachers thought and he often wondered why some people were satisfied with second best. At exam time, he would swot endlessly in a panic of insecurity, missing meals just before exams in order to steal last minute moments of cramming. Contradictory statements from his parents and teachers confused him. Sometimes he was reminded, "Your schooldays are the happiest days of your life" and on other occasions he was warned sternly, "You only have this one chance to make something of your life. Don't waste it." He loved the sport, it made school worthwhile, but nonetheless longed never to have to sit another exam and yearned for the days when his education would be over and he could be free of the stress and tension of endless weekly tests, end of term exams and, worst of all, the ultimate formal examinations – the 'O' and 'A' levels.

Like any school, Manorfield had a mixture of good and bad masters. Alec Fraser was a true inspiration. He never made James fearful of failure. Other less enlightened masters enjoyed the aura of power that they carried and thought that fear and a good challenge would 'make a man out of the boy'. Strangely, it was those of the latter inclination who also demanded obedience, a towing of the line in the common good and a respect for authority. The only masters who ever really encouraged him to enjoy himself without fear of failure were Alec Fraser and Cass Cassell.

In his fourth year, James experienced both approaches, in one incident that he would remember throughout his life. Robert rushed up to him early one summer's morning.

"James, guess what. You've been made captain of the First Eleven."

"Cricket captain! I don't believe it!"

"It's true, it's on the team lists. Go now, quick, you've got a couple of minutes before the lesson starts."

He sprinted from the classroom until, puffing and perspiring with a mixture of excitement and dread, he reached the large board. There it was!

'Manorfield First XI versus Bristol Grammar School'

The list of names was headed 'James Anderson (capt.)'

"Oh no, why me?" James gasped with despair thinking: "Last week I was selected for the team only for the first time. Now captain. Why?"

Many boys would have loved the accolade, accepting the challenge with pride. But James was a quiet and modest young man. Although he enjoyed playing cricket he was younger than his team mates and never liked having to make tactical decisions in the field, preferring to concentrate on his own performance, quietly and effectively following instructions and contributing to the team's success. He had, until his last match, thoroughly enjoyed representing his school's Second XI. Last week he had been promoted to the First XI. Towards the end of the match he had been asked to bowl the last few overs from the pavilion end, with the instructions, "Keep it tight, James. Concentrate on keeping the runs down and don't worry about taking wickets. We can't win but we can force the draw." James had done just that. He had also fielded superbly and fearlessly, at silly mid off, taking three instinctive catches from crashing drives that would have scattered lesser fielders. And he had loved every moment of the match.

But now, he balked at the prospect of captaining older boys at a higher level than ever before. Why did this always happen? Why did everybody always think that he was better than he really was?

"Maybe next season when I'm eighteen," he moaned to himself, "but not right now."

James' stomach churned with anxiety all morning. To the surprise of his Geography teacher he failed the end of week test, forgetting much of what he had carefully learned about the Fenlands simply because of the dread that now sunk like a lead weight deep within the pit of his stomach. At lunch he picked nervously at a pork chop and confided his fears to Alec Fraser.

"Why did they choose me, sir? I'm not as good as Elliott when it comes to making decisions. I just like to play."

"Do what you think is right at the time, James, and have no fear. Mr. Hughes obviously has confidence in you. I think he's right. You always lead by example and you always try your hardest. That's what he's looking for from you as a captain. Don't try to emulate Elliott; he's got other strengths. I reckon Mr. Hughes is experimenting this time with a new approach."

"I'll do my best, sir, but I won't enjoy it, having to make decisions all the time rather than just playing cricket."

"I know you'll do your best. Just remember, follow your instincts and be brave. I won't take you to task if we lose the match. The Grammar School has a good side."

"Thanks, sir."

It was amazing – the effect of a few gentle words of encouragement.

James won the toss and elected to bat. This was the correct decision as it allowed Manorfield the best of the daylight but it was made for the wrong reasons. When his side is batting, a captain has to make very few decisions other than to decide on the line up and, with the First XI, that took care of itself. In electing to bat, James was simply postponing the moment when he would have to lead his side into the field. But he did not realise that the Universe had accepted his negativity and had decided to respond to the weakness by throwing back an immediate challenge.

Manorfield batted well through the afternoon and reached the tea break at 110 for 6. As his players gathered eagerly around their refreshments, James realised that he would now have to make his first decision. Manorfield had batted from 2 pm to 4.15 pm. The match was scheduled to end at 7 pm. With the fifteen-minute tea break, they were nearly half way through the allotted time. Should he now declare the innings? The alternative was to bat on, using up valuable minutes amassing an even larger score but reducing the opportunities to bowl out his opponents. It was a clear choice – declare and give both teams a chance to win the match, or bat on and guarantee a draw by limiting the Grammar School's time at the crease.

James remembered Alec Fraser's advice to 'be brave'. His instincts cried out for a declaration but his anxious conscious-self swithered with indecision. Should he consult Mr. Hughes or should he decide on his own? What was brave about asking another person to take responsibility? No, he would decide for himself. After all, he was captain and wasn't that his role? As the tea was being poured, James approached George Harbourne, the opposing captain and touched the boy's shoulder. He turned with a friendly smile. James felt a small surge of confidence.

"Just thought I'd make a match of it. We're declaring our innings."

George was speechless. He would not have done the same. The initiative was being handed back to his team. He smiled again, this time almost a sneer, and said, "OK by me." James' brief moment of confidence was shattered.

Mervyn Hughes was a short, ginger-haired Welshman. He loved teaching music and cricket and took immense pleasure in coaching the Manorfield First and Second elevens. When things went well, Mervyn's blue eyes glittered with merriment, his singsong Welsh accent bubbling with optimism and humour. But his red hair also matched a fiery nature that meant that Mervyn did not like failure. He also liked to have his own way. Now, with the balance of the match swinging firmly towards Manorfield, he was full of confidence and geniality. He took a huge bite from a buttered scone and strolled towards the strangely glum James.

"Well, boy, I think we've got control of this one, eh? I suggest half an hour more batting to make it safe."

James was close to panic. "I've already declared, sir. I've just told their skipper."

"What's that? You didn't consult me, boy. The decision's a bad one and you didn't consult me first."

The outburst was petulant and thoughtless, and James could do nothing. His respect for authority, combined with self-doubt, drained him completely so that now only fear remained, gnawing at his stomach.

"Sorry, sir. I just thought we could make a match of it – maybe force them to go for a win and hopefully take a few quick wickets so that they feel the pressure."

"Or lose the match because they've now got plenty of time to make 111. Don't you realise that their number three batsman has scored three half-centuries this season. Think, boy, think. Now it's too late. You can't undo the declaration so go out there and captain our team sensibly. Keep the run rate down, at all costs."

The rush of instructions was lost within the reprimand and left James demoralised and alone. One or two of his team-mates heard the diatribe but, worst of all, so had a handful of the Grammar School boys and immediately the teams divided into two groups. Tea was no longer a social occasion. Instead, conspiratorial huddles developed, whispered asides were passed and baleful glances were thrown in James' direction. James cringed and made a point of loading a plate with sandwiches and buns, none of which he felt any inclination to eat. Somehow he summoned up the courage to join a small group of his team mates, where their opening bowler, the cheerful and extroverted Paul Elliott, was holding forth, the only person who did not seem to be affected by the incident. His buoyant mood lifted James who desperately sought the solace of support and companionship. He used his captain's duties as an excuse to enter the discussion.

"Paul, you know what's happened?" Without waiting for a reply, he ploughed on. "I think I've put us in a pickle and we'll have to bowl really well. You open, down the hill. Keep it tight but be as fast as you can. Our only hope is to rattle them. We'll get John to open at the other end, as usual, and I'll take over as first change when one of you gets tired and if we're losing runs. I may not take wickets but I'll try to keep it tight. Sorry about this, but I think we can still win, especially if one of you gets their number three out."

Paul, ever the extrovert, ever confident, grinned conspiratorially. "Don't worry, James, we'll all show old Merv that you were right to declare, just watch me cut into them."

Now that he was involved and had the support of his team-mates, James' confidence returned. He led his players onto the pitch and set a defensive field, placing several men on the boundary to cut off the fours. He stood at Mid Off close to the umpire, Mr. Hughes, at the non-striker's end. The master was in a sulk and ignored James. He was in a foul mood, regretting his own outburst but also fuming at the declaration. Lowering his arm, he called; "Play." Paul began his run up and released a mighty delivery, full of energy but lacking direction. Mr. Hughes sighed audibly. Glaring at James, he called, "Wide." Immediately the first run was recorded on the scoreboard. Paul's enthusiasm and commitment were undaunted. He threw everything into his first over, but lacked control and bowled another wide before being hit for two successive boundaries. The last four balls were left alone by the batsman who could not yet be tempted into playing an unnecessary shot.

"Over," Mr. Hughes called crossly. He walked to square leg to take his position for the second over and passed close to James. "Ten for no wicket. At this rate they'll have the match wrapped up within the hour."

James' heart sank. There would be no encouragement from that quarter!

Fortunately John took a wicket in the second over, a snick to the only slip fielder who took an easy catch. However, a further six runs were scored, and the fall of the first wicket now brought in the feared number three batsman, a short young man with broad shoulders topped by a red face and loose blond hair. He took his guard confidently and faced the final ball of the over, playing it safely with a dead bat – a perfect forward defensive stroke, showing his class.

Once again, Paul threw everything into the next over. And once again he was wayward and expensive. Another eight runs clicked onto the scoreboard. James felt devastated. His mind froze and he made no effort to change the field settings. All he could do was concentrate on his own game and field as well as he could. His head spun with despair as he thought about the predicament and his world became one long, horrendous, never-ending moment of anxiety and shame. He could feel the anger from Mr. Hughes; it prickled between the two of them, invisible, palpable.

And then fate took pity on the lad. The star batsman struck a perfect straight drive, just wide of James, between his body and the umpire. The ball sizzled across the square, a certain boundary. The batsman began his run, confidently expecting the ball to speed into the outfield. It flew like a bullet, hard and dangerous. Mr. Hughes started in fright, instinctively moving to one side, at the same time gasping with exasperation. In normal circumstances no-one would have attempted to stop the ball. It was a dangerous, hard missile. But James was utterly desperate. Instead of ducking out of the way, he flung his body to his right, stretching out a frantic arm. Amazingly his hand deflected the ball into his own chest and it rebounded back to the right, towards the wicket at the non-striker's end. Continuing his roll, James gathered the ball and, from the back of his hand, he flicked it instinctively at the stumps, deflecting the leg stump just sufficiently. One bail wobbled to the ground. The batsman was stranded, four yards from safety. He stood, aghast! One moment he was relishing the perfection of a superb drive and the next he was run out by a feat of courage, instinctive skill and fantastic fortune.

James' team-mates gathered around their stunned captain, clapping him on the shoulders and chattering with delight. John, the bowler, muttered, "We wouldn't have bowled him out, so we did it the only way possible. Well done, James."

James blew on his stinging hand, shaking it vigorously, but he barely felt the pain. At that moment he became a forceful, competitive captain and he loved the experience!

"Two down, eight more to go. Let's get stuck in. Paul, you and John keep going but now concentrate on line and length, not speed. Let's pin them down and get them worried."

James moved in to silly mid off and pulled every man in close to the batsmen, a dangerous tactic. Although he was saving the singles and putting pressure on the opponents, fighting for their wickets, he now ran the risk of giving away boundaries and twos whenever the close wall of fielders was breached. But he knew it would work as soon as he saw the eyes of the number four batsman. The lad took his guard nervously and looked up at the array of faces peering at him. He blocked the first ball, tried the same with the second and it popped up into James' safe hands, an easy catch. The match had turned. From a foregone conclusion, it was now a tense, tactical affair that could go either way. Occasionally the field was breached and runs ticked remorselessly onto the total. But the run rate had been stemmed and, as the tension mounted, wickets also fell. Paul and John were inspired and kept their heads, bowling straight balls that forced their opponents to play. If the batsmen missed, they were either bowled or were given out 'leg before wicket'. Two more catches were taken by the close-in fielders as the ball caught the edge of the bat and flew to the arc of slip fielders or to short leg. With fifteen minutes left, the Grammar School's score stood at 102 for 8 but Paul and John were tiring and a short burst of runs had begun to swing the match in favour of the opponents. It was time to change bowlers.

At the end of John's last over, James took the ball and thanked him for his efforts. Then he turned to Paul who approached, expecting to be given the ball to continue his spell.

"Thanks for your great effort too, Paul, but don't bowl any more. I'll give you a rest and take this end from now on."

James knew that he had been forced by the situation to bowl from the end that Mr. Hughes stood as umpire. The master had said nothing for over an hour. Like all the spectators, he was absorbed in the drama and his mood had slowly improved now that the match seemed winnable. But he was still angry with the young captain. As James handed him his sweater, he glared coldly at the lad. This saddened James who had done his best and was looking for any sign of encouragement.

Before starting his over, James assessed the field and made a single adjustment, pulling mid on closer in – to the silly position. He took his run up, feeling out of touch with bowling. In fact, he felt as if he was dreaming; everything seemed so unreal and so utterly quiet, as if nature itself had paused to observe the occasion. The ball was slightly short and pitched in line with the leg stump, giving the batsman an opportunity to flick it to the leg side. But it caught the leading edge of the bat and ballooned upwards, looping over the head of Silly Mid On before landing exactly where he would have been had James not moved him in. Another run was scored.

"For pity's sake!" Mr. Hughes hissed venomously, full of knowledge that always follows the event.

James pushed the fielder back, aware that the horse had bolted on this occasion, so what was the point other than to placate his irate sports master? He bowled again, a straight ball that was played nervously down the wicket. The third ball was again short pitched; it reared up at the batsman who was caught unawares and only just managed to get bat on ball. The ball popped safely down the wicket and James' instincts cried out to bring in mid on again. The batsman was anxiously prodding and poking and it was inevitable that he would eventually pop up a catch. But James knew what Mr. Hughes' reaction would be so he decided on another course of action.

Intentionally bowling short again, he continued his run forward after releasing the ball. It was too much to expect him to reach the vacant silly position. However, the batsman stepped back, holding the bat up to his chest in an instinctive reaction to the rearing ball. The ball hit the splice and arced tantalisingly towards the advancing captain. James doubted whether he could reach the ball in time but he dived full length, stretching one hand forward in a desperate effort to achieve the impossible. He failed. Just as the ball touched the ground, his hand scooped it up, a fraction of a second too late. James' tumbling body impeded the umpire's view as several fielders appealed instinctively, thinking that the catch had been made.

"Howzat!" The appeal exploded from several excited quarters. Spectators roared their approval, venting full appreciation for another wonderful moment of cricket.

Mr. Hughes raised his finger in delight! "Out!" he spluttered instinctively, all semblance of neutrality lost in the moment of exhilaration. The batsman glared at the umpire, then at James, before beginning a despairing walk back to the pavilion.

James' team mates swarmed around him, full of congratulations, but the young captain immediately recovered his wits and stopped their celebration.

"Wait. Wait a second." He broke through the huddle of excited players and called out to departing batsman, "Come back! The ball was grounded. I didn't make the catch."

Mr. Hughes was dumbstruck but could do nothing. It was the players' prerogative to withdraw an appeal, but it never ever happened. James turned to the furious master and said simply, "Sorry, sir. I think I was the only one who knew it wasn't a fair catch."

"No you were not, lad," a kindly voice spoke. It was the square leg umpire, Derek Hodgeson, the master from Bristol Grammar School. "Very sporting gesture. Well done, boy." At the same time, he looked at Mervyn Hughes. Nothing about the day's events had been lost on the man. He'd observed James' despair and humiliation at teatime, seen how coldly the boy had been treated thereafter and, finally, he knew that his colleague had been unsighted by James' tumbling body as he took the catch. He should either have given the batsman the benefit of the doubt or consulted Derek with his view from the position square of the wicket. "You've got a fine captain there, Mervyn. Whatever happens today, he deserves a lot of praise."

James completed his over and three more runs were scored. The batting side stood at 106 for 8. James was mindful of how peculiar it had felt, for himself, to pick up the bowling so late in the game. He'd felt out of touch and rusty and it would be unfair to ask another new bowler to do the same, especially at this stage of the match. He called across to Paul.

"I'm changing my mind. It's not fair to put a new bowler on at this stage. Can you manage another over?"

"Sure thing."

"Thanks, Paul. If you're feeling knackered, don't worry about speed. Just straight and true. Keep the pressure on."

"No probs."

Paul was magnificent. He drilled five consecutive balls straight at the batsman – medium paced and well pitched up. No runs could be scored. The last ball was his best. It pitched on middle stump and turned on the seam. The opponent was drawn to play a shot and the ball snicked the outside edge of the bat, flying towards the cordon of slip fielders. But luck was on the batsman's side. At perfect catching height, the ball fizzed between second and third Slips, and hurtled over the boundary line for four more vital runs. At 110 for 8 the scores were tied. Almost two full minutes of play were left – just enough time for the umpires to change ends and a final over to be bowled. The advantage was now firmly on the side of the batsmen. All they had to do was prod one single to win. And they had the comfort of two valuable wickets to spare.

Derek Hodgeson was in no hurry. He ambled from his position at the wicket towards square leg and glanced at his watch. Then he turned around. He seemed to notice something was not quite right about the stumps so he strolled back to the wicket and spent a further moment tapping them down and replacing the bails. Finally, with less than a minute to go, he looked up at Mervyn and spoke.

"Don't know about you, umpire, but I make it seven o'clock."

Mervyn glanced at his own watch and saw that there was, in fact, time to start a final over. But he understood the gesture that was being offered.

"Seems you're right, Derek. We'll call it a day." Mervyn withdrew the stumps from his end and announced close of play, "The game is over – match drawn."

After supper that evening, James leaned against the parapet of the school quadrangle and gazed out over the cricket pitch, reliving the memories of the afternoon. He felt good about himself, especially Mr. Hodgeson's kind comments. They confirmed his belief that he'd done the right thing. What would have happened if he had not declared? What would have happened if he'd claimed the unfair catch? What if? What if? He was also saddened by his own master's refusal to give praise, or even criticism, at the end of the match. Mr. Hughes had simply stalked grumpily away, his usual Welsh ebullience pointedly lacking.

"Evening, James." The familiar Scots accent greeted him and he turned from his reverie, smiling at Alec Fraser.

"Hello, sir."

"I'm sorry I missed the match James but I've heard all about it. Mr. Hughes has just briefed me. I've got one comment. Simply and in truth, well done today."

There was a long pause. "So you think I was right, sir? To declare that is?"

"Tactically? You could argue this one to death. But in a short space of time, tomorrow even, the world will have forgotten about the result. How will you look back on it in the future?"

"With pride, sir."

"And will you learn any lessons from the experience?"

"I'll take a few more risks, maybe. It's nice when they pay off."

"And if they don't come off?"

"If I've done my best, then I'll just move on."

"Did it come off today?"

"We didn't win and I hated the match, worrying so much about the trouble I put us in."

"Anything else?"

"The match was drawn, but I know we were the better side on the day. I could see it in their eyes. They knew we were on top, once we dismissed their star batsman."

"Anything else?"

James began to feel uncomfortable. What was Mr. Fraser driving at? Now he groped for an answer, one that his housemaster would like to hear.

"Well, I enjoyed the challenge, nearly pulling it off. It was better than a dull draw, giving them no time to make the runs and us no time to take the wickets. That would have been, well, so … ordinary." James could not think of a better word.

"We haven't mentioned one other thing yet, James. Your calling the batsman back after his dismissal was a remarkable gesture, given your tender years and the state of your mind. The pressure must have been incredible to claim that wicket. Earlier I said that, in future, nobody would remember the result. However, everybody on the pitch, and many of those watching, will remember that gesture. You live your life that way, son, and you'll be a success. Be true to yourself, have courage to follow through and you'll make something of yourself. I feel I'm going to hear about you long after you take your leave of this school. Good night, James."

James sighed as he watched the slightly stooped figure walk away.

"Thanks, sir," he called out. That one, gentle, moment with a man he had grown to love lifted all cares and doubts from his shoulders. Mr. Hughes' rebuffs were forgotten. James walked back to his study and wrote a letter to his parents. He wanted to share the experience with them too.

In his final year at Manorfield, James worked hard at his 'A' level studies. His early interest in the sciences, combined with his father's prodding, then support and finally delight, convinced him that his chosen career, civil engineering, was correct. After all, wasn't his parents' approval a sure sign that this was the right choice? But he struggled with the more sophisticated aspects of mathematics and, before the year was over, he began to worry that he would not be comfortable with the choice of career. But a momentum was now under way. It was too late to change his 'A' level subjects – Mathematics, Chemistry and Physics – and he had already been put down for university places. So, in typical fashion, and not to let others down, James kept quiet about his reservations and put his mind completely, if not wholeheartedly, to his studies, often staying up long after his fellow pupils had retired to bed. With the exception of Dudley Pullinger, whose love of his subject and dedication to the development of young minds ensured that Chemistry would always be a fascinating learning process, his teachers were analytical and dry, churning out the same topics by rote to each new influx of students. And James needed to be led. His creative thought processes had long since been crushed and his natural character traits did not allow him to break free from the intellectual limitations in which he had learned to live. That was just the way he was. He envied the confident and extrovert boys that he saw around him and observed that they fell into two types. Those who were single-minded, apparently selfish in their ambitions and who did not appreciate how their own behaviour could sometimes upset those around them. And those, like Paul Elliott, who were generally cheerful and supportive and who did not seem to worry about anything. James was the opposite. He was naturally introverted and worried excessively about seeing a task or responsibility through to perfect completion. He also became overly sensitive to how his actions would be perceived by others. Very often, he'd sacrifice his own well being for some other 'greater need'.

He knew that people were different. Sameness in everybody would be awful. But he yearned for the ease with which some of his fellow pupils glided through both their studies and now, as senior boys, their responsibilities to help administer the running of the school. In the senior common room, James observed how some boys seemed unconcerned with their duties.

"You know, James, you spend too long preparing the rosters. When I was in charge of sports facilities last term, I did it in half the time. You do a great job, better than me, but when all's said and done, nothing has changed. Everybody ends up playing their matches on the right pitch and on the right day."

Paul's words of wisdom struck home. James kept quiet, unable to think of a response that would not be challenged.

What worried James most of all was the way some boys would suggest ideas or solutions that were so obvious and sensible that he could hardly believe he had not thought of them himself! This applied to academic lessons just as much as to extracurricular aspects of his school days. Why did some people cope so much better with the order and structure of the British education system? Why was it so easy to limit, even crush, the creative freedom and mental flow of an introverted boy, with highly developed feeling traits, whereas extroverted boys with a tendency to 'think' rather than 'feel' would confidently and successfully go their own ways? His only conclusion was that he was 'just a bit thick' and would have to compensate for things by making extra effort. And, after all, if his actions hurt nobody then surely that was all that mattered? In these moments of self-doubt, James failed to recognise his own strengths. The same traits that he regarded as weaknesses were, in fact, when used correctly, incredible strengths. His growing lack of confidence was letting him assume that a conscientious, supportive and gentle nature was a weakness. Sadly, many years would pass before he could begin to live at peace with his own self and realise that there lay within him a massive strength – perhaps the greatest one of all – the strength of gentleness.

But the education system simply did not allow for different traits in children. All were treated in the same way. On the face of it, this seemed perfectly fair. But was it? Boys like James could not bring themselves to challenge. They simply succumbed. And there could be no flourishing under the stultifying effect of mindless discipline, and of learning by memory and by rote. The wonder of imagination was so easily crushed by the formality of analysis and logic.

At the time, James' cooperation was rewarded but, later in life, he would pay the penalty until, perhaps, maturity and self-confidence would allow him to rediscover the potential of imagination, possibly to discover for the first time, independence and peace of mind which, in turn, could eventually lead him to interdependence and a true fulfilment of the human spirit.

But it was not always difficult. As ever, sport helped to make James' school days acceptable and even enjoyable. Sport and the 'Never Again Club' offered physical activity, a chance to interact within a team, and a sense of fulfilment that academic studies and 'official' responsibilities never could. With his variety of challenges and excitements, Cass Cassell continued to draw from James different strengths – like fitness and physical courage.

"Have you read 'Ill Met by Moonlight', James?" Once again, Cass was about to suggest another hair-brained scheme.

"Here we go again," he thought with delight. "No, sir."

"It's going to be a fine, moonlit night tonight. Are you doing anything?"

"Just the usual, sir. But Mr. Fraser will let me off my duties, as it's Saturday."

"I've already had a word with Alec. Right then, dress for a night outdoors – rough clothes and good walking boots. I'll provide sleeping bags and food this time. This will be your last chance to do something with Billy Nichols. He's joining the army and will be off within the month. How would you and he like to take on a two-man challenge?"

James was delighted. He and Billy had formed a friendship that crossed the class system. They had enjoyed each other's company on several 'Never Again' projects but, knowing that this was to be the last, James' joy was tinged with regret. He had always intended to invite Billy to join him during the school holidays – sometimes he spent a week with his Aunt Jean before flying out to Africa. But he'd been nervous about broaching the subject with her, fearing disapproval. After all, she was somewhat staid. Now the opportunity had been lost forever. Maybe it was just as well, but on the other hand … "Damn. Another opportunity missed because I was afraid of someone else's reaction."

"Great, sir. What's going to happen this time?"

"Wait and see, unless you can read the book in the next few hours! Just don't expect to get much sleep."

The Land Rover's headlights cut a swathe in the sky as the vehicle crested the steep track. James and Billy crouched in a ditch beside the deserted road, high on the Mendip hills. It was just after midnight, the agreed hour. Clouds scudded across the face of a full moon, almost as if nature had decided to cooperate in the re-enactment of the famous wartime story when, in Crete, a group of British commandos had kidnapped a high ranking German General before transporting him across hostile territory to an allied submarine.

"Hey, Billy! That's the Land Rover, for sure. See how the headlights are close together."

"Yeah! Quick then – lie down, James. Play dead."

James rolled into the middle of the road, lying prone beside a mangled bicycle. Billy ran forward, waving his arms to the approaching vehicle. When it stopped, he jabbered to the driver. "... hit by a personnel carrier ... just a peasant … they didn't stop … can you help, please?"

As the jumble of words distracted the vehicle's occupants, James rolled to one side then, crouching low, he scuttled to the passenger's side where Cass sat reading documents with arrogant disregard for the flurry of activity that surrounded him. Until he felt the cold metal of the pistol at is forehead.

"Out," James whispered. "Now lie down. On your face. Hands behind your back. Schnell, schnell." It was fun to use a few words of German.

Billy made a wonderful 'show' of clubbing the driver with his own pistol.

"OK mate," he hissed at the amused Alec Fraser, "You're unconscious and trussed like a f***ing chicken. It'll take you all night to escape, or be rescued. Either you act like that's the way it is or I do it for f***ing real."

James gasped at the lack of respect for his housemaster. He finished handcuffing Cass and looked up crossly. "Hang on, Billy. Don't overdo it."

Alec grinned and winked. "It's OK. I take it I'm out of action from now on – paralysed with horror at the your compatriot's language no doubt." He slumped back in the seat and closed his eyes, feigning unconsciousness.

"Right, let's go!" Billy took over. He had picked up the mood of the occasion and was relishing every moment. "You map read and lead the way. I'll hold the Kraut and slip a knife in his back if he makes any f***ing move to escape."

Billy pushed Cass vigorously and the old man stumbled forward.

"Are you OK, sir," James whispered. "Shall I tell Billy not to swear so much"?

"I do not know English good. What are you speaking, Britischer?"

Cass scowled furiously, playing his own role with Teutonic arrogance and outrage. James relaxed, accepting now that they had entered another world. In fact, Billy had been right all along, throwing himself wholeheartedly into the challenge.

With his pencil torch, a compass and a map, James found no difficulty in leading the trio eight miles across broken hilly countryside, through bracken and dark woods, towards their destination. They crossed streams on foot and, using a rope, abseiled down a cliff face. Cass made one break for freedom when the lights of a farmhouse glowed encouragingly, enticing the belligerent General to test their resolve, especially as they were exhausted by lack of sleep, nervous tension and physical effort. Billy made the mistake of holding the General's belt, simply to keep contact and a degree of restraint. Cass surreptitiously slipped the belt from his waist at the moment they ducked through the strands of a barbed wire fence. Then he ran towards the lights, shouting "Achtung. Achtung!" Billy was stranded on the wrong side of the fence.

"Get the f***er, James!"

James flung himself at Cass' legs – a perfect rugby tackle. Cass crashed to the ground, feeling a stab of pain sear through his chest as his ribs thudded against a fallen tree. He cursed, muttering, "Too old for this sort of thing. Shouldn't have tried it on with these two." He sat up gingerly and crossed his arms around his chest, easing the ache of bruised ribs. James also sat up, blinking in consternation. Cass' foot had caught his forehead, just above the left eye which was now puffing up. They grinned at each other and James felt true affection for the game 'old timer' whose love of boys and desire to educate and entertain manifested itself in such strange ways. How many schoolboys would ever find themselves in this crazy situation – cold, tired and bruised, on the Mendips at 3.00 am – and loving every minute of it?

When they reached a short stretch of road at 4.00 am they avoided search parties. Alec Fraser was at it again, this time in his old Austin Cambridge, patrolling the road, hoping to catch a tired and distracted group, perhaps no longer intent on evasion, just desperate to complete the cross country trek. But he was wrong! When they reached the road, James took one last look at his map.

"Nearly there, Billy. Just half a mile along this road and we get to the barn. You stay here, out of sight with Herr General. I'll walk on, a hundred yards at a time, ready to duck into the bushes. When it's clear, I'll wave you forward."

James was confident and relaxed. His eye throbbed, but so what? They'd nearly done it! He realised that now he had taken command. He was so relaxed that his mind had fallen into a sort of autopilot, when everything seemed so instinctive and easy. Why couldn't it be like that all the time?

"This is great" he thought, as he walked quietly forward. On his fifth forward 'pass', he heard a car engine idling and froze, raising a hand dramatically in warning to Billy. Then he edged forward and peered round the bend in the road. There was Mr. Fraser, sitting in his car, having 'patrolled' and 'lurked' for over an hour. Again, James felt a surge of affection. Here was another master that he loved, who had given up a Saturday night for the benefit of his charges. James wanted to greet the man but restrained himself. Unfortunately, Mr. Fraser would have to 'die'. He was all that lay between them and their destination. Keeping out of sight, he crept up to the vehicle and emerged beside the startled occupant, the gun pointing to the kindly forehead.

"Puff. That's a silenced gunshot, sir. Clean kill in the side of the temple. You're dead."

"Why, James," Alec grinned. "You have changed. No mercy at all? Would you have done it for real?"

"I, er, well. I don't know, sir. I suppose not. It's easy to pretend. Would you prefer to be unconscious again?"

Alec enjoyed the ridiculous humour. It was a surreal moment. He chortled.

"Given the two choices, I suppose that's the better one. It's been quite a night. Knocked out twice. But not for real like you. How's that eye of yours?"

"It's nothing, sir. Worth it for all the fun. Cass is a tough old bird."

He ran back to the bend and waved at Billy, who led the disconsolate General forward.

"He's unconscious." James pointed at Mr. Fraser. "Last dash to safety. Come on, we've won!"

They reached the barn and were delighted to find a hayloft, full of loose straw. Two sleeping bags welcomed them. James felt his exhilaration drift pleasantly away, to be replaced by a feeling of contented exhaustion.

Cass understood. "Right, lads, a few hours kip. We'll return for you at 9.30 am. There's a gas cooker on the floor over there and tea, milk, sugar, bread, and bacon and eggs, in the cold box. We'll get ourselves bathed back home and give you time to yourselves before we return to pick you up. Sleep well."

Alec and Cass drove away. It was just after 5.00 am. James looked at Billy.

"Cass could have taken us back right now, but he's given us a few hours together, alone, to have fun. Let's sleep and have a 'fry-up' in four hours time. We'll have a last chance to chat. Well done today, Billy and thanks for your friendship."

The two young men stripped to their underwear and wriggled into sleeping bags. Billy's eyes were heavy; he barely remembered his last words to this strange friend.

"You're OK, James. My first real friend. You just can't see a difference in us, can you?"

"Nope. We're just the same. Except for one thing."

"What's that?"

"Your f***ing language."

The bacon and eggs that they shared a few hours later were memorable, the best James could ever remember. Burned, crisp rashers and hard, overcooked fried eggs, garnished with grit and straw. James picked a feather from his plate and flicked it from his fingers.

"You don't need haute cuisine to satisfy a hungry, happy body."

"Oat what, mate?" Billy wiped a thick wedge of bread across the grease on his plate.

"Oat nothing, Billy. Just a good friend to share it with and a sense of physical and mental well being."

"Lah de dah, mate. There you go again with your posh words."

James smiled. Even though they would say proper farewells in an hour or so, he always remembered Billy by those last words, and his reference to 'my first real friend'. It reminded him so much of someone else.

"Anderson! I want you to be school captain of boxing."

Sid Dormer did not ask – he simply made the statement. He was a former professional boxer, a solid, well-muscled middleweight. Now retired, Manorfield employed him during the winter to coach the few boys who were prepared to follow this least popular of all sports, even less so than cross-country running.

James hated boxing. Unfortunately, he was good at it! He was, however, not good at saying 'no' and even though he had expected this request, and had prepared his script, he blabbered unconvincingly.

"Sir, I'm house captain, of boxing that is, and that's enough. I really must concentrate on my studies this term. My 'A' levels are looming. I hope you don't think I'm letting you down but there's so much to do. If you're unable to find anybody else …"

"I'll ask Matthews instead. Just giving you first refusal but, if that's not OK, then I'm sure he'll do it."

And that was it! The issue was closed, quickly and painlessly. But not for James, who felt that he'd let the side down and worried for several days, long after the world had moved on. He even spoke to Alec Fraser whose reply, as always, was full of understanding and wisdom.

"Boxing's just not your scene, is it? You can't do everything, James, and I respect the serious manner in which you're approaching your 'A' levels. No harm's been done. Actually, use this to your advantage. Why don't you put your sporting effort this term into rugby, which I know you love and, instead of captaining the school, make a last determined effort to lead Wishaw to the inter-house boxing title. Shouldn't take too much time but it'll give you a chance to pass on some of your skills to the newer boys."

James thought it over. Relief refreshed his mind giving him an injection of renewed enthusiasm. He had intended to go through the motions in leading the notoriously weak Wishaw House boxing team to its usual unremarkable performance. School House always won the tournament, led by Alan Matthews and a core of hard, competitive boys. In fact School House tended to dominate at all sports – it was the oldest house in the school and was regarded as the most prestigious; so it had no problem in attracting the best boys, both academically and sports wise.

But now, James took his role seriously. He planned a strategy, looking at the likely teams and comparing Wishaw with School House. It was clear that, if Wishaw could beat School House, they would beat any of the other six houses. Any number of boys could enter and would be drawn, by weight group but otherwise at random, in an individual knockout competition. A point was awarded for each entrant, and thereafter it became a free for all, with points being scored by those who won their bouts and progressed to later stages. Bonus points were also awarded for skilful boxing, irrespective of the result. Apart from himself, James was unable to identify a single Wishaw boy who had any chance of winning his weight group, so it was unlikely that points would be gained by progressing into the later stages. Yet, if he 'flooded' the competition with entrants, a few would inevitably be drawn against each other and someone would have to win, at least to one more round, gaining valuable points for the house. So he put it to everybody during an evening assembly.

"Nobody's being forced to enter," he summed up. "But many thanks to those who choose to do so and I promise to give you all the coaching you need. I also promise that you won't get hurt. Sid Dormer always stops fights that are unfairly matched and I'll be in the corner as the main second. I'll pull you out if you're unhappy or frightened. But look, if we can be a team, a close-knit supportive team, we WILL have fun over the next four weeks and some of you may discover something new about yourselves. We'll be brave for each other – it's always easier that way."

Wishaw House contained sixty-two boys. A few, mainly the older ones, grouped together and approached James, taking him to task for his 'cringing' approach to motivation.

"Next you'll be talking of King and Country. Also, we don't believe you when you say nobody's going to get hurt. How can you be so sure?"

James was stunned, and demoralised at the fact that they had not trusted him. Was it worth going on, especially as he was no lover of boxing himself? But before the week was over, he realised that things were not like that at all – twenty-five boys volunteered for the competition, all but four of whom had never boxed before. Most of them were youngsters and had not yet developed the crust of cynicism that had closed the minds of the others.

"Thanks for your trust," he said to each newcomer, with heartfelt gratitude. "I promise to look after you."

He entered all their names and surprised the whole school. Wishaw started the competition with 26 points and immediately led School House by 15. Now, Wishaw would have to hang on grimly to a lead that would inevitably diminish. Before the first round of the competition began, James held a nightly boxing class showing the youngsters some basic techniques and demonstrating the art by way of exhibition bouts with faithful, clumsy Robert and one other older boy who had some experience and was, at last, revealing an amazing hidden talent. The evening sessions were filled with fun, the constant laughter drawing a regular contingent of interested onlookers. James kept it simple, teaching the correct stance, how to move around the ring 'like Mohammed Ali', how to lead with a fierce points-scoring jab rather than go for haymakers, and how to block punches to the head and body. They all practised conscientiously, growing in self-esteem as they realised how easy it was to absorb sudden sharp thumps and feel no pain. A few of the boys were naturals and began to move with fluid ease, gently teasing their clumsier opponents and drawing cheers and more laughter from the onlookers. James ended each session with a reminder that they were 'a team'.

"Nobody's better than anybody else because those who are not naturals must be showing lots of courage just to take part."

The laughter was good-natured and several boys bonded with each other in a way that they could never before have imagined possible.

Alec Fraser added his support when he addressed the whole house one Sunday evening.

"Tomorrow, boys, the first bouts take place. I want all twenty-six participants to stand up. Thank you. Let's give them all a cheer. Thank you, boys. Now, I'd like to hear that same cheer whenever any of our lads competes. Let's all go and support them whenever we can over the next month. And when you hear that cheer, know that you are not alone in the ring."

James was nervous, but not for himself. The first match of the tournament was about to start and he took Teddy Glanville through a warm up routine, knowing exactly how the lad was feeling. He'd experienced it himself many times before. The nerves before a boxing match had an added intensity, an edge of fear, a real visceral fear of physical harm that never came with other sporting events. They both stood in an ante-room to the gymnasium, ignoring Teddy's opponent and second, and listened to the echoing clatter of raucous conversation, harsh laughter and clunking scraping benches. Spectators took their seats and vied for best positions. Some had come simply to observe with gruesome interest. But the Wishaw support was there in numbers too, occupying the benches along the back wall opposite the door.

James put one hand up and to the side.

"Make some jabs at my hand, Teddy. Follow it around as I move it. That's great. Good sharp jabs, well done. Keep moving, 'dance like a butterfly', duck and weave, breath out through the mouth. Good, good."

The distraction worked perfectly. He saw the intense concentration in Teddy's eyes and felt a glow of gratitude that this tiny twelve-year-old creature had been the first to volunteer for the team. He was so light that a special weight group had been introduced – 'Paper Weight' – to accommodate Teddy and his opponent, the only two entrants in that category. In effect this was the final.

Teddy blew out his cheeks and looked earnestly into the older boy's eyes.

"How was that, James? Will I be alright?"

James squatted onto his haunches and grasped the youngster's waist. He whispered quietly and with a confidence that he did not really feel.

"Don't look right now, Teds, but do it in a moment when they're not expecting it. Have a look at your opponent. He's rooted to the spot. It may be fear, or maybe he's forgotten to warm up because he's too interested in you. He's been watching you practise and he knows you're better than him. I can see it in his eyes. He's worried. If you are too, just remember that he's really worried. You won't just be alright, you'll win this. But don't go crazy. Remember, box properly and get us a bonus point for skill. Just three one-minute rounds. That's all it is. I guarantee you'll win this one and think how you'll feel afterwards. Fantastic."

The door opened and Sid Dormer summoned them. James mussed Teddy's hair.

"Go, tiger, I'm right behind you."

Teddy raised his tiny fists in front of his head and jogged on the spot before leading the other three boys into the gym. A lump formed in James' throat as he watched the wee figure bob through the door, trying for all his worth to be like a professional. The lump thickened and James gave a small, involuntary sob of gratitude when he heard the huge cheer. Teddy was greeted like a hero by the Wishaw contingent. The youngster ducked between the ropes and turned to his corner, looking up at his captain with large frightened eyes.

"Big breaths, tiger, in through the nose and out through the mouth. Keep your guard up at all times. Quick left jabs. And you WILL be alright."

Sid called the boys to the centre of the ring to receive their instructions. They touched gloves and returned to their corners. James gave the big-hearted youngster a huge wink.

"Seconds out. Round one."

The timekeeper clanged the bell and Teddy turned and bobbed intently towards his opponent. He jerked out a quick jab and the other's hair flapped upwards with the impact, a perfect points-scoring punch. For a moment, Teddy froze in amazement. That was easy, so he continued to lead with left jabs, following his opponent around the ring. The bell sounded for the end of the round and Teddy had not yet been hit. His tiny frame trotted confidently back to the corner, and he sat on the stool. James massaged his stomach.

"Well done, tiger. Now get your breath back. That's it – in and out." James fingers pressed gently into the diaphragm to provide the rhythm. Then he stooped through the ropes and flapped a large green towel in front of the small frame and looked straight into the eager blue eyes. "What a fantastic first round. More of the same. Remember. Don't go wild. You'll easily win this one on points. When you start again, throw two immediate left jabs followed by a right cross. Try the combination. He's not expecting you to use your right."

The bell sounded and again Teddy edged forward, lightly, his two hands guarding a serious red face. Bip, bip bop. The combination landed beautifully and Sid Dormer called, "Stop boxing!" He pointed Teddy to a neutral corner and looked carefully at the opponent whose startled eyes gleamed back, shining alertly. He was unhurt. Nonetheless, Sid mussed the lad's hair and said. "Brave lad. I know you want to go on, but I think this fellow is a bit too good for you. I'm stopping the fight."

He turned to Teddy and called him forward, then, lifting the skinny arm into the air, he announced, "Blue wins. Also, a bonus point is awarded for skilful boxing."

Teddy hugged his opponent sportingly and trotted back to the corner, his eyes gleaming with pride and happiness. The cheer from the supporters was massive – a thunderous cacophony of clapping, stamping and shouting, rough adolescent tones mingling with immature, high pitch shrieks.

James felt a huge weight lift from his own shoulders. He wrapped the towel around Teddy's shoulders and spoke with mock formality.

"Edward Glanville – Paper Weight champion of Manorfield School. Well done, Teddy."

"Fisherman's Retreat"
Seaton Lane
Chipping Norton
Somerset
15th November

Dear James,

I recall with much pleasure speaking to you on the first day of the term, when I brought Edward to Manorfield at the start of his first year. You were in the front hall of Wishaw House and very politely asked if we needed help. Do you then remember our discussion? I pointed out how nervous Edward was and you immediately empathised with his position, fully appreciating how daunting it was to begin one's first term at public school. I asked you to place young Edward under your wing, which you kindly undertook to do.

I have today received quite the most remarkable letter from him in which he praises you in no uncertain terms! In general, he has been most appreciative of your 'kindness and support' in making him feel 'at home among friends'. But he specifically mentions your role as captain of the house boxing team, guiding him to his win in the 'Paper Weight' category. He says that he only entered the competition because he felt that he 'owed you one' for being so kind at the start of the year. He never believed it possible that he could be a boxer, let alone a winner, and I can say without exaggeration that his self-confidence has blossomed over the past month ("I feel accepted ... part of a family at Wishaw").

I am copying this letter to your housemaster, simply to express my true appreciation for your part in Edward's wonderful development. He is no longer the shy, self-conscious lad of three months ago and is brimful of enthusiasm about his future at Manorfield. Much of the credit must go to you, and I now express my deep gratitude.

You are a credit to the school and I hope to have the pleasure of meeting you again before you move on. I wish you every success in your own future.

Yours appreciatively

Sir Michael Glanville

cc Mr. A. McG. Fraser
Wishaw House
Manorfield School
Bristol

"Robert, will you be my second?"

"Sure thing."

The boxing competition was almost complete. All of Wishaw's remaining entrants had been eliminated, with the exception of James who had reached the Light Heavyweight final, now scheduled for the next day as the climax to the tournament. James felt a deep satisfaction in what they had all achieved over the past few weeks. After Teddy Glanville's wonderful opening bout, the rest of the team had been galvanised with an enthusiasm that buoyed the spirits of the entire house and became the only talking point for days on end. Nobody was hurt although, in the heavier weight categories, it was clear that blows from the mature contestants did take effect and several bouts were stopped early, especially when the outcome was beyond doubt. Sid Dormer carefully ensured that nobody was pushed beyond reasonable boundaries of punishment. In very closely fought encounters, Sid allowed more leeway, to give both boxers a chance of winning, and a few of the lads emerged with minor bruises, which they wore with pride. Knocks from the rugby field were always more serious. James was relieved, especially that his promise that nobody would be hurt had been proved true. And his relief was now overwhelmed by the thrilling realisation that everything was now to play for.

"There are ten finals tomorrow, Robert." For the umpteenth time, the possibilities were being recalculated. "We still lead by seven points. School House has got six people through to the finals and we've got just one – me. Forget my bout with Alan Matthews for a mo. Now, assume the other School House lads all lose, which they won't, but just assume. Then they'll score a certain five points. That still leaves us two ahead so it won't matter if I lose to Matthews. BUT if they all win, they'll score ten and we'll be three behind so we'll lose whatever I do – my bout will be academic. So, for us to have a chance to win, they must lose at least two of their five other finals, preferably three because then we'll be equal going into my clash with Matthews. Wow! It's possible, just possible. But none of all this takes account of bonus points. The more they get, the sooner we're out of it."

"Do you think you can beat Matthews?"

"I'll have to be extra good because he's captain of the whole school and will be given the benefit of any doubt. But, yes, I think I can. We've never fought before, only just sparred together in training, and I held my own. Caught him a corker too, which may have dented his confidence a bit."

The next day, it seemed as though all the Wishaw boys had turned up from the outset, even though their only direct interest was in James' bout at the end of the afternoon. Obviously everybody had been doing their own calculations and wanted to track the score.

Their excitable captain had pumped up School House. They won their first two bouts by technical knockouts in the first round, simply overpowering their opponents in a flurry of energetic but clumsy punches. James listened calmly to the hysterical cheers from their supporters.

"Robert, they've forgotten about skill. Brute force doesn't win bonus points." Then School House lost a bout, in line with expectations. "And STILL no bonus points," James whispered gleefully. "We're still two points ahead of them with two more bouts to go before mine."

In the final two bouts, luck moved in both directions. School House lost a fight they expected to win, but won the last match against the odds. Again, no points for skill were awarded. Clearly, Alan Matthews had asked for a supreme effort from his team, thinking that they could bludgeon their way to overall victory.

"It's probably worked out more or less as they expected, Robert. They're now one point ahead and Matthews can do it for them if he wins. He's pretty sure he will, I guess. It's simple. Even if I win now we can only tie overall, unless I get a bonus and he doesn't. Unlikely that he won't – he's probably the best boxer in the school. Unless, unless, unless! Can't help what we can't control. OK, I'm on after one more bout. Let's go and warm up again."

In the ante-room, James went through his usual routine. But his stomach was churning with that same familiar combination of nerves and fear. He always wondered why he got himself into these situations. And it was worse this time. So much depended on this one bout and he was desperate not to let his wonderful band of fellow boxers down. Alan Matthews came in and grinned at him, but said nothing. James grinned back and added a wink to the greeting, remembering what he'd said to Teddy and all the others: "You may feel nervous, but so does the other guy." Faithful Robert could think of nothing to say so just sat close by on a bench and smiled encouragingly whenever James glanced at him. Suddenly it was time. The previous bout had ended and two perspiring boys walked in, bringing with them a smell of leather and sweat that further refreshed the already ripe atmosphere of the ante-room.

"How'd it go?" James asked without real interest, hoping only to relieve the tension. He did not listen to the reply. All he now sensed was a complete silence in the gym; heavy with expectancy, broken only by nervous coughs and murmurs. Sid's head appeared round the door.

"Right lads. In you come."

James looked at Alan and nodded with his head, indicating politely that his opponent could lead the way. The young man looked surprised and paused for a moment seeming to change his mind. But suddenly he acquiesced and walked quickly through the door, to be greeted by a huge cheer. James waited intentionally, for just a few seconds, and timed his entrance to perfection. The original cheer had begun to dwindle and was now interrupted by a renewed explosion of noise when James appeared – shouts and whistles merged with the thumping of feet and the chant "And-er-son, And-er-son" pulsed through the air. It was a staggering reception – one that clearly unsettled Alan and warmed James' heart, helping to dowse the dread in his stomach. During his short walk to his corner James could barely hear Robert's stunned whisper, close by his ear, "Wow, wowee. This is quite something."

"...and when I say break, you both stop boxing immediately and step away from each other. Is that clear, lads?" James nodded automatically and pushed his gum shield against his upper lip, looking at Alan who returned the gaze vacantly. "Good luck to you both. Make it a good, clean fight."

They returned to their corners and turned waiting for the bell. It sounded, unnaturally loud in an otherwise total silence, like an ominous knell from the bowels of the earth. They approached each other, arms up in a perfect defensive pose. Then Alan attacked, like a berserk warrior. He flung himself at James, throwing a flurry of punches. James felt several concussive thuds against his head, accompanied by brilliant explosions of light. He backed away, realising that he had to weather this storm, or lose ignominiously within seconds.

"Stop boxing!" Sid examined James' eyes and smiled knowingly. He'd been there himself many times before, at levels way beyond that of these two youngsters. But he knew courage when he saw it.

"I'm OK. I'm OK." James pleaded, "Please don't stop it sir, please."

"You're fine, lad." A friendly hand patted the back of his head. "Box on."

This time James was ready. He watched his opponent moving towards him, and waited for the first punch of the inevitable onslaught. Then he whipped forward a single vicious left jab that caught Alan flush on the forehead. It was a stunning punch, combining perfectly with his opponent's own forward momentum. Alan staggered back three paces before sitting abruptly on the ground in an ignominious bundle. The roar from the onlookers spurred him instantly and he leapt up, ready to rush forward again.

"Stop boxing!" For the second time in fifteen seconds Sid peered closely at a pair of alarmed and furious eyes, grinning to himself at the commitment of both boys. "OK, box on."

James had taken the wind from Alan's sails. His opponent's confidence crumbled as, time and again, a fierce left jab halted his advance. Alan felt a wash of desperation. He simply had to finish James off. He was losing too many points to the deadly scoring punches, whereas his own were becoming increasingly wild, landing harmlessly on James' shoulders and arms. The bell sounded and James returned to his stool, his chest heaving for breaths, sucking in the luxurious energising air.

"Well done, James! You've got him on the run. Finish him off." Faithful Robert was trying so hard to be supportive.

James could barely speak so he waited for his own gasping breaths to moderate, becoming slower and more controlled.

"I've got to win a bonus point. I must outbox him, not bludgeon him. That's the mistake he's making. Sid won't give bonuses for brute force. For God's sake Rob, get that sweat out of my eyes."

"Oops, sorry!"

In the second round, Alan's onslaught continued. But they were both tiring and came together, clinging fiercely to each other, jabbing short punches at the solar plexus. Still James remained calm. This would not earn points for skill. So he looped a quick overhead hook and stepped back, looking intently at the angry face. Jab and move, Jab and move. James concentrated on defence, only attacking when he saw a clear opening. His arms were feeling leaden but the punches still carried weight and he felt his opponent wilt as he threw a solid right into Alan's ribs. Then he stepped back and ripped two further left jabs to the forehead.

Alan threw caution to the wind. Bravely he surged back and, amid another flurry of punches, one solid right caused another explosion of light in James' head. He backed away, hearing the roars from Alan's supporters and knew that another charge was imminent. When it came, he moved quickly to his left and ducked beneath another vicious right. Then, returning his weight to his right side, he threw a perfect left hook over Alan's' outstretched right arm. It landed cleanly on his opponent's forehead. This time Alan dropped to his knees.

"Stop boxing! One, two, three …" The count began.

"Get up, please get up." James knew that he needed to box on to gain the vital bonus. Alan rose on the count of five and Sid looked at his face seeing despair reflected dully in cloudy eyes.

"It's been a great bout, Alan, but I've got to stop it there. You gave your all." He led the distraught captain back to his corner, then called James to the centre and held up his exhausted arm. "Blue wins."

Thunder erupted from the benches. James walked across to Alan and hugged his fellow competitor who had striven so hard, yet to no avail.

"Sorry, Alan, sorry."

The urge to apologise welled up for no reason. Both boys clung to each other, a merging of despair and delight in a single momentary sculpture. The thunder reduced to continuous applause, before calming to a total silence. Sid waited for the silence.

"And a bonus point to Blue."

Chapter 9

A False Dawn

During the month in which Lisa gave Kinord notice that she wanted to move Chelsea, the Scottish winter refused to ease its grip. It seemed as though Kinord had shrivelled in despair in the cold, exhausted with winter and waiting in vain for the first signs of spring warmth. The centre now carried an air of hopeless gloom, like a bleak, grey prison whose warders were the biting winds that relentlessly patrolled the bare, open fields. Lisa longed for final confirmation that a place was available for Chelsea at her new home – Braehead – where warm stables awaited and, in any case, the weather was kinder away from the high ground, closer to the seaside.

"Jean, It's Lisa. I'm in London just now. Please bring Chelsea in at night. She's utterly miserable and needs some respite from the cold." Lisa emphasised the 'please' and Jean sensed a touch of desperation in the normally cheerful voice.

"OK, Lisa, I'll see to it."

The next morning, Lisa phoned for news of Chelsea. Jean was immediately defensive, her tone full of forced assertiveness as she tried to cover her embarrassment.

"No, she was not brought in last night. Gail tried but Chelsea kicked out at her so she gave up. I'm not having any of my staff put in danger."

"Is that all you have to say, Jean?"

"Yes." The defensive tone was clearly evident, even in that one word.

"Then, that is the end of the matter. Goodbye, Jean." Lisa slowly replaced the phone, thought for a moment, and picked it up again. She pressed the memory recall for Braehead and sent up a silent positive prayer: "Thank you, God, for making available a place for Chelsea right now."

"Hello, Sheena? Lisa Graham here. Sorry to trouble you, but is there any chance at all that you've got space for Chelsea right now, rather than at the end of the month."

She closed her eyes and looked upwards, sensing God's presence and knowing what the response would be.

Sheena's cheerful Scots accent bubbled confirmation, "That's fine, Lisa. Amazing that you should phone now, but last night we had a cancellation and I was thinking of you, but I thought you'd want to see your notice through with Kinord, seeing that you've paid them in advance."

"It's expensive but unimportant where Chelsea is concerned. Sheena, you're a star. Can I bring Chels in this evening? Great! Thanks so much. She's had a dreadful time and needs looking after."

Although tempted, Lisa knew that there was no need to ask for a nice deep bed of fresh straw and plenty of hay. The only other place she'd seen beds like those at Braehead was at the National Stud at Newmarket, home to the cream of Britain's Thoroughbred brood mares and stallions.

Sheena smiled at the phone, knowing that she would enjoy Lisa's company and looking forward to the new client's presence in the yard.

"Of course, Lisa. We'll bed up the isolation box, nice and warm. When will you get here?"

"I'll get the early afternoon flight home. All being well, I'll see you no later than eight this evening. Sheena, once again, many thanks. And a kiss from Chelsea too."

Lisa rang off with a jubilant "Yes!" then phoned Andrew with instructions to get the transporter ready.

They arrived at Kinord at 6 pm and saw Chelsea, alone in the paddock, a picture of misery, her head lowered in unhappy sleep with her back turned against the biting February drizzle, driven across the field by a harsh, gusting breeze. Their headlights swept across the scene and Andrew gasped with dismay.

"She looks so sad, poor Chels."

They jumped from the vehicle and called across to the forlorn figure, who raised her head in delighted relief and blew soundless nickers of welcome – only evident in the quiver of her nostrils. She caught easily and was led into a nearby stable where Lisa and Andrew clucked and fussed about, cleaning and drying her, and feeding her hay and carrots. Soon she was groomed, rugged and booted, ready for the short journey to Braehead. Sensing that this was indeed an end to an ordeal, she loaded without demur, breaking wind as her final gesture to the bleak and heartless scene behind her.

Later that evening, Chelsea was led into Braehead's isolation block, where she would spend four days in quarantine before being introduced to the other horses. A welcoming glow shone from the door of the stable block and, as she walked through it, then down a short aisle and into her box, she was alert with interest, sizing up what she instinctively knew to be her new home. The knee deep, fresh straw, rustled, dry and welcoming, and the manger was piled high with fresh malty-smelling haylage. Chelsea circled the box twice, her ears pricked upwards, alert with delight. With a single huge harrumph, she spread her hind legs and peed a long stream of territory-marking urine. Then her entire body relaxed and she began to feed on the wonderfully sweet haylage, so different from the brittle hay that she had become used to. Lisa and Andrew leaned against the half door and quietly watched a scene of utter contentment.

Early the next morning, Lisa returned to the yard and saw Chelsea's rug covered in straw and marked by stable stains, a sure sign that the mare had lain down to sleep during the night, obviously completely relaxed. She took her out for a short walk in hand just to stretch her legs and let her become familiar with the new surroundings.

Two days later a major two-day show began at the yard. When Lisa went to find Chelsea, she discovered that she had been moved, a day early, into her permanent quarters in the main stable block in order to provide two visiting stallions with accommodation for the show in the more secure isolation boxes. The main block buzzed with activity – horses were being groomed and studs fitted into shoes for jumping, and the bustle of coming and going gave Braehead an air of busy excitement as horses were led to and from their competition rounds. Amidst this activity stood Chelsea, head bowed contentedly downwards as she enjoyed a mid morning nap, taking the weight off a hind leg, a picture of relaxed comfort. What a change! What a wonderful and immediate acceptance of a new home.

Chelsea and Lisa loved Braehead. Although it was much bigger than Kinord, it was incredibly friendly and all the horses were treated as individuals. Which, of course, they were. Braehead was a private livery yard, with no riding school or other facilities for the public. Most of the animals were competition horses – mainly show jumpers and eventers, some competing at high levels – and no-one worried too much about their quirks and peculiarities. Although the staff did all the day-to-day chores, mucking out, feeding and taking the animals to and from the fields, very often the owners helped out. In any case, each animal was groomed and worked regularly by its owner. Lisa no longer needed to worry about being away from home, at last knowing that Chelsea would be well cared for. Furthermore, with another slice of good fortune, Lisa discovered that one of the girls who had once worked at Kinord was now employed locally by one of the oil companies. Chris loved horses but was as yet unable to afford to own one so she was delighted when Lisa offered her the chance to earn some extra money by exercising Chelsea when she was away. Everybody was delighted – Chelsea remembered Chris as one of the caring humans at Kinord and responded happily to this new arrangement. Chris was thrilled to have the opportunity to continue her own riding and to earn money in the process and Lisa, at last, had peace of mind.

Within a few weeks, Chelsea's condition had improved dramatically and she was back to her old spirited self, once more happy and cooperative, and also keeping her old touch of mischief and spice. It was important to Lisa that Chelsea never lost that touch of spirit! The calm routine of the yard and the kindness of those around her were working like a reviving tonic, just as they would have done for any human being. Yet again, Lisa marvelled at the similarity between horses and humans.

"There's no doubt that you can train the body if the mind is right, but it doesn't necessarily apply the other way round."

Chelsea was still undergoing her fitness programme following the episode with her hocks. Now she began to work well, able to trot for longer periods and even do a little school work. So Lisa turned her mind once again to competition, her main aim being endurance riding, preferably close to home, until Chelsea could once again return to the world of jumping.

In the meantime, Lisa received an entry form for a prestigious annual horse show, to be held that year at Braehead early in July. It looked like fun and, importantly, was a home fixture, so the lure was irresistible. Lisa read through the classes and decided to re-introduce Chelsea to the world of competition gently, by showing her 'in hand' in the adult hunter class. Lisa did not feel that her rehabilitation was sufficiently advanced for any of the ridden classes nor was she certain how Chelsea would react to the atmosphere and excitement of a return to competition so, taking everything into account, the 'in-hand' class seemed to be a good place to start. On top of which Chelsea was a real eye-catching beauty and it would be interesting to see how the judge would react to her irresistible charm. So they began to practise walking and trotting in hand. Chelsea approached this return to basics with bemused good nature, and the practice lessons served to sharpen up her movement and posture. They also worked on standing straight and square reducing Chelsea's pigeon-toed appearance. Normally Lisa did not worry about her being 'in' in front and 'out' behind; that was often the mark of a good jumper. However, on this occasion, she wanted her lovely mare to look her best for the judge. And Lisa wanted to look the part too! She invested in a whole new wardrobe – hacking jacket, show shirt, tie, beige jodhpurs and short, black boots along with gloves, a black silk for her hat and a show cane. It all felt very strange after her usual, casual riding dress.

During the week before the show, Lisa pulled Chelsea's mane and tail and trimmed her feathers. On the eve of the big day, she bathed the mare using 'Fiery Chestnut' shampoo. "How appropriate!" The bath left Chelsea glistening with a healthy coppery sheen. On the morning of the show Lisa rose at crack of dawn and arrived early at the yard. The first and main task was to plait Chelsea's gorgeous mane, something that she'd been practising hard. Then Lisa brushed the mare till she shone and put some oil on her hooves. Finally it was time for eye make-up – an old show trick – rubbing baby oil around the eyes to make them stand out. With her bridle on, Chelsea was at last ready, looking a real stunner; her beautiful Thoroughbred head was perfection, alert and ready. Lisa did a quick change and 'voila!' – they were both ready for the judge's scrutiny.

From the moment they walked out of her box, Chelsea acted as though she was royalty. She walked regally across to the show park and waited quietly until they were called in for her class. Lisa was unaware of Chelsea's first experience, with Eric years earlier, of being shown in hand but she sensed that Chelsea was a natural, having an aloof presence in the ring that made everybody smile. It was a hot day and all the competitors were troubled by flies, even though most horses had been sprayed with fly repellent. As they stood waiting outside the ring, Chelsea shook herself vigorously. But once inside, she simply ushered the flies away with gentle, discreet shakes of her head and swishes of her tail. So well mannered, just as though Lisa was riding her. Chelsea was on the ball, completely aware that this was serious stuff!

They walked and trotted around for the judge in a large circle with eight other horses. As she passed him, Lisa remembered to smile, and Chelsea turned her head to smile too! To Lisa's delight and surprise they were called in second after the initial group inspection. Although this was a fairly small, local show the competition was severe as there were several horses in the class bred from well-known stallions. So Lisa was thrilled that Chelsea was able to hold her own amongst the others. But she was also under no illusion that when the judge made the individual inspections he would spot the arthritic hocks. Nonetheless, it was pleasing to know that they had made a good first impression. During the individual inspection Chelsea accepted with good grace the judge's handling of her silken body. Then they walked and trotted alone for him and once again took their place in the line. Chelsea continued to behave impeccably, standing quietly even when another horse in the class lost patience and broke loose, cantering out of the ring. Shades of her first show with Eric! Soon they were walking around for the final time and eventually Chelsea was called in at fourth place. Lisa couldn't believe it – this was more than she had dared to hope for, especially as the mare had been placed ahead of many of the horses from high quality stallions. Clearly the judge liked good, old-fashioned Irish hunters and, of course, Lisa completely agreed with his preference. This was her first competition with Chelsea so the beautiful rosette would always hold pride of place in her collection, proving that competition is simply about doing one's best in the company of others whose intention is the same. To have won would have been a truly wonderful accolade yet, in coming fourth, Chelsea attracted the loudest applause from a very partisan local crowd, well filled with Braehead's own stable girls all of whom had fallen in love with the gorgeous, sassy mare. Chelsea received the acclaim with cool aplomb, as nothing more than her due. After all, what was the big deal? She knew she was the best, even if the judge was inept – but there again, he was only human, and a male at that!

A fortnight later, they entered their first endurance ride together. This too was great fun although it was a much more serious test of Chelsea's hocks. It was also their first away competition together and a chance to test out Lisa's new lorry. Andrew accompanied them as groom and driver so, as he claimed later, "No wonder everything went smoothly." They passed both the vet's examination and the tack inspection and were soon on their way. Chelsea had been at the location before, last year, when she had done the cross-country course with Tony. Now, because the first part of their route passed some of the fences, Lisa had to take a good hold and redirect Chelsea who immediately assumed that they were there to be jumped!

"It was so funny," Lisa reported later on to Andrew. "Do you remember that first jump – the low hedge between two gates? Well, as we approached it, Chels was sure we were going to do a cross-country and she began to fidget and align herself with the hedge. When I held her back and started to point her past the fence, she must have immediately thought: "If it's not the hedge then wehey, we're going for the bigger jump – the gate" and I had a real fright. At one point I thought she was going to go for it, but she was only having fun and held back. Then, when we walked past the fence she gave me that look with her ears. You know the one, "Spoilsport, I could have done it." And I know she would have done. She's got her spirit back again, that's for sure. It was so funny, and yet that one simple moment made me so happy."

"We soon settled into a steady rhythm and headed towards the hills. I'd been a little anxious about Chelsea's highly competitive nature and wondered how she would react to faster horses coming from behind, overtaking and going on ahead. Endurance riding at our level is not a race, but a test of physical fitness at a steady pace so I didn't want Chels to regard the occasion as a race. But I needn't have worried. She was as good as gold.

She cooperated as part of our team, warning me with her ears when other horses were approaching and then was so good, always standing to one side to allow them to go on ahead."

Clearly, Chelsea was happy with Lisa's company, a sure sign that the good old days were returning, when she had been fit at Kinord and had formed such a trusting and enjoyable relationship with her wonderful mistress.

In the end, their time was slower than planned, only because Lisa had been reluctant to push Chelsea too soon. Andrew met them at several points along the route, with water for Chelsea, and also just to check that all was well as Lisa was still not entirely sure how the hocks would cope. In fact she need not have worried – they had great fun and, most important of all, Chelsea finished in excellent shape. Her heart rate at the end was lower than when she started! Next morning Lisa trotted her up and was delighted to find that she was 'sound as a bell'. So Chelsea was turned out into the field for a well-earned day's rest. The period of sensible, gentle recuperation seemed to be paying off.

Their next outing was a twelve-mile supervised charity ride along a local beach. Lisa chose to accompany a 'mostly trotting' group that comprised a mixture of horses and ponies. The leader was a ferocious woman who insisted; "Everyone must stay behind me at all times." Chelsea always respected Lisa but was not averse to letting her feelings be known as well. This was just such an occasion and frustration got the better of her as she began to jog and skitter in anticipation of things to come. The leader observed Chelsea's exuberance with disdain and insisted that they ride close-up behind her, presumably to keep an eye on them! Lisa bit her lip and concurred. When they reached the beach the leader's horse baulked at a narrow path over a small stream leading to a shoulder of sand dunes. Not even a tap with her whip would encourage it to go forward – clearly the horse was less afraid of her than the humans were! The second horse in line also refused to go, having seen the lead horse refuse.

"Chelsea will lead," Lisa found herself saying with quiet confidence and the other two riders gratefully moved their horses to one side. Lisa urged Chelsea on with an encouraging pat and a gentle squeeze with her legs, for Lisa never carried a whip. The path was narrow and awkward but, brave creature that she was, Chelsea plunged into the soft sucking sand and on across the dunes down to the firmer surface on the beach. All the other horses followed obediently.

As soon as they reached the beach Chelsea was ready to go; she was tired of having to 'amble' along at the speed of ponies. Her ears spoke volumes for her outrage. "I mean, after all, the indignity of it!" And Lisa sympathised, knowing that her beloved mare was trying to be good but was at the limit of her patience and was not at all happy in the group. So she decided to risk the wrath of the ride leader and asked for permission to go ahead at her own pace. Having signed a verbal disclaimer to absolve the world of any responsibility for disaster, Lisa was finally allowed to go it alone. Both horse and rider sighed with relief and began to trot towards their destination – Northport. Chelsea's humour immediately improved as she covered the ground easily with a flowing trot, interspersed with the occasional canter. At Northport, they had a short break before turning around and beginning the return leg before Chelsea's hocks began to stiffen.

It was a strange day but, even with the sticky start, Lisa's comment was simply, "That was just the best – alone with my lovely horse and twelve miles of glorious sunny beach. Sometimes we forget; it's often the simplest of things that give the most pleasure."

They had one more endurance ride, in October, to finish the season. This time Chelsea was back to full fitness and Lisa pressed her a little harder to finish in a good time. And this even though Chelsea lost a back shoe six miles from the finish. When it happened, Lisa immediately offered to lead her home but the mare had other ideas and clearly indicated that she wanted to end the season well. So Lisa decided to go with Chelsea's messages, knowing that it would be less stressful just to let her go, so she stayed aboard and they enjoyed several canters along lovely soft, grassy forest tracks. At the end, Chelsea proved that she was right by trotting up perfectly for the vet. Obviously the shoeless hoof had caused no discomfort and, once again, her low heart rate confirmed her overall fitness. In the lorry on the way home Lisa chatted with Andrew about the day's events, putting into words for the first time what she had long suspected.

"She's such a star. She'd give you her last breath in a competition."

Lisa's patience had once again paid off. Their move to Braehead had been inspired by love and concern, contributing to Chelsea's return to her usual equable nature, spiced with true chestnut character. The gentle activity during the year had also guaranteed Chelsea's physical well being. Meanwhile, Lisa too had benefited. For her, riding time offered an opportunity to simply *be*, to experience a kind of meditation. So often Lisa had started out riding with thoughts and issues running chaotically through her mind. Then she had become engrossed in the ride, forgetting everything until suddenly a solution popped into her head. On other occasions, Lisa had felt weighed down by worries but had returned from her session with Chelsea feeling much better, with a true sense of perspective. Gradually, she began to see a meaning to her life. This sense of purpose was grounded in her relationship with Chelsea and the fact that she had brought the mare to fitness and happiness by simply listening to her silent, 'whispered' messages. She had learned that Chelsea would never have recovered her spirit, or her physical health, if she had been coerced. She had learned too that Chelsea could be trusted, that she was not a difficult, petulant chestnut mare, but an authentic creature wanting desperately to serve a mistress whom she loved unconditionally. And all because Lisa always listened to her whispers and never failed to serve Chelsea in return.

"I've learned so much from you, Chelsea. You've rewarded me beyond measure for my effort and love. Surely there's a message here for my life with humans?"

One of Lisa's favourite management gurus was Charles Handy, whom Lisa had once had the pleasure of meeting whilst doing a year's course of study in Oxford. He had presented an interesting and, as was now becoming ever more apparent, a very accurate picture of the world of work. Lisa had read all his books and now found herself re-reading 'The Hungry Spirit'. Here, she found much food for thought, and much that reminded her that the approaches that had worked so well with Chelsea could also be used as a bridge to people. Lisa began to understand that her own business ethics were not so different so maybe her values were not so way out after all. These feelings were confirmed when she was introduced to Lance Secretan and realised that in his book, 'Reclaiming The Higher Ground', she had discovered a perfect encapsulation of her own beliefs.

With winter approaching, Lisa began to look forward to furthering her riding skills with Chelsea. She felt that it was time to start show-jumping again so, at the first opportunity, she booked a grid session. As gridwork was basic training for show jumpers, what better place was there to begin jumping? There was time for one lesson before Christmas. After a somewhat nervous start, Lisa soon became accustomed to the experience, immediately acknowledging that she had forgotten how much fun it was, and exhilarating, to jump. She therefore began to make plans for more fun during the festive break. Sadly, this was not to be for once again she and Chelsea were to face further challenges. It had been a false dawn.

Lisa's patience and determination were to be tested yet again. Like black clouds gathering before a storm, two setbacks combined to challenge her upbeat nature. Sadly, Andrew's father died just before Christmas. He had been frail for several years but his gentle determination and refusal to wallow in self-pity had always drawn admiration from Lisa. So much so that she often gave him credit for helping her to mould her values. Like Chelsea, her father-in-law was a perfect role model. Strangely, like Chelsea he also always seemed to recover from setbacks and somehow Lisa had come to think him of as eternal so it was a shock when the indomitable spirit passed away. Christmas and the Millennium celebrations were muted for both Lisa and Andrew and they were glad to escape for a week's break in the New Year. With all the upheaval at home, she also gave Chelsea an extended holiday over Christmas, planning to get back to work with her when she returned from her own break.

As ever, Lisa was filled with joyful anticipation of their first ride together in the new millennium. Chelsea welcomed her with the usual quiet nickers of delight but otherwise seemed a little agitated. As the saddle was placed on her, her ears went back and she reached forward to bite the bars that ran along the top half of her box.

"What's up, lass? Holiday's over. Yes, I know, back to work, but also fun."

Lisa chattered on happily and soon they were alone together on a beautiful crisp day, in brilliant sunshine, the bright rays of the low winter sun flickering between the branches of tall bare beech trees. As they walked along the woodland path they passed, momentarily, through blinding flashes of light and welcome shade. To start with, Chelsea seemed fine, her pleasure at seeing Lisa again more than compensating for any discomfort. But not for long. As the hack progressed, it soon became clear that all was not well. Instead of a smooth trot, Chelsea jogged, throwing her head agitatedly from side to side. Lisa was immediately aware that the mare was in pain, her understanding now honed by their close relationship, and a growing experience coupled with genuine intuition. She dismounted and, side-by-side, they walked companionably home. During the walk Lisa had a careful look but could not see any obvious signs of injury. She ran her hands over the mare and could feel no heat or swelling. Back at the yard, she checked the saddle and found nothing untoward.

The next day, she made another close inspection, this time using her intuition after a night of 'sleeping on it'. During the night, she had dreamed. Chelsea was standing in an idyllic pasture with other horses, the mares from Braehead and Kinord in friendly harmony. A sultry summer sun bathed the herd in gentle, energizing rays and all the horses were head down, contentedly grazing. Lisa felt herself float effortlessly over the pasture until she reached Chelsea who raised her head in welcome. Then, turning her neck stiffly as far back as possible, the mare peered past her own withers and Lisa felt a sharp stab of pain. Immediately she awoke. Now Lisa knew exactly where to look. Sure enough, there it was – a warm spot on Chelsea's back! The skin fluttered to Lisa's touch; she was not comfortable. Within the hour, Lisa had called the vet who came immediately. Sarah was on her way anyway to check out other horses at Braehead. It seemed as though everything over the past twelve hours had been pre-ordained.

Lisa was relieved that she had called Sarah for, by the time the vet arrived, Lisa had taken Chelsea out of her box and had walked and trotted her in hand and, sadly, was clearly able to see signs of lameness in her right hind leg. Sarah carried out her own examination and concluded that the most likely cause of her pain was that the spavin in her right hock had not properly fused.

"However, it will take X-rays and other tests to confirm the diagnosis. What is clearly evident is that Chelsea has indeed been adopting a poor posture to accommodate the pain in her leg. The result is that her back has also been affected."

Lisa could hardly contain her sadness, feeling so much sympathy for the wonderful brave mare who certainly did not deserve this further turn of misfortune. When would it all end? Yet amid all the doubts and regrets, Lisa's resolve strengthened, making her ever more determined to see things through to a proper conclusion. Never once did it occur to her that she should cut her losses and sell her beloved mare. Infinite patience was being called for and Lisa would respond with all the love she could muster, fortified by the absolute certainty that the road ahead would eventually lead to hidden rewards and joys. Lisa was firm in the belief that 'infinite patience produces immediate results'. The first task was to admit Chelsea to the animal hospital during the following week whilst, in the meantime, she was left to rest.

Fortunately, the hospital was close to Braehead so Chelsea did not have to endure a long journey. She sensed that the process was for her benefit and loaded into the transporter with quiet cooperation, emerging ten minutes later to a strange world of human activity.

Andrew was still grieving his father's death, but was anxious to receive Lisa's nightly reports. He knew that his wonderful father had been re-united with God and he was thus eager to share with Lisa the progress of the living. Somehow, to his simple but sincere belief, the link between the souls of the departed and those of all living creatures was inexplicably present. His father's comforting presence calmed both Lisa and Andrew during this worrying time, as if his essence had re-entered their lives through Chelsea.

Andrew could not dispel the feeling that Chelsea would emerge from the experience whole and recharged, in the same way that Dad had emerged from his setbacks for so long. It did not surprise Andrew when Lisa reported on their experience to the hospital in terms that reminded them both of God's presence.

"She was an angel all day, especially throughout the three hours of tests. Despite being lame, she behaved with unnatural calmness, almost with pleased anticipation, just as if she was going to an endurance competition. Maybe this was because she saw another horse being trotted up for the vet. Anyway, she was very much on her toes but also, ever so cooperative. Then, she gradually got the idea that it wasn't a competition and resigned herself to the various tests and all the hanging around in between. She didn't even mind the X-rays. Alarm on her part wouldn't have surprised me at all, yet she simply walked straight in to the X-ray suite and stood quietly whilst all manner of machines were placed around her back legs. Andrew, there's no doubt that Chelsea knows what's going on. Just like your dear Dad, putting up with all the inconvenience and indignity without a moment of complaint. I couldn't help thinking that your Dad was there, telling Chelsea to be calm, that all would come out well in the end. Now, I'm really convinced that all will be well too."

The tests confirmed that the spavin in her right hock had not fused naturally. Fortunately, the one on her left hock had. Given that the first level treatment – painkillers and gentle exercise – had not worked, Sarah recommended that she should have a steroid injection in her right hock to encourage fusion to take place. Lisa was alarmed but, trusting her vet, she was happy to accept the recommendation. Treatment was scheduled for the following week.

A steroid injection is as painful a process for animals as it is for humans and so Chelsea was heavily sedated. The injection had to be placed very precisely, another reason for a still, sedated patient. On the morning of the treatment, the stable staff made up her bed with deep straw, well banked up around the walls so that, if she lay down and found it harder than usual to get up, she would come to no harm. Sarah arrived and gave Chelsea a friendly pat. Although Chelsea associated her with unpleasant experiences – needles for flu jabs and all the tests for her spavin – she understood that Sarah was intent on helping her. So she bore no grudges and was quite happy to accept any number of Sarah's seemingly endless supply of Polo mints! With a sigh from Lisa, they began work. They stood Chelsea diagonally across her box giving themselves plenty of room to work behind her. Then Sarah injected Chelsea with a 'pre-med' followed shortly afterwards by a full sedative. The mare remained on her feet, as intended, but her head sank slowly downwards and it was clear that she was no longer aware of her surroundings.

Sarah inserted the needle several times, searching for the exact spot in the joint. She quickly found it; clear joint fluid soon flowed back into the syringe. Then she attached the steroid syringe to the needle and a few seconds later the treatment was complete. They expected the sedative to last for about one hour and Lisa naturally wanted to stay with Chelsea so she settled herself on a comfortable pile of straw in the corner of the box, watching her friend and talking constantly to her – Lisa had once read that 'hearing' is the last sense to go so she thought that Chelsea would be comforted by a familiar voice. Remembering how jumpy her cats had been when they emerged from sedation, Lisa put aside her instincts to stroke Chelsea. She did not want to startle her when she began to become aware of her surroundings. Gradually the sleepy mare returned to consciousness, looking just like any human recovering from an anaesthetic.

"How are you feeling, Chels? It's all over now."

Slowly, the head lifted and the eyelids opened wider, revealing increasingly alert eyes whose first sight was the caring and concerned face of her mistress. Gingerly she took an unsteady pace to the loved presence and nuzzled Lisa's hand. Lisa was immensely touched by this gesture, certain now that Chelsea had heard her voice chattering to her throughout the experience and now wanted to reassure Lisa that all was well. She stroked her gently whilst murmuring further encouragement. "You'll be fine, lass. You'll be fine." Then, wonderfully, Chelsea turned around and started to munch hay.

With the injection behind her, the next stage was to get Chelsea working again. At Sarah's suggestion, Lisa tried to ride her and, with the vet watching, Lisa used a mounting block to edge slowly into the saddle.

"It feels terrible; just like sitting on a rickety table."

Lisa was close to tears. Would Chelsea ever be sound again? But Sarah was not overly concerned and suggested lunge sessions instead.

"Don't ride quite yet, not until she's less stiff. I'll also arrange for Chelsea to see a physiotherapist."

Once again, they were being forced to walk a familiar road, long and uncertain, to rehabilitation.

The physiotherapist was a kind lady but for some reason, known only to herself, Chelsea took an immediate dislike to her. To start with, this made it difficult for Jean to assess Chelsea so Lisa undertook to do the tests under her instruction. Then, eventually, they discovered that as long as Lisa laid her hand on the mare's neck, she would tolerate the physiotherapist's touch. Chelsea obviously trusted Lisa and accepted discomfort when she sensed her mistress' calming contact. Her treatment included daily use of an electro-magnetic pulse rug. This made Lisa slightly anxious because it involved Chelsea being 'plugged-in' to the mains, via the rug, and hence having to stand still for twenty-minute spells. But Lisa need not have worried because this was obviously a perfectly blissful form of treatment that involved no physical manipulation. In fact, as soon as the rug was plugged in, she was perfectly content to doze happily in peace and quiet. What an animal!

The lunging was more difficult because Chelsea was clearly very stiff, and yet she simply had to work through it until, gradually, more and more movement returned. The physiotherapist was both caring and intelligent. Whilst watching a lunging session one day, she remarked, "She's a good athlete, Lisa, and has every chance of recovering well." Lisa's concentration had been devoted to working Chelsea as sympathetically as possible with the lunge line so, as the words were spoken, she imagined that another Jean was speaking – Jean Walker! Simply the same confident intonation, that's all it was, conjured an image of the owner of Kinord.

"That's it!" Lisa exclaimed to her astonished companion. "That's why she doesn't like being touched by you, Jean. You remind her, the sound of your voice that is, of another person; somebody she knew last year who was not so kind. It's amazing, but with Chelsea there's always a reason. She's never gratuitously unpleasant or uncooperative."

And so the schooling continued. Lisa observed the gradual improvement, bolstered by Jean's encouraging comments, and was interested to observe the way Chelsea moved when left to herself. Not surprisingly, the horse tried to avoid using her right hind leg whenever possible. Although the steroid injection was providing pain relief, as well as encouraging fusion, Chelsea was clearly anxious about hurting herself. Nonetheless, she was eager to press on and, working with Lisa's subtle hints, she gradually regained the confidence to trust her weaker leg. So, sooner than expected, Lisa tried to hack her out again. Although she still felt very stiff, they enjoyed for the first time in several weeks a walk together in the woods. And recognising the improvement in her movement, Lisa urged her into trot. Chelsea responded eagerly and was fine on her left side but, when asked to use her right, the difference was clearly apparent – a distinct stiffness. Even so Lisa persisted, but oh so gently, watching for signs of pain or signals from Chelsea that things were moving too quickly. She could see Chelsea thinking about the process and whenever the mare flicked her ears into the 'quarter to three' position, Lisa smiled with relief knowing that her companion was concentrating hard but was untroubled. After a few strides, her wonderful, willing partner felt the stiffness ease and started to step out more confidently.

"Good girl," Lisa whispered giving her a pat of approval and thanks.

After a few more good steps, she let her come back to walk and gave her another pat. Then she asked her to trot again, on her right side, and this time the movement seemed easier. Ending on this high note, and full of encouragement, Lisa jumped down and, together, they walked back to the yard, 'conversing' happily together through sound – "I love you for your willingness to try, Chels; you're so honest AND tough. Thanks for really wanting to get better", and through body language – "That's OK, Mum, just pleased to back into riding with you."

Chelsea's favourite pace was gallop or, at least, a good going canter. Lisa had always known this but, during her continued rehabilitation, it became clear that this state of affairs really was very dear to Chelsea! She kept dropping hints, "Walking and trotting is all very well, but what about it?" Lisa resisted the temptation, taking great care to increase the severity of exercise only very gradually. They soon reached the stage where they were able to enjoy plenty of walking, and a bit of trotting too, without mishap, but Lisa was convinced that canter was still a few weeks away. One day, however, Chelsea became incredibly stuffy. There was no obvious problem; just that she was not her usual enthusiastic self. Fortunately this coincided with a check-up from the vet and Lisa explained what was happening. Sarah watched Lisa ride and agreed that there was no obvious problem. But she also concurred that something was amiss and asked if she could take a turn in the saddle – what a joy to have a vet who was also a competent rider! Again Sarah confirmed that there was nothing actually wrong. Then the vet had an idea.

"I wonder what will happen if I ask her to canter? Is she likely to buck?"

"No. Only if she's really sore, and that's clearly not the case. But watch out! You'll certainly know when Chelsea moves up to canter! She's like a hard-suspension sports car so take care! As she strikes off her hind legs, you'll certainly know about it!"

Sarah laughed at the analogy and trotted around before asking for more. Then – wow! 'Enthusiasm' was an understatement! Chelsea simply bounded across the school, grinning from ear to ear.

"AND there appear to be no after effects, Lisa. I think it's time to tear up the last part of the rehab schedule. Clearly Chelsea hasn't read the part that says 'no cantering yet'."

"Hey, that's wonderful, Sarah," Lisa called out with joy.

"What do you think I've been trying to tell you all this time?" Chelsea's indignant snort told its own story. "Now can we get on with some fun?"

And they did. But Lisa kept her head. They did not gallop on every hack, just a couple of times a week on good going. It worked a treat, helping Chelsea to accept, even cope with, the steadier, more mundane work that was essential to rebuilding her strength. But Lisa had to admit that she enjoyed those little bursts too!

Soon, Chelsea was able to use her right hind leg as easily as her left and her balance was improving. So much so that Lisa was tempted to start competing again. However, she decided to resist the temptation. Chelsea was using herself better than ever before but was also finding it hard to sustain so Lisa decided that a more gradual fitness programme would be time well spent. It was more important that Chelsea developed all the right muscles now in order to prevent problems in future. So, although for both of them, this meant that life lacked excitement, it was nonetheless a worthwhile approach and even repaid Lisa with a fair share of surprises, most of them pleasant. Like her beautiful extended trot through mud, or wonderful flying changes to stay balanced as they cantered around bends in the forest, or her ability to see her stride over rough ground and, best of all, her joy at finding any opportunity to show off her athleticism, such as the mound that became an Irish bank or the sharp corner that could be cut with a single thrusting bound that provided an effortless launch into an uphill canter.

Lisa continued to read widely and her research led her to a variety of new techniques. Sadly, not all of them worked. She knew for certain that Chelsea had had a chequered past and at one time had not been treated kindly. This became ever more apparent when, in order to encourage Chelsea to use herself correctly, Lisa tried a Harbridge. This was a very mild, elastic device that simply encouraged a horse to use its legs, back and neck in a proper and efficient manner. With Andrew in attendance, Lisa clipped the Harbridge into position, loosely, with no tension even on the elastic. Chelsea stood quietly, trusting her mistress, but the strange sensation stirred her memory and, from the corner of her eye, she saw in Andrew the brutish figure of Mike Feherty. So, as Lisa swung her leg over Chelsea's back and eased her weight gently into the saddle, it seemed as though she was settling herself onto a volcano about to erupt. She patted her and stroked her neck to let her know that all was well. Even so, Chelsea, with all her trust in Lisa and her desire to cooperate, was unable to show her usual 'quarter to three' ears. She tried as Lisa edged her into a strong walk. She tried as they trotted. And she tried as they practised their transitions. But the volcano erupted the moment that Lisa asked her to walk and trot over poles, lying on the ground at easy intervals. Chelsea stiffened in alarm, her ears lay flat back and she baulked at the poles with a mixture of anxious backward steps and small, reluctant attempts to rear her front legs.

"For a horse that loves jumping, this should be a fun exercise. She always enjoys trotting over branches and logs when we are out and about. Now, she's completely terrified."

Andrew, whom Chelsea loved, stood by the side of the poles but this made things even worse.

"Somebody's been cruel to her, maybe using draw reins and forcing her to trot over poles. You know how she hates whips. I bet someone standing on the ground by the poles once threatened her, or even used a whip on her. Poor lass. It's quite likely that her back was sore at the time. The very mild contact from the Harbridge must have brought these terrible memories flooding back. Well, that's it. We abandon this exercise. It's a definite no-no. I guess I'll just have to be prepared to use my legs correctly to send her forward!"

Lisa could not have known just how accurately she had described what had happened to Chelsea in Mike Feherty's dark barn.

That was the wonderful thing about Lisa. Occasionally she made mistakes, but she always listened to Chelsea's whispers or, as was now the case, her occasional 'shrieked' messages, and she never pursued a course of action that would cause the mare unhappiness or discomfort. Lisa had recognised, almost from the first day that she saw Chelsea, that there was well of experiences – sadness and pain, and possibly even cruelty – behind those deep, intelligent eyes. The story would unfold over time, gradually, as significant moments occurred in their life together. Moments when Chelsea would react, just like now, for no apparent reason. So Lisa watched and 'listened' and observed, and came to conclusions that were based on the powerful mix of solid common sense and intuition.

"What a tale she could tell me. I'd love to sit and listen to it all in one go. And yet I also love the piecing together of the parts, slowly, as time passes, as we develop a deeper bond. I wouldn't miss a single experience, even the bad ones, because the whole package is one huge gift from God, full of lessons for life, rewards and joys, and all wrapped in shining love."

Late one early summer's evening, Lisa was reminded of how well attuned animals are to a world that humans cannot perceive. Darkness was closing in and the forest was filled with a mystical air as, low on the horizon, the last rays of sunshine shone below a bank of storm clouds. The woodland was musty with the smell of dampness that follows heavy showers. Chelsea was used to being out in all weathers but something clearly troubled her on this occasion. She was reluctant to move forward – very unlike her. Only as a result of Lisa's firm urging did she edge forward, but soon she was trembling with fright. Lisa could not see nor hear anything unusual. However, true to her instincts, she decided to dismount and lead Chelsea, talking to her all the while, a measure that normally calmed her. Then Lisa too felt a sense of foreboding; something was wrong. She also felt anxious, fearing the presence of humans or dogs that might emerge from the gloom to startle her mare. They were on a narrow track though a dense part of the forest so her chances of guiding a frantic horse safely between the tree trunks and low branches were limited. Realising the danger, Lisa changed her route home, by moving onto a broader path half a mile away. This would lead them to Braehead by a circuitous route but one that was more open and would allow her to lead the anxious animal in safety. With Lisa beside her, Chelsea's tension eased but she was still upset, nuzzling her hand and clearly relieved to feel reassuring pats. After twenty minutes of slow, reluctant progress the crisis seemed to pass and Chelsea became calmer so Lisa remounted, in almost total darkness. The detour had certainly done the trick but now they were very late. Fortunately Chelsea's anxiety passed and she quickly reverted to her old self, trotting and cantering amongst the leaves that permanently carpeted the ground on their way home.

Lisa remained puzzled about the strange incident. Normally, she could work out the reasons for Chelsea's behaviour but, on this occasion, she was perplexed.

"Must have been an animal or human that I didn't spot."

As usual, she mulled things over in bed after turning out the light, hoping that an answer would come to her as she drifted down the delicious path to sleep. No thoughts came but the night was restless, full of 'busy' dreams of issues that could never be resolved. The following day, she picked up her local newspaper and glanced at the bulletins. She became rigid. There, in the column for late news items, she saw the answer, and it made her shiver. At the time they had been out the previous evening, at the exact moment that they would have normally crossed the road between the woods and Braehead, a serious car accident had occurred, claiming the life of a young policeman and injuring several others. Again, Lisa shivered; a cold dreadful tingle ran down her spine. Chelsea could not have heard the accident. At the time she became fraught, the accident had not yet happened. But it was going to happen later, at the time they would have crossed the road. It was uncanny, yet Lisa knew, deep down she knew – Chelsea had sensed the future, knowing that she was carrying them both into danger. Once more, Lisa thanked the Universe for sending this animal into her life, her wonderful, loving Chelsea whose whisperings and perception extended to dimensions that could not be explained. Lisa knew that she would never cease to listen to and respect her feelings.

And so, finally, it happened – Chelsea recovered fully. With the pair of them, how could there be any other outcome? Yet another healing journey had passed and, at long last, once again everything was going well. As Lisa had planned, they missed all the summer's jumping and endurance competitions but it didn't matter; giving Chelsea that little bit of extra time had been so worthwhile.

Lisa began to take lessons again, this time with a twenty-eight-year-old, open-minded teacher called Sally, with whom Lisa very quickly developed an immediate mutual liking, based on respect for each other's different strengths. Sally had observed Lisa's patience with the gorgeous chestnut, often in the face of criticism, and had felt drawn to the pair. So she had made the first approach, offering to help Lisa in any way at all, maybe exercising and schooling Chelsea when Lisa was away. At first, Sally found it hard to explain why she had wanted to befriend Lisa, to become part of her life. Then she realised that there was more to it than any one personality. Lisa came as a package. Yes, that was it! It was the pair – Lisa and Chelsea – that was so attractive. Individually, they were characters in their own right, likeable and charismatic. But together, they were a soaring example of the beauty of a human-horse partnership. The energy, that they exuded together, loving and positive, was like a magnet, an irresistible draw that Sally could not ignore. Now that's chemistry!

At first, Sally rode Chelsea a few times, keeping her in trim when Lisa was away. They immediately developed a rapport simply because the Scots lass was kind and sensitive but also firm when necessary. Sadly, Sally's main competition horse had broken a foreleg during a madcap session in his field with fellow geldings and, although expected to make a full recovery, Wally was destined to be out of work for several months. Sally had been looking forward to doing the winter dressage series with him and so she asked Lisa if she could compete with Chelsea instead. Lisa was delighted. Dressage was not her scene but it would do Chelsea good. Chelsea mirrored Lisa's lack of enthusiasm for dressage, probably because it required regimented obedience, not at all her cup of tea! However, she was a natural show-off and was always keen to be involved in any kind of competition. So the deal was struck – lessons for Lisa, schooling for Chelsea, and competition for Sally.

Their first competition was out of doors and much to everybody's surprise, except of course Chelsea, she won her class and came fourth in a major qualifier for a spring competition. She and Sally made a wonderfully elegant pair and, amazingly, Chelsea did everything that she was asked to do for each of the required movements. Encouraged by this, they continued to compete all winter, going on to win several more competitions and never failing to be placed on the other occasions, eventually qualifying for both the Prelim and Novice spring finals, a great achievement for a first season's competition.

Lisa helped Sally prepare for all their competitions. Because of her unorthodox approach, Lisa's dressage preparation often gave rise to much amusement amongst the other competitors, particularly those from Braehead who knew Chelsea well. Unless she was away on business Lisa continued to do most of Chelsea's schooling, and always the hacking, whilst Sally would ride her a couple of times, on the day, just before a competition. Even in the run up to competition days, Lisa always set off for the woods and their favourite pastime together – cantering. Many times she was asked, "Isn't Chelsea doing dressage this week?" to which her reply was always the same: "Yes, and we're off to do our preparation in the woods!" In truth, the forest tracks gave them plenty of opportunity to practise all the dressage movements, apart from the tighter circles, and Chelsea found it far more fun than being restricted to the schooling arenas. Lisa was convinced that Chelsea's freshness was a major factor in her success. Those who mocked often looked on in good-natured surprise whenever Chelsea took the honours. More pleasing than the rosettes, however, were the judges' positive comments about her way of going. Although she was occasionally tense, a natural consequence of her efforts to concentrate and be totally obedient, there was never any mention of stiffness. This was indeed a tribute – to Lisa's patience and Chelsea's resilience.

Lisa would not be unduly perturbed when, in the spring of the following year, both finals had to be cancelled as a result of an outbreak of Foot and Mouth disease that was to plague the British countryside.

Chelsea's performances in the qualifiers had satisfied her that she was well on the road to recovery.

Lisa always enjoyed watching Andrew with Chelsea. He had no desire to ride – he was too tall and heavy for the Thoroughbred – but 'he loved her to bits'. Chelsea knew this too and regarded him as a source of cuddles and carrots. Although not interested in riding, Andrew was always happy to get involved in 'looking after' Chelsea and he soon became an excellent groom. To begin with, catching her had been his greatest challenge, partly because of his height. She often misunderstood his approach as 'squaring up' to her and she would respond in the appropriate equine way – by running off. Then Andrew joined Lisa on the first occasion that she went to see Monty Roberts. He was spellbound by Monty's approach to 'joining up' and immediately set about practising on Chelsea. So now, Andrew was the best person at catching Chelsea, indeed his services were often needed as a last resort when she took one of her 'moods' and refused to come in for anybody else. Even Lisa was not excluded from Chelsea's mischief. But Lisa didn't mind for, when it really mattered – when they were riding – Chelsea never took advantage of her mistress. But in the field she recognised, in Andrew, a determination never to give up, never to be too rushed to persevere, and always willing to pat and to praise afterwards, carrot ready in pocket to slip to her once the lead rope had been duly attached. So why bother to avoid being caught? Andrew spoke to her in the right language, gave her the signals she understood, and was always there to pat and praise and reward. In the field, Andrew was Chelsea's best friend.

Lisa was not jealous of this small relationship. Often it made her smile. On one occasion they arrived at the yard, hoping to find Chelsea in her box, ready to be tacked up. But no, that day Chelsea decided that it was not to her convenience! "I'll stay in the field, thank you." She had resisted being caught by any of the yard's staff. Andrew arrived, dressed only in his 'office' clothes so he had no suitable footwear for the muddy fields. He borrowed the yard manager's boots, even though they were two sizes too big. With suit trousers tucked safely inside the boots, he set off across the field hoping that there would be no nonsense as a chill wind cut through the light cotton shirt. He was not dressed for a long 'catch me, but only if you're nice' session.

Chelsea sensed his mood and put up no resistance, not even a token minute, and allowed herself to be caught before accepting a carrot with insouciance. Lisa watched with delight, a small smile tracing her lips as she waited for them to make their way to the gate. In the meantime, several other horses noticed Andrew with Chelsea and decided they wanted to come in too. Several galloped up to the gate, causing a melee of confused excitement. Chelsea remained as calm and as polite as ever, walking quietly in with Andrew, ignoring the 'lesser beings' whose antics were beneath disdain! As they approached the cloying mud patch that had formed in the poached ground by the gate, one boot was sucked from Andrew's foot forcing him to take a single step with his stockinged foot, placing it firmly into the mud. He was now stuck, unable to put his foot back into the boot because that would soil it horribly for the yard manager, and now barely able hop on the other foot which had also been sucked into the mud. And all this amid a melee of excited animals! Lisa's smile was quickly replaced by concern.

Then, Chelsea came to the rescue. She simply stopped, just where Andrew had lost the boot, and waited patiently until he picked it out of the cloying mud before walking, boot in one hand and herself in the other, quietly through the cluster of other horses to meet Lisa at the gate. Forgetting his frozen, soggy foot, Andrew gave Chelsea a huge, grateful hug for being so kind. Of course, so did Lisa!

Chapter 10

"I am your Friend"

"Wake up, James darling."

At first his mother's voice was distant but when it no longer mingled with his dreams he felt the inexorable and unkind pull of consciousness drawing him to the surface of a luxurious sea of sleep. The heavy drag of the anchor that he longed to follow, back down into the depths of intriguing nothingness, became lighter and lighter until at last he opened his eyes and saw the faces of his parents peering down. Immediately he panicked. Something had to be wrong. Why would they both be there, waking him from this delicious sleep?

"What's up?" He struggled for words but was cut short by his father's huge smile.

"Your 'A' level results are in, Jimbo. Take a look."

The plain postcard was placed into numb fingers. He could barely feel anything so he squeezed his fingers tightly around it. They felt almost painful as sleep-weakened muscles slowly came to life. He peered at the card and noticed his own handwriting, remembering the day several weeks ago when he had written his address on it, together with three words on separate lines – Chemistry, Physics and Maths – leaving space beside each for Manorfield to add his grades.

"Two Bs and a C!"

His panic washed away, replaced by a surge of lovely, warm elation. The results were good enough for entry to his university of choice – Paxton College had required exactly those grades as their minimum requirement for the Faculty of Engineering. And there they were, too good to be true! Exactly what he had striven so hard for, even though he had often been filled with self-doubt and a gnawing feeling that he should have followed a more artistic path. But surely this was proof positive that he could indeed become an engineer? Then, true to his nature, he became self-effacing.

"Shame about the C in Maths. I knew I'd done badly in the calculus paper, but I'd hoped that overall I'd done enough for a B. Never mind – better than an F which is what I was so sure I'd get on the day I did the calculus."

The jumble of words bubbled out, but was lost on his delighted parents who had also lived through their own turmoil of anxiety as they waited for this day. Helen stroked the tousled hair from his eyes and murmured with delight, whilst Jim continued to set his son's path out clearly.

"Well, Jimbo, you're in and that's all that matters. Four years of study and in no time I'll have you with me at Arthur Garland. Now that I'm a Partner, there will be no hiccups – just get your degree and, once you're articled with us, the world's your oyster."

The certainty of the future, expressed so hopefully, should have filled James with excitement. Instead he felt another clutch of despair that he tried hard to put to one side by smiling back at his father.

"At least now I can enjoy the summer holiday. The waiting and worry is over. I've never had seven weeks of nothing to do before. No exams, no getting up early, no school duties. What luxury."

"For a while Jimbo, but maybe you should get a summer job. We'll speak to the owner of the Jousting Inn, as planned. A good job as a barman or waiter will introduce you to the world of work and give you plenty of pocket money. It'll be no more 9.30 am rises for you. Can't get into bad habits now can we?"

The inward groan was lost in Helen's flurry of cheerfulness.

"9.30 James, darling. Rise and shine and I'll provide a big fry-up for breakfast. Be ready in fifteen minutes. And well done, darling, you've done well to pass all those exams. Yes, you deserve a good holiday before you make a start at the Jousting Inn."

She kissed his forehead and slipped happily from the room. James buried his head under the sheet and moaned.

"Why don't I feel happy?"

But, fifteen minutes later, he peered down at the sausage, bacon and eggs, mounded on the centre of his plate, and the blues were put to one side He tucked in with gusto, looking forward to a game of golf. Life wasn't so bad.

The summer holidays sped by. For the past year, when 'A' levels had been all consuming, James had lived for this moment when, with no exams and an enforced pause in his life, he could be carefree. And yet it wasn't like that. He still carried a permanent gnawing feeling of doubt about his future. His father had taken control and now, too late, he realised that he hated the science subjects that he'd felt obliged to take and wished he could have studied Geography, learning more about his favourite continent – Africa – where he felt drawn to spend his life. But nobody had asked him what he really, really wanted from life. It had all been assumed – that he was a chip off the old block, that the only useful subjects involved the sciences, and that a guaranteed path to prosperity lay ahead with the Arthur Garland Partnership. He didn't even want to go to university – yet. What made matters worse was that his best friend Robert had taken a gap year before deciding his future. He had signed up for VSO and was, at this very moment, heading for Botswana.

Robert had spent the previous weekend with James and they had discussed their futures together, sympathising with each other's lots in life.

"I envy you, Rob. My parents – actually it's Dad mainly – keep pushing me on to the next thing. I'd love to be coming with you. I really would. Actually, I'd like to spend my life doing VSO-type things all the time. I love Africa and I love Africans. You know, apart from you, I don't really have any proper British friends. None of them understand me, especially when I talk about Uganda. They all think I'm weird and a throw back to colonial days. But I love Africans – Uganda's full of friendly people and I want to work with them. AND there is so much hardship out there. Yet they just get on with it and live their simple lives. God, I wish so much I could start all over again."

Robert smiled sympathetically. At school, gentle as he was, James had been the leader whilst Robert had followed. With his frail frame and short-sightedness, he had never excelled at sport and, academically, he had even trailed behind James. Although they were of similar intellect, James had worked harder than Robert, always driven by his self-doubts and a desire to prove himself and to please others. Robert had cared too, but not in an all-consuming way so, instead, he had followed his passion for listening to music, often content to sit back in their shared study chair and absorb himself in the popular groups of their time. He was not a musician, but he was a mine of information, with intelligent predictions of the way the music industry was moving. In the face of opposition from his own parents, he had announced that he was going to manage pop stars. And that was that; simple and vague. Yes, he would get his 'A' levels. Yes, he would go to college, if that's what they wanted.

"I'll take a Business degree somewhere." And no; he had no idea how it would all happen. "Maybe it'll come to me when I take a year off."

He had opted for VSO to escape the pressures that were being placed on him to become respectable, but he also wanted to have an adventure and James' tales of the magic continent had tipped the scales.

Their lives, for so long parallel paths with similar opportunities and challenges, were about to move in very different directions. On the one hand, Robert – quiet, unassuming Robert – was casting aside the security of a 'proper' career to follow his passion. On the other hand, James – diligent and hardworking – was about to follow an established, safe and respectable path of further education and a profession. Yet, it was Robert whose eyes sparkled with anticipation of the freedom of adulthood whilst James' eyes were dull, reflecting an inner turmoil, even fear. Robert shared his friend's sadness.

"You can still change your mind."

"No I can't."

"You can. You can. And if you don't do it now, you will one day."

Robert's words were full of a wisdom that he did not yet have. He simply could not imagine himself being dragged into a way of life he did not want. He was speaking for himself. But at that moment, he was speaking to a young man who could not countenance any life that did not conform to others' expectations.

James and his father sat in the bar of the Selby hotel. In an uneasy silence, they sipped their beers. Two rounds of ham and mustard sandwiches were placed on the table between them. Limp stalks of watercress were sprinkled over the unappetising snack that was so typical of bars in the student district of the town. Jim Anderson picked up a quarter wedge of tomato, popped it into his mouth and took a bite of sandwich.

"So how do you feel, Jimbo?"

A cress leaf stuck to Jim's front tooth looking like a vast cavity. James did not bother to point it out.

"Nervous, Dad."

"No need to be, son. This is the start of the most enjoyable years of your life. All you have to do is study hard. I'll take care of the rest. You'll have no financial worries or responsibilities for the next four years. Just relax and have fun, but also work hard and make friends too. I remember in my student days …"

Eventually the piece of cress worked itself loose, long before his father came to the end of yet another discourse.

"… and so you see, Jimbo, university was the making of me, as I'm sure it will be for you."

"I'll do my best, Dad. I'd better be getting on back to the room to unpack. Thanks for the lift today and all the help with lugging my possessions about. Oh, and give my love to Mum. Tell her I'll miss her, as usual, and will write regularly."

Later, back in his digs, James finished his unpacking, feeling as hollow as the empty suitcase he placed on top of the ancient wardrobe. Then, with a sigh, he went out to face his new world. He headed to the student union and the freshers' hop. Disco music and a fug of smoke welcomed him, but no faces turned to smile at his inconspicuous entrance. James looked for a soul-mate. Surely there would be others who felt as lonely and as nervous as he did. Nobody else was alone. The room throbbed with cheerful vibrant life as couples danced and canoodled and small groups of first-year students laughed and chattered as if they had known each other for years. He bought a pint of beer and, summoning his courage, he walked to the smallest group he could see and introduced himself. They welcomed him with interest rather than warmth and James was immediately struck by the variety of regional accents. All of a sudden, he was the odd man out; his perfect public school intonation grating in his own ears and reminding him of his holiday at Millport when he had happily mixed with the boys from Glasgow, holding his own and defending, with naïve good humour, his 'posh' background.

Now it was all so different. Older and more self-conscious, he held back from the conversation as much as possible, smiling politely as his party friends laughed and chattered with abandon, talking freely of 'birds' and 'grass', and enthusing about the year that lay ahead. Not one of them mentioned their studies. So James enquired and they responded politely, without real interest, until the line of conversation inevitably petered out. He would have loved to talk about sport, cricket or rugby especially, but again he realised that this held no interest for the others. To have mentioned Africa would have been utterly inappropriate! What else? "Yes, I am from another world." James sensed that, as well as being from a different background, he was also immature, at least in his own eyes, compared with these street-wise students. So he contented himself by listening politely, occasionally murmuring words of agreement and encouragement, and by getting drunk for the first time in his life. That night he danced with nobody and stumbled out of the union in the early hours of the morning, remembering very little about the night's experience, instead feeling alone and sad. After being sick on the pavement he staggered back to the refuge of his room where, fully clothed, he collapsed on his bed and fell asleep.

The next morning things improved. The day was free of lectures. It had been set aside for the 'Societies' fair. He walked around the hall looking for activities that might interest him. In autopilot, he signed up for the Golf and Rugby clubs and was then attracted by the sound of well-spoken accents. So he joined the Conservative Society with the promise of good parties and the chance to get involved in student politics and 'rivalries', whatever that entailed. At least he was now meeting a wider variety of people than at the previous evening's hop and he began to realise that, maybe, he was not alone in his loneliness.

An American accent caught his attention and he turned to see an earnest, pretty girl completing her registration with the secretary of the Conservative Society.

"I hope your parties are better than the one last night. It was awful – full of folk just drinking. I left after half an hour."

"Hello, I'm James. I stayed at the hop all night. God knows why."

"Hi, I'm Harriet."

"What're you studying, Harriet?"

"Geology."

"Oh!"

"What's wrong with geology then?" The flash of mock irritation was softened by a lovely twinkle.

For the first time in his life James' heart missed a beat. "Nothing at all, except that I'm not studying it too."

"My, my. You are forward."

Suddenly everything was easy. Free of tension and, simply enjoying the company, James took a step that for months he had wondered about, even dreaded, but which was now so natural.

"Can I buy you a cup of coffee, Harriet?"

"Sure, that'd be great."

"The student union has a coffee bar and, I'm told, great cheese rolls."

"Not so great." Again the twinkle defused any possibility of rebuff.

"OK then, just a coffee."

Together they walked from the hall and sat in the union lounge, sipping cups of coffee and swapping notes about their first experiences of the university. James learned that his own discomfort was exactly mirrored by Harriet's and that she too felt like an outsider. It was worse for her because this was her first experience of Britain. She described her disappointment at the lack of warmth in the students' welcome, their lack of interest in anything academic, and the drunken single-track mind of her 'partner' the previous evening. James agreed.

"You know, sometimes I don't feel British." And he explained his background – Uganda and boarding school – and ended by describing a small black crippled boy who, somewhere in Kampala, 'if he is alive', may still have a tattered bald bear. "Now you see why I often think I come from a another world."

"That's a great story, James. I'm glad we've met. Makes me feel better to know there's somebody else who's feeling like a fish out of water right now."

James struggled with Maths. Calculus was his bugbear. He had got away with it for 'A' levels, knowing enough about other aspects of mathematics to compensate for his weakness in this area. But, as the term progressed, his worst fears were realised and, try as he might, hard work did not carry him through his difficulties. This time he was alone, without the personal support and guidance of schoolteachers. In any case, his heart was not in it. With nobody to turn to, he understood that the freedom of student life could also be a lonely place for the troubled. He thought of speaking to his father, but dismissed the idea, not wanting at this early stage to be lectured about commitment and 'giving it time'. He wished there was somebody, like Alec Fraser, with whom he could confide. Even Robert was out of his life just now, probably relishing every moment of his first experiences of Africa. So, quietly and with a feeling of dread, he knuckled down and did his best.

But after a few more weeks, he became desperate and eventually consulted one of his lecturers. Miles Penham had been driving James particularly hard. The man had an air of authority and certainty that impressed the young man whose innate decency and respect allowed him to accept anything that Miles said. So, although the man was a taskmaster, James felt that an open and honest approach would lead to sound advice and a resolution of his worries. He approached the tutor after a late afternoon lecture, hoping that he would have no further commitments that day and would be prepared to give him some time.

"I can give you five minutes, Anderson. Then I must prepare for a faculty meeting."

James' issue was not a 'five-minute' one. Inexperienced as he was, he did not recognise the warning bells and ploughed on, repeating the well-rehearsed script. Miles' face glazed with disinterest and dismay, not of sympathy but with the realisation that he was, for the first time in his ten-year career, being asked to deal with a human being in turmoil – not at all his inclination and quite removed from the realms of pure mathematics.

James saw the impatience in the other's face and assumed the fault was his own. He hurried his explanation before ending lamely, "So you see sir, it's advice I really need about what to do. Should I continue with mathematics and, if not and I have to abandon Engineering, what are my options given I'm half way through the first term of a four year course? Can I change faculty, maybe begin a Geography and Economics degree?"

"Young man, you are no longer a schoolboy. These are issues you should be able to resolve for yourself, or at least in conjunction with your parents. I am surprised that you did not choose to resolve them before you applied for this faculty. Mathematics is a wonderful subject and, although mastery of its inner secrets may not come easily to every student, I am convinced that through application and commitment, you can indeed find the key. My advice is to apply yourself so that, like me, you can enjoy a most fascinating and intellectually rewarding subject. If you choose any other course of action, then do not attribute your decision to me. I now bid you good day."

James had experienced patronising behaviour, and a degree of pomposity, from the less enlightened masters at school. But he was staggered by what he had heard. A rush of despair and outrage made his head spin. Without a word, he crept from the room, utterly humiliated.

"I'll show the bastard. I'll pass his beloved Maths exams and decide what to do next year."

Harriet listened in silence. Like James, she could not believe the insensitivity and pomposity to which he'd been subjected. But she did not agree with his reaction.

"Listen, James. First off, do nothing for a day or two, until you've calmed down and can think straight. Then reconsider. I mean really reconsider. Who is important here – is it you, or is it your father? What is the worst that can happen? What do you dream of doing? What would stop each day at university being a long drawn out hell for you? Think of all these things. I'll be here to listen but why don't you speak to your mom? She sounds so neat and understanding. Now come here."

James looked into her eyes and saw deep, caring affection. Without thinking, he went to her and for the first time in is life he felt the softness and warmth of a woman's body. Harriet traced the faint line of his scar with her lips, edging closer to his own until their mouths met and James was transported into a world beyond the present – one in which dread and anxiety were forgotten, replaced instead by a wonderful oneness with another human being that transcended all pain. On the day of his worst humiliation at the hands of one human, James experienced the magnificence of another. He fell in love.

James lived term by term. His plan – a compromise – was to study hard so that nobody could complain later of laziness. Then, if he failed any exams, he would use that moment as the catalyst for change – an opportunity to discuss with his father a possible new direction. Meanwhile, if he passed his exams, he would get his Engineering degree, but would consider other careers when the time came. As with many compromises, he fell between stools. With Harriet's love and support, he maintained his morale through the first year and, loathing his studies, he scraped through to the second year. At this point, he could not keep up with the technical nature of his subjects and he failed his second year exams.

"I'm truly disappointed, James. Have you stopped trying or is something else the cause? What about this girl Harriet? Don't allow her to distract you? You mustn't fail the autumn resits."

"Dad, the only reason I've survived this long is Harriet. She's full of common sense, but she's also full of love and a genuine concern for what's happening to me. No, it's the subjects. I've tried. Please trust me. I really have. Look, I've passed my first year. I don't want to take the second year resits. I want to change subjects, and do Geography, Geology and Economics. I've discussed this with the college and they say I can keep the credits for my first year and take these three new subjects at second and third year levels. That will get me an Ordinary BSc., not as good as the Honours I was hoping for but still a degree. Then I'll look for a job, any job that takes me back to Africa. Maybe Arthur Garland employs non-engineers?"

He had not considered the last point. It had been thrown in at the last moment out of desperation. But, at last, a small flicker of acceptance showed in his father's face so James pursued the point: "Look, Dad. Accept it. I'm not cut out for engineering. But Arthur Garland has work in Africa and I'm desperate to get out there again. Surely they employ people in administrative positions as well as engineers. Couldn't I be considered for one of those positions? Please, Dad, please!"

It took several days. As ever, Helen's quiet support was there, gently edging Jim towards the inevitable. So, with his mother's help, James' pleas were accepted.

"I'm still disappointed James, but OK I've consulted the firm and they do accept a few trainees who are not engineers, in the Contracts Department. You can even get your Articles eventually, through a track record of experience with the firm."

"And do Arthur Garland still have projects in Uganda, Dad?"

Jim could not suppress a smile.

"Yes, Jimbo, they do. But you're ahead of yourself. Remember, two more years of study and a degree. Then we'll see about getting you back to your beloved Uganda."

For the first time in many years, father and son hugged each other breaking through for a single, wonderful moment the veneer of formality that Jim Anderson had unwittingly introduced into their relationship.

"You're a good lad, James. I ..." There was a pause as Jim struggled to find the next, the most important words. James' heart pounded in anticipation and he waited. Jim struggled. "I ... admire you ... for your determination."

"I'll live with that at least," James thought happily, his momentary disappointment soon forgotten in the height of relief.

That was the last day Jim Anderson called his son 'Jimbo'.

Because of his wasted year, James completed his Ordinary BSc. at the same time that Harriet completed her Honours Geology course. For two years, they enjoyed each other's company – lovers and friends, but most of all soul mates whose love for each other became a balm in times of pain, a source of laughter and of creativity, and a foil against the occasional bouts of fear and doubt that plague most human beings. For two glorious years, James relaxed. Although he continued to wrestle with self-doubt and worry about other peoples' opinions, he became more easy-going knowing that he had a companion who loved him for what he really was – a gentle and caring soul who may never set the world alight but who was sincere in his love of humanity.

Harriet shared his dreams and, through many hours of discussion, she felt ever more drawn to the Africa that she had never visited. During their last term, James produced a small diamond ring and proposed to the only woman in his life. He faced her earnestly, determined to do it right.

"Harriet Carson. You've saved me from insanity. You've loved me despite everything, stayed with me through thick and thin, accepted my parents, been a rock of decency and of courage, a never-ending source of fun and laughter, and a fount of wisdom beyond your years. You've been my adviser and confidante; you are clever and loving, perceptive and witty, beautiful and oh so sexy. I mean every word of it and I do not want to let you go. I'd be mad to let you go, and I'd go mad if I did. More than anything else I'd love to have you in my life forever. Will you marry me? Allow me to repay all these things over the course of a lifetime, because that is how long it will take to balance the mountain of love that I have received from you over the past four years."

Harriet mimicked his solemnity.

"James Anderson, that's the longest continuous speech I've ever heard from you. Now get ready for my own."

She smiled and held her hands on either side of his face, running a thumb along the line of his scar.

"Yes."

"Is that …?"

Her lips touched his own, like softly scented rose petals, smothering his words. They continued to kiss, a long sweet moment of happiness and love.

"Yes, James, that's it. And for those few folk in this world who don't know it – you're the catch of a lifetime. Now take me to this Africa of yours and let's share our lives."

"What about your parents and your career? You've got a fantastic degree. Won't you be bored not working? What about you?"

"After that great proposal, are you trying to talk me out of it now? Listen, my lovely James. Stop being so full of doubt, so wonderfully considerate. Didn't we say we've got a lifetime together? I'll work out what it is I can do, if anything, when we get there. I guess you're not planning a fifty-year contract with Arthur Garland, or are you? Let's see what's what in a year or two. Also, I really, really do want to see what Africa is like. Oh and finally, so you don't get all guilty, I really, really do want to live the rest of my life with you, Mr. Anderson."

James would always say that the best thing he brought away from university was his wife.

The VC10 banked over Lake Victoria and a pair of eager eyes peered down at the welcoming sight. A small strip of sandy beach was cluttered with bathers, mostly white-skinned, sun bathing in the glorious equatorial warmth. Tiny figures, children mainly, splashed in the lake's blue-brown waters. The beach was broken by a high craggy promontory that jutted rudely into the lake. On it, a swimming pool reflected the sun in a single blinding gleam of light that flashed momentarily into their eyes.

"Look, James. Lots of people. What a lovely sight – all enjoying themselves."

"That's the swimming pool at Entebbe, Harri. I used to go there every Saturday. It's only about twenty miles from Kampala. Look beyond it, on the other side of the promontory from the sandy beach. You can see a hippo. There, look to the left of the flock of birds. It's underwater but it can't be very deep. It's moving slowly towards the shore; looks like a huge black boulder."

Harriet's eyes widened in horror.

"My God, James. Aren't they dangerous? What about the bathers?"

James loved sharing this moment. As the memories flooded back he realised that this was indeed a return home.

"When threatened, they're incredibly dangerous creatures. But see the promontory, it divides the flatter sandy area where the people are from that ugly mucky bay beyond where the hippo is? They always keep away from noise and activity. They're not carnivores and are happy to graze on vegetation, so they avoid humans. That headland is as good as any artificial barrier, protecting the humans from stray hippos. And crocs too!" James enjoyed his moment of knowledge. "But more than that, they'll avoid any hubbub. I used to swim in the lake too, like those people. Mum and Dad brought a picnic and we'd often take it down there. Nobody seemed to worry. But one day, when I was very small, I remember walking in the water, maybe up to my neck, and I stood in a hippo's footprint and disappeared from sight below the surface! So, at night, when nobody's about, hippos must come into the beach. We were always told, "Never get between the water and a hippo." That's when they'll charge you, especially if they've got calves. I'm told they can bite you in half with their massive jaws."

"No kidding!" Harriet's eyes widened in horror. "There's no way I'm gonna swim in that lake."

The scene below passed out of view behind the small oval window and their attention moved to the fast approaching ground as it rose upwards to meet the aircraft. In silence now they watched thorn trees and red dusty paths and tracks flash beneath them until finally the runway greeted the plane. With a single screech of rubber, it bumped and rolled gently into Africa's embrace.

"Here we are. Uganda at last! How'd you feel?"

"Nervous, excited, intrigued. A little frightened." The words came thoughtfully, almost haltingly as Harriet responded seriously to the question. "But, hey, I wouldn't change this moment for anything."

They entered the immigration hall and were struck by the air of nervous tension, close to fear, that such places can engender. But here it was palpable and the reason was evident. Hanging on most walls, large photographs of the jovial face of Idi Amin beamed down at the arriving passengers reminding them of who was now in charge of the country. Behind his smile, pig-like eyes flashed; evil black buttons that carried not a flicker of humanity.

"Dad met him, you know." James raised his eyebrows towards the slug-like face. "Before independence, when he was just a sergeant-major in the army. He was apparently quite good at boxing. Dad says he was very friendly and nobody would have guessed …"

"Hush, James, we're nearly there."

"Suppose your right."

They reached the front of the queue and smiled at the young black immigration officer.

"Jambo." James had been looking forward to practising his Swahili again.

"Your passports." The cold face did not acknowledge the greeting. Instead a black hand snapped officiously towards the white couple, open palm upwards ready to accept the documents. With disinterest the officer asked, "What is the purpose of your visit?"

"It's all there, tucked into the passport. Work permit for myself, and my wife is here to live with me. I'm on a three-year contract to work, up at Fort Portal, on road construction projects."

Suspicious eyes scrutinised the couple, satisfied that they were suitably ill at ease. Eventually, he looked downward and, with deliberate formality, the passports were examined.

"You were born in Uganda?"

"Ndio, at Nakasero Hospital in Kampala."

"Why are you not Ugandan? Why do you choose a British passport?"

"Because, my parents are British," James snapped back.

He felt Harriet's hand close around his fingers and squeeze a brief warning. He composed himself, although disappointment flooded through his body. This was not the smiling, friendly Ugandan that he had been so used to.

The official nodded. Long, slow nods. An eternity passed – fifteen interminable seconds before the decision was made. "You may enter

Uganda." With exaggerated slowness and an excess of formality, the passports were stamped and handed back. The beady black eyes met James' brown eyes in a look of cold loathing. "You will go." The permission to pass through, on into the customs hall, was expressed as an imperative statement.

James recognised the cultural difference and stooped to pick up his hand baggage. They moved on, out of earshot.

"Things are different now, Harriet. But he was just an officious little twerp. I'm looking forward to introducing you to ordinary Ugandans. I hope I can find a few who'll remember me, or my parents at least."

Having been forewarned by Arthur Garland's travel department, James did not use the Green channel through customs, but declared new goods and paid a nominal customs fee, even though he genuinely had nothing to declare. "It will save you a long delay," he had been instructed. "They have all the time in the world to search your possessions, and are quite prepared to use it. Just pay something and save yourself the bother. You can recover it later on expenses."

They were learning the ways of the new Africa. Outside, the whitewashed walls of the terminal building reflected back the harsh glare of a burning late morning sun. They squinted in bemusement, and so did not see the friendly face approaching.

"You are Mr. Anderson." Again, a statement, with no inflexion of a question.

"Yes." James smiled back, responding readily to the universal language of friendship. "What's your name?"

"It is Bilasto, Bwana. I am official driver for Mr. John Hare."

"Are you taking us to his office, Bilasto?"

John was Arthur Garland's Kampala representative. The company needed a presence in the capital although all its main construction sites were in far-flung regions. John was well known, renowned even, for his knowledge of Africa, particularly post independence, and he had become an invaluable asset, oiling the wheels of bureaucracy and negotiating contracts on behalf of a western company in a land with such different customs and values.

"No. I will take you to the Intercontinental Hotel."

This was a relief. It had been a tiring non-stop flight with little sleep. They settled into the aging Mercedes and enjoyed the journey to Kampala, with James sharing memory lane enthusiastically.

"See that bay there? That's where they shot the film 'African Queen'. That's the hotel that Humphrey Bogard stayed in. Apparently he was quite a hell-raiser." Later, James sniffed the air, breathing in ostentatiously, and exclaimed, "Smell that. That's Africa. It brings back fantastic memories."

They were now in the open country and the car swept through the Savannah landscape, brown and immense. Africans walked or cycled along the roadside, women with huge loads balanced perfectly on their heads, and 'totos' strapped in loose cloth pouches on their backs. The babies lived most of their early months in this position, whilst the long-suffering mothers worked without complaint in fields, or transported water and food to their small rondavel homes. Harriet loved it.

"Oh, it's all just as you described James. I feel it too, just closing my eyes and letting my intuition speak. It's got its own energy. Vibrant, but primitive too. You know you're not far from nature, or hardship for that matter. Oh, this is so exciting!"

She waved enthusiastically at a file of women and was rewarded with huge smiles. Laden as they were, unable to wave back, the shining friendship in their faces was a most wonderful response. "Jambo, jambo," Harriet called through the open window and clapped her hands with delight when she saw their smiling, giggling response. "Now I know I'm out of Britain."

James could not resist the temptation. He was desperate to speak to a Ugandan about the country so he took a chance, aware that the dictatorial regime may well have closed the door of human interaction.

"Bilasto?"

"Ndio, bwana."

"What's Uganda like now? I was born here but left about ten years ago. What can I expect?" Intentionally he left the question vague, giving the driver an opportunity to avoid a difficult topic.

"It is bad, bwana. There is much suffering."

James clucked sympathetically but otherwise remained silent and patient, not pressing the conversation into dangerous, unwanted areas.

"There is much killing. Amin promised us release from Obote's corruption. Now we have death and cruelty."

Harriet was staggered at the young man's outspoken words, obviously trusting his white companions.

"Where is it worst, Bilasto – in the city or in the countryside?"

"In the city, it is bad because of the secret police. People are arrested and they disappear. But there is work in the city so we have money and food. My family is from the Toro region and they also suffer, for there is much lawlessness in the country. Bandits take their crops and they go hungry. Indeed madam, it is bad. Mbaya, mbaya sana." He shook his head sadly.

With typical American openness, Harriet continued. "What about the white people? Are they welcome?"

"Yes, memsab. When they bring wealth and work, it is good."

"Is it safe for us here?"

"In the city, it is safe for those who do not speak against the government. But everybody fears the secret police. When you are stopped, offer the soldiers a cigarette and do not make an argument."

"And in the country, Bilasto? Tomorrow we go to Fort Portal."

"Always there is danger in the country. There are many bandits. But you will travel safely with the company. You will not travel alone. Nobody from Arthur Garland is harmed."

By now they had entered Kampala, and the conversation ceased, as if they had crossed a hidden force field and that everything they now said would be overheard. James smiled at Harriet and took her hand, squeezing it encouragingly. She winked back. James amused them both with more memories.

"See that shop there? It used to be a clothes store run by a white man called Bill Green. I remember he made my uniform when I joined the cub scouts. Because he and Dad were friends – they used to play Solo together – he left me a fifty-cent piece in the trouser pocket. I'll never forget that. It was worth an old sixpence in those days, a fortune to a youngster like me. Oh and there, look! That used to be the Colonial Provision Stores, run by Indians. Mum used to call them the 'Col Prov'. She'd place her grocery orders with them and when they made the deliveries, in a battered old red van, I used to love meeting it at the top of our driveway. They let me stand on the running board as it drove down to the house. Mum went bananas. And there, see, it's still there! That's where I got my haircut. I used to ask for a crew-cut as I hated having to comb my hair in the mornings. It never lay flat. Mum never liked it so short, so we had a constant battle with each other over what to tell the barber. Mum always insisted on coming with me and told him not to overdo it. I kept pestering him for more and more off. He was an Indian barber, like the owner of the Col Prov Stores. They'll have been expelled now, by Idi Amin when he cleared all the Asians out of the country a few years ago."

And so the chatter went on. Harriet had heard some of the stories before. Now she saw the real backdrop to her husband's life and was completely absorbed, loving listening to every word and realising what it meant to James to re-live his early days. He seemed to revert to his childhood as he told the stories and she watched, fascinated by the experience, understanding so much more about this strange and lovely human being that was her husband. All too soon they reached the hotel and the stream of chatter ceased.

As he said goodbye, Bilasto looked at the open, friendly white man with respect. He'd also enjoyed 'listening in' on the trip down memory lane because he too had remembered Bill Green and the Asian businesses. He also regretted their demise and, albeit reluctantly, had to admit that those days had been more beneficial to his countrymen than the disintegration of a nation, especially of values, that they now experienced.

"Kwaheri, bwana mkubwa. I will collect you tomorrow and we will drive to Fort Portal."

"What was that he said, James?"

"Kwaheri means 'goodbye'. Bwana mkubwa is 'big person' although bwana is a person of higher rank than the one speaking. It's a term of respect, something like addressing somebody as 'sir'. I was quite touched by it. He's a good chap is Bilasto. I'll enjoy chatting more in the car tomorrow. It's a long drive, an all day job, so we'll have lots of time to talk."

"I'm looking forward to it too. Gee, I'm bushed though. Can we have an early night tonight?"

Later, as she lay in bed, Harriet thought about the day. What a strange country! This was an adventure indeed. With heavy eyes, and to the sound of a squeaking ceiling fan, she drifted into an exhausted sleep. Beside her, James lay back, arms behind head, and let the moving air cool his bare chest. Then he turned and looked at her sleeping form and felt a rush of pure love. She had so much courage, and such certainty of purpose. What a woman! Here she was, in a strange country with no hope of work. Yet she was far cleverer than him and could have insisted on her own career, on a different course of action after they had married. Not once had she complained. Her trust in him was humbling, especially as James was beset with doubt. Once again he sensed that he had chosen the wrong job and had been lured into Arthur Garland with the promise of a return to his beloved Uganda. But was it a pipedream? Would he find nothing but disappointment in his attempt to recreate past days? The present had opened his eyes, and in doing so he had been unsettled, and now felt a little foolish, realising that he had been drawn into living in the past. Wonderful as memories are, reality always intrudes. At the end of every reverie is a rude awakening.

But sleep came to comfort him and his last thoughts were more positive. For there, beside him, was a gift from life that was immeasurably greater than any challenge. "I won't let the allure of the past take away from me what is under my nose in the present." He leaned across and lightly, with the back of a finger, stroked away a loose wisp of golden hair from Harriet's cheek. Then, gently, he kissed a closed eyelid feeling a deep surge of love and appreciation.

"Jambo, bwana. Habari?"

"Msuri, Bilasto. Thanks and I hope you're well too. What a lovely day! Will it be hot for the drive west?" The old Mercedes did not have an air conditioner.

"It will be hot, but then it will be cold."

James understood. Uganda straddled the equator but much of the land was at high altitude and the heat was seldom oppressive, even in Kampala. But as they headed west, towards the border with the Congo, they would rise higher, until they reached the Rwenzori Mountains – the Mountains of the Moon. Fort Portal lay twenty miles below the foothills of this magnificent range, with its own different climatic conditions. There, the temperatures would be cooler, although James noted with amusement that Bilasto regarded such conditions as 'cold'.

After meeting John Hare, and collecting the site mail and other vital supplies, they set off. Both James and Harriet sat in the back seat so that they could share the experience and the scenery, much of it now new to James who had never travelled so far west of the capital. Soon the tarred road came to an end and they swept onto the dusty red laterite surfacing that was common in the country regions of Uganda. They had moved from the open, dry Savannah into wooded areas, a foretaste of the densely forested region ahead. Plantains abounded, the green banana-type fruits that provided 'mtoki', a staple food along with the universal maize or 'posho' that sustained a majority of the population. They passed through villages and small single-street towns where shops bordered the main street and men congregated to drink beer whilst the women wrapped their purchases in brightly coloured cloth bundles and balanced them on their heads before beginning the long journey on foot back to their homes. Several men passed on bicycles, some loaded with bundles and sacks of meallie meal, others transporting themselves in style through the bustling streets. Harriett watched with childish enthusiasm, absorbing every new sight and experience with relish, and exclaiming with glee or sadness whenever something touched her heart.

"Look, James. That poor woman. How can she cope? The bundle on her head is massive. It's clearly weighing her down. And the baby on her back – it's so cute, fast asleep."

"I know. The 'totos' never seem to be distressed, do they? It must be the body contact with the mother. You don't see prams here, do you? I bet if you did, the babes would be wailing away like back home. Prams may be comfortable and convenient, but body contact seems so appropriate, so calming. It all looks so natural, doesn't it?"

They stopped for a cold drink at dilapidated 'duka' advertising 'Tusker' beer and Coke. A bicycle swept passed the Mercedes, carelessly scratching the paintwork with its handlebars.

"Mbafu!" Bilasto leapt in pursuit, remonstrating in fury and beginning his tirade with an expletive. It was the only word that James recognised as the two men harangued each other, to no avail, before eventually going their own ways.

"Never mind, Bilasto. Have a beer. It's not very cold but it's wet. You must be thirsty." They all sat together on the chipped stone steps of the 'duka' and chatted amicably. "How much further, Bilasto?"

"We are close, four hours, no more."

"What is it like in Fort Portal?"

"It is a good place, bwana, but do not go close to the border. There is much fighting." And Bilasto shared his knowledge, openly and without exaggerating. He painted an attractive picture of natural beauty, gentle climates and a friendly, safe community well removed from the worst excesses of Amin's regime. They learned that they could golf and play tennis, that there was a social club based in the old fort that gave the town its name. James explained to Harriet and Bilasto how Portal was an early explorer, of the era of Speke and Stanley. And so the two races sat happily together, as a single friendly community, sharing their knowledge and perspectives. Bilasto's respect for the quiet young man and his charming, open hearted wife, grew steadily over the course of that day. It was a pleasant relief to drive a white man who neither patronised him nor stood aloof and remote. James was also relieved to be back in a country he loved, interacting with its people without concern for the appropriateness of his behaviour, with no peers to impress and, above all, with Harriet – uncomplicated, unchanging Harriet who would always be the same, generous and upbeat, whatever her circumstance.

They arrived with the dusk, in time to see a magnificent red sky above the distant, snow-capped mountain peaks. Nature was welcoming them to their new home. And the welcome from the resident engineer was equally warm, especially when Neil met Harriet and succumbed to her beauty and charm.

"You'll want a quick meal and an early night, nae doubt. Bilasto will take you to your house now – it's number five, Bilasto – but freshen up and come straight back here in due course. Morag says it's potluck night, but that means a big stew so it can wait till you get here. You're welcome whenever you're ready. Bilasto, thank you for your day's work. Can you check in at the bachelor's quarters? They know you're coming."

Neil was a Scot – one of the many typical, blunt, friendly Scots who appear in every corner of the world, happy to fit in wherever he was to whatever lifestyle was needed, and to bring a no-nonsense professionalism to his work. He was also happy to squirrel away the fruits of his labour, with canny care, so that one day he could enjoy a comfortable retirement in 'God's own country'. He was a young man, in his early thirties, and this was his first Resident Engineer's posting, in charge of a site of his own. It was a small site, a minor road and bridge construction scheme, but he was the boss, proud of his promotion and determined to do well. His team consisted of eight employees from Arthur Garland's U.K. office – engineers, a surveyor, a laboratory technician, and James as trainee contracts administrator. He also had two inspectors, poachers turned gamekeeper, former artisans whose duty it was to check the day-to-day quality of the work done by the civil engineering contractor. James was the last to arrive and would help relieve the burden of the engineers who, in the absence of a quantity surveyor, also had responsibility for the monthly measurements of work done and certifications of payment to the contractor, a British/Ugandan joint venture called 'Roadbuild Uganda'. Neil was delighted with his new team and was intent on delivering a quality project to the Ugandan Government. The road scheme involved the surfacing and partial rebuilding of a fifty-mile stretch of road between Fort Portal and Kampala. It was being funded with British Overseas Aid.

When James and Harriet arrived later in the evening, they were welcomed by a warm-hearted Morag, cold beers and a delicious casserole. In a friendly, very sociable and somewhat alcoholic fashion they were briefed about the site community and the 'tricks of the trade' for survival in remote regions where the simplest things, like toilet rolls and flour, could not be taken for granted.

"If worst come to worst, keep your Guardian Weekly. It's airmailed here every week from our London office so we can catch up with the week's news from back home. Not that that's worth much these days – nothing but strikes and economic woes to report. Anyway, it makes good standby loo paper. Last I saw of Harold Wilson doesn't bear describing! Have a whisky, compliments of yourself, James. You brought it up from Kampala today. Good for John – he slipped a bottle of Glen Grant in with the latest batch of drawings. Do you play bridge, by the way?"

The welcome was all that could have hoped for and the young couple tottered back to their house after midnight, tired, elated and mildly intoxicated. Even at the late hour they heard, from a small native hut nearby, the rhythmic strumming of a guitar. The sound combined with the chirrup of locusts and the occasional screech and rustle of wildlife from nearby tall clumps of elephant grass. They knew they were experiencing the essence of Africa – lulled to sleep by primitive, throbbing pulses of energy that seemed timeless.

James enjoyed his life in Fort Portal. He loved the country and was always happy when his work required him to take one of the company Landrovers and visit the various sites where the construction work was taking place. But that was not often. As a trainee his own work was mundane, checking endless columns of figures to ensure that the measured quantities of work done were recorded and paid for. He was too green to take responsibility for negotiating, with the contractor, the resolution of the many claims that were submitted for unforeseen conditions. And there were plenty of those! Normally Neil or one of his section engineers would lead the discussion, with James in attendance so, gradually, he began to get his head around the complexities of Conditions of Contracts, Specifications, Bills of Quantities and Drawings. Eventually he was allowed to process the simpler claims. But it was all office-based work and he constantly wished he could get out and about. Even so, there were advantages to the office. Edward, the tea boy/clerk, and Gideon, the site driver, both saw in James a polite and friendly presence. It was not long before his approachability attracted his African assistants – they would often discuss their problems over a cup of tea, or a glass of freezing cold limejuice. James learned about wayward wives, difficult cousins – everybody seemed to be another's cousin – and illness, even death.

One night, James' and Harriet's meal was interrupted by a knock on the door. Edward stood outside, two hands clasped together low down in front of his body (a typically subservient attitude amongst Africans) and a look of concern on his face. Behind him stood a young black woman carrying a small bundle. Her face was wracked with misery.

Edward explained, "Sir, it is my cousin's daughter. She is dead."

For a moment he could only gape, appalled at the suffering in the girl's face. She could only have been sixteen years old.

"Edward, that's dreadful. What can I do?"

"My cousin must return to her village to bury the child. It is many miles and she has no transport." Clearly, Edward was asking for a lift.

Harriet listened in anguish. Her heart went out to the girl and she placed a consoling hand on the bony shoulder.

"We must do something, James."

"I know. I'll get the Landrover from Dave. You phone Neil and say what we're doing." He grabbed a light sweater and strode from the house. "Wait here, Edward, I'll be back with a car soon."

Within five minutes he was back and the two Africans clambered aboard. Harriet emerged.

"I can't raise Neil at home, but I'll try ringing around. He and Morag often play bridge with the Carters. Don't you think you should wait until he gives the go-ahead?"

"Edward says it's about twenty miles. I should be back in a couple of hours so don't worry. We're all allowed use of the Landrovers out of hours so I'm sure it'll be OK."

He kissed Harriet's cheek and sat behind the steering wheel. They turned out of the short driveway and headed west, towards the mountains. After twenty minutes, James heard a small wail – childlike and feeble. He looked in the mirror and saw the girl's face peering down at the small bundle on her lap. Puzzled, he stopped the vehicle and turned around. The infant's face was now visible and it was clearly alive, whimpering weakly and mouthing the air pathetically.

"Edward, the toto – it's alive!"

"Yes, bwana, but it is sick. We must take it to the village doctor."

"I cannot do that, Edward. There's a site clinic where it will get proper treatment. We must go there quickly."

Edward said nothing. Although the girl did not understand what had been said, she exclaimed in horror as the vehicle made the tight turn and headed back towards Fort Portal.

"Why, Edward? Why did you lie?"

"The mother is afraid of white medicine. Her village doctor knows how to cure such illness."

"OK but I cannot take the chance. Even if she does not want to go to the clinic, I have to take her there now. I would not forgive myself if the child dies. Sister Antonia is a wonderful person and she will look after the baby. She'll call the doctor if necessary. Please trust me. Ask the girl to trust me, would you?"

Edward spoke to the mother, but her eyes filled with tears as she looked up at the mirror and into James' eyes and said nothing. It was unsettling. She gave no indication at all of approval or otherwise; she simply looked fearfully, without a sound, into his eyes.

When they reached the clinic, James rushed in and saw the kindly figure of Sister Antonia. Relief flooded through him. The Catholic nun was an Italian, serving her church and humanity by running the small medical centre for the benefit of the community. 'Roadbuild' had placed a qualified doctor on the site. He was primarily there to help the construction community, but was available for emergencies within the local villages. Often he would treat cuts and fractures but there was reluctance, even in the current times, for some villagers to trust anyone other than their own witchdoctors. So, when illness struck without reason, superstition often prevailed. James was taking a risk, but he was also following his instincts and using common sense. Even so, he prayed that the child would survive. It was not his intention to thrust his values onto the villagers. So he felt cornered, caught in a dilemma that would only resolve itself if the child lived.

He went to collect Harriet and together they sat with Edward, waiting for news. Nobody felt able to speak, but they gained comfort from each other's presence. Harriet shared a thermos of tea; they took turns to drink from the plastic cup and nibbled chocolate digestive biscuits absent-mindedly. It was an extraordinary sight.

An hour later Sister Antonia emerged.

"There is no need to wait. We will know in the morning. You must go. Go and sleep." She touched James' elbow. "God bless you. If the child lives, your action saved it. Sleep with peace in your mind."

"James, I don't know what to say to you. It is not our job to run a taxi service for the locals. After this incident, they'll expect you to run them about at their whim. Don't let that happen. On the other hand, a life has been saved, so well done!" Neil could not resist a smile as he continued, "By the way, we need an office manager. You're always keen to be out and about so can you take over those duties as well as the contracts work. I'll see if the Partners will give you a bit of a pay rise as well."

James was delighted. He left Neil's office and called to Edward.

"Have you a moment, Edward? Tell me how your cousin's daughter is. She is out of hospital, I hear."

"She is well bwana mkubwa. We wish to thank you. Please accept this gift."

Edward handed James a painted bottle – an empty wine bottle – painted by a craftsman from Edward's village, depicting a forest scene with men in canoes fishing for tilapia with spears and nets. The colours were typically African – gaudy and stark – but the image was perfect, skilfully crafted, and James knew that he would treasure the gift for the rest of his life.

The whole episode had given him a surge of self-confidence.

"Thank you, Edward. Senti sana. Please thank your cousin for me. By the way, I am now your boss. My job is to run this office. Please tell the others that I look forward to working with them."

His new duties included managing the salaries and welfare of all the African staff – the office and laboratory clerks, the drivers and the surveyor's chainmen. He took to these duties with relish and, for the first time, he even began to feel that his career with Arthur Garland held potential. The only unpleasant task was the monthly certification of payment to 'Roadbuild'. As each monthly deadline approached the prospect of number-crunching the payment figures became ever more demoralising. But otherwise he ran the office with enthusiasm and each day had its own interest.

As part of his duties, James made a monthly trip to Kampala. This was mainly so that essential supplies for the households could be purchased and important mail collected by hand rather than be subjected to the vagaries of the postal service. As time passed, the trip also entailed more business-related activity such as visits to the Client office and banking. In James, Arthur Garland had a conscientious and trustworthy employee. Sometimes he was accompanied by other members of staff, or their wives, giving everybody an opportunity to enjoy an overnight stay in Kampala and to do personal shopping, or simply relax away from the sameness of site existence. James looked forward to these trips. He enjoyed driving the Landrover and occasionally he would ask Gideon to take a rest whilst he took the wheel.

Often, as they approached the capital city, they would encounter roadblocks, mainly manned by the army but always there would be at least one civilian – clearly the secret police. As time passed, they were recognised and were often waved safely through although James kept a packet of cigarettes in the glove compartment and always offered a few to the two or three men who hovered close to the vehicle, peering in to see if there was anybody hidden in the back. One or two of the soldiers were prepared to smile, and were courteous, but generally the atmosphere was sullen, especially when the policeman listened to the brief interrogation.

This became a routine that James and Gideon accepted and they often had bets with each other as to which soldiers would be manning the checkpoint. They were given nicknames. James always liked it when they saw 'the Good, the Bad and the Ugly' standing in the road ahead waving them down. 'The Good' was a genial sergeant, easygoing and always anxious to chat. He never stopped smiling, as if life was a continuous cause of wry amusement. James played him along often joking about the usefulness of the roadblocks.

"How many criminals have you caught since I was last here, Ephraim? None! You should be shot."

The sergeant roared with laughter and banged the roof of the vehicle with the palm of his hand. "You may go, bwana." Then he continued to chortle to his more sullen colleagues, giggling with a high-pitched "hee, hee, hee."

Occasionally, and only when it was appropriate, James would discretely slip Ephraim a bag of sugar or rice, knowing the value that was placed on these luxuries. On other occasions they knew that polite respect and silence was required, having learned that they should never complain about inappropriate treatment. Once they were forced to waste an hour unloading the supplies from the Landrover and watch helplessly as the soldiers picked through each bag and container, openly stealing groceries and vegetables.

James became experienced in the routine of 'checkpoint diplomacy' to the point of complacency. He was therefore taken aback one day when they passed several roadblocks, some of them many miles from Kampala.

"Why are there so many, sergeant. You are the fifth we've passed today."

'The Good' clucked sadly. "There are many criminals. We must arrest them, but there are too many." He shook his head at the enormity of the task.

James knew that 'criminals' were, in fact, those who had fallen out of favour with the regime. He was careful not to be drawn, preferring to make light of the inconvenience.

"Well, Ephraim my friend, I travel happily knowing that you are always on this road to protect me."

The genial sergeant's shoulders shuddered in merriment as the giggles once again overcame him. "It is good, bwana. Msuri sana. Travel safely. Kwenda – go."

The next day, as usual, they began the return journey, passing fewer checkpoints, all of which were close to the capital. Gideon drove whilst James dozed, slowly succumbing to a pleasant sleep. He was now used to the sights of the journey and boredom often set in, especially on the return leg when he was anxious to get home and see Harriet. If he could sleep, he always would and on this occasion, as they had no fellow passengers, he was able to stretch out across the back seats. This saved his life.

He awoke to Gideon's cry of alarm, in time to hear a volley of gunshots and feel broken glass from the Landrover's windscreen and driver's side windows cascading over his body. Bullets clanged and thudded into the vehicle, slicing through the air above his head. Gideon was not so fortunate. A bullet snapped past his face, gouging the side of his temple and tearing off his right ear. Another bullet shattered his right shoulder, throwing him back into his seat, making him lose control. They swerved off the road and over a steep embankment, rolling sideways for twenty yards in a terrifying jolting crashing slither before slamming into a tree and stopping upside down in a small stream.

Water swirled around James' face, filthy with mud and rotting vegetation. He swallowed a mouthful and immediately vomited, then struggled to pull himself to the surface, gasping and gagging, still not fully in control of his senses. From the roadside, he could hear exultant shouts and further gunshots. More bullets slammed into the Landrover, but this time they were lucky as many ricocheted from the solid metal parts, wheel axles and drive shaft, and those that did penetrate the floor thudded harmlessly into the passenger side. The instinct to survive took over. James dragged himself through the window on the protected side of the vehicle and crouched behind it, in shin deep water. He saw Gideon's body slumped upside down, his head beneath the surface of the foul water. Fortunately the driver's door was not jammed, so he was able to heave it open and drag the unconscious body into the stream. He placed Gideon in a seated position, propped up his back against the side of the Landrover and checked for breathing. Spittle and filthy green water dribbled from the mouth, joining the rivulets of blood that flowed freely from his head wound.

Until now, James had acted on impulse, unthinking, aware that this was a crisis and feeling a panic and confusion. Now, as bullets whipped past them, thudding into the ground behind, clanging or snapping into the vehicle, or whining off it with vicious ricochets, he was struck with the stark realisation of their danger. He crouched low, waiting for the fusillade of random shots to end, knowing that there was no chance of survival. The cruel shouts of jubilation from the road above reflected a bloodlust, a chilling relish of the chaos being inflicted. What hope that they would show mercy? All he could do was cower. He did not want to leave Gideon but even if he had made a rush for the cover of the trees, he knew that it would only spur his attackers into a renewed frenzy of shooting that would have shredded his body before he could run more than a few paces. So he squatted and prayed.

"Dear God, help us. Please help us."

The gunfire eventually stopped and the bandits began to scramble down the bank, high on an adrenalin charge and chattering like over-excited children.

"This is it!" James thought and he began to staunch the flow of blood from Gideon's head wound and ear, certain that death was imminent and now coldly determined to show courage and dignity.

"Hey, wewe. Kuja hapa." The guns were levelled at his stomach. James raised his hands and, obeying the command, looked coldly into the eyes of the speaker and walked slowly towards five gun barrels.

"This must be a dream!" When he was in view, he half turned and signalled towards Gideon with a gesture of his head.

"My driver is injured. He is unconscious and cannot move. He is of no danger. He needs help. I will give you no trouble."

It was all he could manage. The short sentences were blurted out in barely coherent gasps – his chest was so tight with fear that he choked between each utterance, desperately trying to draw breath into rigid lungs. He saw the elation of blood-lust drain from their eyes to be replaced by a mixture of emptiness and disappointment. His stomach knotted dully. They gestured to him, indicating that he should go back up to the road. There, at the top of the bank, stood another group – the gang must have consisted of more than fifteen badly dressed, ill-disciplined thugs. With the urging of harsh shouts and sharp, painful jabs from gun barrels, he was ushered up the embankment into waiting hands. Then he was thrust to the ground, face down onto the hot abrasive dust of the road. His wrists were bound with sisal and he was pulled upright. His face and white shirt were stained in a rust-coloured, grimy coating of laterite, making him look like a Red Indian smeared with war paint. This lightened the mood of his captors, whose disappointment at not finding a scene of carnage was slowly replaced by a marked curiosity at the strange white captive. James was relieved to be subjected to the jeers of amusement; the alternative was unthinkable. Then he heard a scream of pain and turned to see Gideon being dragged up to the roadside with no thought for his wounds. The pain must have been excruciating, jerking him back to a terrifying and agonising consciousness.

His arms were also bound, but to the front, a small and hopeful gesture of some degree of humanity.

A few remained behind to ransack the Landrover – that had been the point of the ambush. The others quickly formed a single file and marched into the jungle, pushing their captives impatiently onto narrow, secret tracks, making their escape before they could be discovered by an armed patrol. Gideon whimpered constantly, and occasionally screamed when his shattered shoulder jostled against trees or was prodded by a rifle. James had read stories describing human cruelty. He had seen news reports on atrocities from within Uganda and elsewhere. But this was now his world. So real and frightening. He was shocked to the core by the gratuitous pleasure that the gang took in tormenting a helpless human being. At one point James was driven beyond reason, fear overwhelmed by an indignant anger that welled within him. For no reason, a brutish thug aimed a blow with his rifle butt at Gideon's injured shoulder. The driver shrieked once before collapsing, briefly losing consciousness and lying where he fell. His tormentor kicked the prone body.

"Stop that, you bastard. Mbafu, mbafu, mbafu."

He felt so helpless and could think of nothing to say other than to shout expletives, hoping that this would distract the man's attention from the hapless Gideon. It worked! The outburst surprised the thug who contented himself with a final vicious kick at the driver's ribs and a backhanded slap at James' face. Blood seeped from his nose and split lip but he had experienced worse in the boxing ring and, anyway, he was now numb, outrage and fear deadening all pain. When Gideon recovered consciousness they walked on, briskly, deeper into the jungle. At least the urgings for speed were spoken, rather than physical, and the two-hour trek continued in silence broken only by exhortations of "Pese, pese."

They reached the bandit's hideout in the late afternoon. James' hands were untied and he was bundled into a small rondavel hut with only one door, outside of which stood an armed guard. Gideon's body was thrust through the low entrance, so low that he had to stoop onto his knees and wriggle like a wounded animal. Yet again the pain of his ruined shoulder racked his body. James gently untied his hands and eased Gideon's head onto his thighs, pillowing it whilst he examined the wounds. The shoulder was a pulped mass of gelatinous, purple-red goo. Encouragingly, blood only seeped slowly from the wound. The temple was superficially scratched and the skull was intact but the ear looked awful, shredded by the bullet, leaving only the lobe untouched. The upper half of the ear no longer existed. Raw red mince was all that remained.

"Maji, mimi nataka maji. Maji, maji, maji."

James called for water refusing to stop his pleas even though the first response from their guard was to jabber incoherently and point his gun through the doorway at their two bodies. But James' outrage was now venomous and persistent, fear long since overwhelmed by a cold, indignant fury. How dare they be so callous in their barbaric treatment of a wounded human? He was determined to prevail, whatever the consequences. At last an old woman stooped into the hut, carrying a tin demijohn of water. She smiled self consciously, an ordinary human gesture, but it meant so much, breaking as it did the nightmare of inhumanity and proving that normality was possible even in this hellhole.

"Senti sana."

His thanks were heartfelt with relief and appreciation. Then his limited fluency in Swahili failed him and he could only gesture towards the quietly moaning Gideon, indicating the need for bandages. The crone nodded and left, soon returning with a well-worn cloth that seemed clean enough. It had recently been washed, but only in the mud-stained waters of a stream.

"Still, better than nothing," he muttered. "At least it's not a soiled clothing."

First, he washed the wounds, taking as much time as was necessary to minimise Gideon's agony of movement, bathing him as gently as possible Then he set about tearing bandages and making a sling for the arm. With what was left, he balled up the cloth and stemmed the shoulder wound before making as firm a bandage as he dared, and finally he eased the sling under the arm to take the weight off the shoulder. He was not a medical expert, but he did sense that this was acceptable, if incredibly crude, first aid. Without proper 'second aid' in a sterile environment Gideon's wounds would fester but for now he contented himself that he had done all that was possible. And it did seem to help. Gideon calmed down and was even able to speak a few words of appreciation, croaking his thanks between moans. He vomited. The natural numbness of trauma had long since faded, replaced by relentless throbs of pain. Soon the agony in his ear had heightened beyond that of his shoulder. But Gideon's morale was bolstered by James' ministrations. Simply being in the company of a sympathetic fellow human was a great solace. It seemed to Gideon that James was trying to share the pain as he cradled his head in cupped hands careful to ensure that the torn ear touched nothing. James' hands seemed to have a healing energy and his every touch was steeped in concern and love. Mercifully, Gideon slipped into a blissful sleep released, at least for a short while, from pain and fear.

He awoke during the night and revisited his world of pain. James was always there, sharing the agony and stroking his friend's dust-encrusted wiry hair. "God is present," Gideon murmured at one point, slipping between coherence and delirium.

Early morning light rimmed the small doorway of their prison. The camp began to stir. A cockerel crowed arrogantly rousing the humans. James had not slept at all. He had spent the night deep in thought during the moments when Gideon slipped into the blessed release of a sleep-coma. He had dreaded the morning, understanding that his captors faced a dilemma that could not be postponed beyond the coming day. Gideon's wounds would soon fester and they would have to kill him or allow him to seek proper medical treatment. Clearly they had not intended to take prisoners – the prolonged hail of bullets that had poured relentlessly into the Landrover had shown their certain intention to kill all the occupants during the main ambush. Afterwards, something had prevented them from shooting the two men. Possibly they had sated their blood lust or maybe, and this James fervently hoped, they had not at first noticed the white passenger in the vehicle – he had been lying out of sight across the back seats – and, seeing only Gideon at the time, they had felt safe in their choice of an uncomplicated, soft target. In the months that Arthur Garland's staff had worked on construction sites there had never been any incidents of dissidents from the Amin regime attacking expatriate workers. Mainly the attacks had been on Government troops and supplies. So James hoped that they would be released, but he dreaded the alternative. Had he seen too much? Or was he now a valuable asset, to be ransomed for money? And what of Gideon? Whatever lay ahead, James resolved to stand by his companion.

A continuous coughing signalled the approach of a bandit, clearing his tar-raddled lungs in the early morning routine of a heavy smoker. He spoke briefly to the guard before hacking loudly and spitting the foul contents of his throat onto the bare earth in front of the entrance. Then the figure appeared in front of them, squatting into view but making no attempt to enter. "Kuja," he commanded through the doorway.

"Hapana." James was determined to stand his ground. If they were to be killed, it would make no difference if he refused to move.

"Kuja, pese." The tone was more urgent, showing stirrings of irritation.

"Hapana. Mimi nataka chakula."

James' request for food was genuine – he was hungry. But it was also a feeler, to test the intentions of his captors. Bullets thudded into the earth in front of the doorway. James leapt in fright jostling Gideon, who moaned.

But the angry bandit departed. Soon the same kindly old woman appeared with a plate of 'posho' and a tin mug filled with brown water. James fed Gideon, pushing the stodgy porridge into his mouth with his fingers and asking him to chew and swallow with sips of water. It took time as Gideon could only eat a few mouthfuls very slowly. James' spirits were boosted by his victory.

"Have courage, Gideon, they would not have agreed to feed us if their intention was to kill us today." However, he could not stop thinking, "Is this the last meal of a condemned man?" Was his optimism giving him false hope? Surely not – his captors were not that considerate. If they were to die, they would not have been fed. "Today I am going to ask that they release us, Gideon. We have nothing that they need and we are a burden on them."

Gideon was lucid once more, although his face occasionally contorted with continued waves of pain. In a moment of relative ease, he reached to James' hand and squeezed it. He spoke with a thin, cracking voice.

"Today, bwana, I will die. I cannot walk and the bandits will not carry me to safety. God will welcome my soul and I shall tell him tales of your bravery. You are my brother. If they release you, you must leave me. Tell my wife that I faced death like a man and my love for her is great. Tell her also that our unborn son is to be named James. It is my wish."

Another wave of pain racked his body and he squeezed his eyes tightly. The grip on James' hand tightened like a vice, but he ignored the discomfort, hoping that Gideon's own agony was eased by the contact.

Again their tormentor appeared. "Kuja."

This time James obeyed. He crawled through the doorway and stood in the early morning sunlight, blinking with bemusement. Two guards carried Gideon from the hut. They were taken to a council of bandits who had clearly been discussing their fate. James was pushed to the ground, where he sat with his knees drawn up to his chin. It was a good sign that his hands were not bound. Gideon was dropped carelessly beside him and moaned as his body jarred on the hard sun baked earth.

The leader stood and spoke.

"You cannot remain with us. And if we release you, you will tell the forces of evil that we are here. We should have killed you at the roadside. But it is not our wish to fight against white men. So we must decide what to do."

"If you release us, we will not tell the police where you are. I give you my word. I am not a lover of Amin – just a man like you, working to help Uganda build roads. I have no interest in taking revenge on you."

"How can we trust you?"

"I cannot give proof. I can only give my word."

"We shall keep the Bugandan scum." He was referring to Gideon, whose tribe was not theirs. "He cannot be trusted. If you are lying, we will kill him."

"I think you will kill him anyway. He will die without medicine."

"Then we will kill you both. The choice is yours."

Gideon whispered weakly. "Bwana James, leave me to die here. You must save yourself."

The temptation was irresistible. His overwhelming instinct for self-preservation was supported by common sense. What was the point of two people being killed when one was inevitably going to die? Gideon would never manage the trek back through the dense jungle, unless he was carried on a litter, and the enmity between the different tribes was such that none of the bandits would ever consider helping him. James was being offered a lifeline back to normality, out of this hellish nightmare. He had struggled all his life to make decisions. At school, he neither had the courage nor the temperament to challenge authority, preferring to acquiesce to his betters in his desire to please. He had embarked on a university career that only his father wanted, again in his desire to please and because of a lack of self-confidence. Now, he had to make a decision where others were offering an obvious solution. He could do what he was told, yet again. He could return to his Harriet, to safety and normality and escape this dreadful predicament. He could, once again, blow with the wind. And nobody would blame him.

Gideon repeated, "Kwenda. Go my brother."

Even his friend was pointing the way, to ease his conscience. What would it serve Harriet to remain and be killed? In his mind, at that moment, he made the decision to leave. It was the only sensible thing to do. His terrified self cried out to be spared, to accept the offer of life and leave Gideon, taking his brave friend's message to his wife. He opened his mouth to speak, to accept the offer of life.

But another James spoke. The James who had called a batsman back to the crease, who had shared a ledge with a borstal lad, high above Clifton Gorge, and who had faced up to school bullies.

"No, I will not leave my friend. We will stay together and I will care for him until he dies."

"Then you must both die. Bind them."

Once again, they were bound, brutally. This time Gideon was dragged to the edge of the clearing in which the tiny village was built. Why bother to carry a man to his death? His agony would soon end. Several bandits brought their guns – a motley firing squad of hard-bitten, cruel thieves.

James' instincts cried out to change his mind, to plead for mercy, to awaken from the nightmare.

They were dragged from the village past a young man sitting alone outside his hut on a smooth, rain-washed rock. The stump of one leg protruded from torn shorts and homemade crutches lay beside him. He had listened to the discussion, but could not take part because he was a dead weight on the community, crippled from childhood and unable to fight. Only his mother had kept him alive. Now she emerged from the hut and James saw the kindly old crone who had shown them compassion the night before. His terrified eyes caught hers, the last desperate look of one human seeking comfort from another. James' face was flushed with terror so the thin white scar that traced his face down one side across to the nose, seemed suddenly so stark, so vivid.

The cripple looked at the white man in amazement, memories stirring deep within him – memories of a pavement in Kampala, of a small white boy with a strangely disfigured face and eyes that shone with friendship. He remembered a white arm falling across his shoulder and a moment when all fear left him and, for the first time in his life, another human being, apart from his mother, had offered gentle, unconditional friendship, simply wanting to share a moment of his life, a moment when colour meant nothing and when love meant everything.

"Wait!" Azenzio spoke Swahili to his fellow tribesmen. "I know this man. Let me look into his eyes, that I may be sure."

Azenzio held no sway in the village. Many of the men despised his frailty and regarded his worth as nothing. But they heard a timbre to the cripple's voice – it cut the air with authority and, to their own surprise, they stopped in their tracks. To a man, they obeyed Azenzio. He struggled to stand and, unaided, he hopped across to James. The two men looked in each other's eyes. James' terror masked the natural caring depths of his true character and Azenzio began to doubt his earlier certainty. He put a finger up to James' face and traced the scar. Suddenly, he was no longer certain. If this was the same person, then indeed much magic had been performed on the face, by a powerful witchdoctor. Suddenly, he felt foolish. His confidence drained away. No face could have recovered like this. No medicine could have been so powerful. Azenzio felt stupid. He should return now to his rock and sit there in anonymity for the rest of his life.

"It is nothing. I am mistaken."

Before the others could continue, dragging James to his death, Alija, Azenzio's mother held up her hand.

"What is it? Why did you think you knew this man?"

"Do you remember when I was child, on the streets in Kampala? When my father put me there to beg, and you were angry with him? I thought that this man was the boy who comforted me on that day, the one who gave me the toy animal that looks like a man-dog. But his face has changed – his nose has been rebuilt, and such magic is not possible. There is no medicine strong enough. I am mistaken."

Alija thought for a moment. "What do his eyes say?"

"They are not the same eyes."

"Azenzio, the man is about to die. His eyes are filled with fear. Show him the toy animal and look for a spark."

Alija ran into the hut and returned with a small ragged bundle clutched to her shrivelled bosom. She showed the bear to James.

"Baldy!"

The word exploded from James. He had not understood the complexities of the conversation, but he sensed that the cripple was trying to help. Now, he too remembered that day many years ago when he had felt such sympathy for the undernourished black child. He remembered the moment so clearly – the fly-infested scabbed stump and the mucus-encrusted face. And he remembered the wonderful oneness of their moment together, arms on each other's shoulders, as James asked the cripple to be his friend. The man who now stood in front of him had been that friend, showing no revulsion at James' own ravaged features.

The friendship had survived eighteen years. Azenzio cried out with pleasure and recognition when he saw James' eyes come alive with animation. He hopped close to James and put his arm on the white man's shoulder speaking with a quiet intensity that James understood, even though he had not fully mastered the language.

"I am your friend."

Chapter 11

Jumping for Joy

The following year began with the heaviest snowfalls for many winters. To make matters worse, Foot and Mouth Disease arrived in Britain in February. Although horses cannot contract this terrible disease, just like humans they are able to carry it so once again Lisa and Chelsea found themselves confined to the yard. Initially, with all the snow, this did not concern Lisa who made good use of Braehead's extensive indoor facilities. She was happy to play her part, along with everyone else at the yard, and accept the relatively small sacrifices involved. Far more important was the plight of all those farmers whose livestock and livelihoods were at risk. For months their fate lay in the balance as, daily, they examined their stock for the dreaded symptoms that would mean a death sentence for entire herds – often dearly loved herds – and financial ruin. Simply, they would lose everything. Many ordinary, decent human beings were forced to live with that prospect for months on end.

The nearest outbreak of Foot and Mouth was a hundred and fifty miles away, to the south in the Scottish border areas, so it was essential that everybody cooperated and that the disease was held at bay. For a few fleeting days, a chill of concern and desperation spread through the close north eastern community. A farm close to the small village of Fyvie, only forty miles from Braehead, reported worrying signs in its livestock and was visited by government vets. But the farm was soon cleared. The false alarm frightened everybody in the country areas around Aberdeen for, although it was Scotland's third city and oil capital of Britain, the surrounding country was renowned for its agriculture and the consequences would have been devastating. With great responsibility, the rural community, including all the equestrian folk, responded seriously to the crisis and the area remained clear throughout the months of outbreak.

Work in the indoor and outdoor schools was, however, very limiting for athletes like Chelsea. As February gave way to March, she became increasingly restless, showing signs of boredom and, true to character, a growing grumpiness. The world had to know that Chelsea was not amused! Then, to add to her woes, she developed an abscess in a hoof and had to be confined to her box whilst it drained and healed. Strangely, her mood improved, as if she understood that this was again time to behave so, as Lisa reported, "She's such an angel to nurse, standing quietly twice a day with her foot in a bucket of water and Epsom salts, and then always holding still whilst I bandaged it." Clearly, their weeks of confinement within the grounds of Braehead were no guarantee that they would be protected from the usual bout of incidents and accidents.

Lisa accepted philosophically whatever was thrown at her: "Owning a horse is a never-ending commitment. I now know never to expect a smooth life. But it's always worth it. For with every setback, sometimes even WITHIN every setback, there is a joy and a reward. That's a lesson I've learned for life in general. After all, there will always be challenges in life. If you let them turn you into a victim, you'll only get weaker. But if you meet them head on, you'll be stronger after the experience. And, let's face it, there are few better at meeting the world head on than Chelsea!"

Andrew and Lisa had planned a week's holiday in March, joining two dear American friends for a return to childhood and a few days of escapism in the magic of Disneyland. They set off with easy minds, knowing that Chelsea would be well cared for in their absence. Even with the setbacks in Chelsea's health, Lisa never became downhearted and optimism always exuded from her like radiant sunshine. Yet, she never took anything for granted, so her joy was palpable when they returned home to find that Chelsea was completely fit. The mare's delighted nickers of welcome carried the message, "Look Mum, well again, so NOW will you take me out for a proper canter in the forest." And, wonderfully, the answer was 'Yes'. The Foot and Mouth restrictions had indeed eased and the forest tracks were open again. Next morning there was no stopping them. Although still jetlagged, Lisa's excitement helped her to leap from bed at 5.30 am and an hour later she was alone in the chill April air with her beloved companion – the first early morning ride of the year. Chelsea was delighted to be with her mistress, and to be released from her confinement, comfortable as it was. As she was led from the stable, this time past the entrance to the outdoor school and over the road to the forest, Lisa could feel the mare's anticipation – "Yeesss, Mum – here we go at last!"

Lisa had planned on a gentle walk as she was certain that Chelsea would be stiff from a fortnight of box rest but she soon realised that, on this glorious morning of early spring sunshine, accompanied by singing birds and scampering squirrels, her companion had celebration in mind. She certainly was not stiff. Instead, her swinging steps at walk told Lisa that pent up energy was ready to burst forth. They rode round the edge of the forest under a canopy of still bare branches, enjoying the sunlight and the gentle breeze. Lisa abandoned the idea of a sensible walk and, with the slightest nudge of her legs, Chelsea exploded into her typical energetic canter up to the farmyard, dancing in the wind and playfully spooking at the shadows that swayed in time with the breeze.

The farmyard comprised a few outbuildings that, at this time of year, served as a maternity unit for a small flock of sheep. The lambs had arrived and were enjoying the freedom of a frolic in the early morning sunshine. Their mothers bleated their warnings summoning their offspring as soon as they heard Lisa and Chelsea approach. Lisa stopped for a moment and silently meditated putting out strong positive thoughts to the flock that all its members would resist Foot and Mouth disease. For that brief two-minute vigil, Chelsea sensed that she should remain quiet and the sensitive mare shared with Lisa her communion with fellow creatures. Even the frantic mothers ceased their bleating as the energies of nature's creatures merged with one loving purpose.

Nature thanked Lisa – along the track, they met some deer. Chelsea spotted them first – she always did. They were enjoying the shoots of new grass but they did not run, allowing Lisa the privilege of sharing with them another silent, harmonious moment. Lisa wondered if they were the same little group who had warned them, early in January, of the approach of a final burst of severe weather. Back then, the herd had been making its way deep into the shelter of the forest. Lisa was delighted to see that, from their condition now, they had wintered well and she wondered hopefully how many babies she might see in June. Again, Chelsea restrained her energies and stood quietly. But the mare was delighted when they turned up towards the 'Gallops' – a well-named stretch and one of her favourite tracks. Lisa ignored the need for discipline. It was not generally appropriate to let a horse decide what to do but then again, why live by rules – sometimes there was a reward and joy simply in their breaking? Chelsea was desperate to fly. Normally Lisa would make her wait for the command, but today she simply leaned forward in the saddle and without the usual nudge, whispered, "Let's go."

Chelsea was off! Up, bounding up the hill like a deer, mane flying in the wind and her chestnut coat gleaming its copper sheen in the sunshine. Her hooves pounded rhythmically on the path – ba ba bom, ba ba bom, ba ba bom. This is fun, oh what fun, oh what fun! They paused at the top and then walked down the far side of the hill. At the bottom they cut the corner and galloped back up again using a track on the opposite side of the hill and thus completing a circuit. On this more sheltered side, Lisa noticed the green fuzz of new growth on the silver birches.

The morning experience reminded Lisa of life and latent energy. As they turned for home, they watched, in the distance, commuters making their way to work in the city and she hoped they would take a moment to enjoy the glory of that early morning, to carry a little of it to their desks and to their colleagues. In her communion with nature that day, Lisa had received encouragement – a message of hope for the future, of rebirth and of new opportunity. She was delighted to have shared her own supportive energy with the provider, knowing that her own strength had been renewed, that Chelsea's injuries had been cured and that both gifts had been an inevitable part of their oneness with a single source of life. With these thoughts came an overwhelming feeling of responsibility. Lisa responded with a brief prayer of thanks, ending with her own commitment: "I will always respect you."

They ambled back together, both thinking of breakfast. Lisa gave Chelsea a grateful pat for sharing, in her own unique way, joy at being out and about once more, for spotting the deer and for helping Lisa to appreciate the beauty and joy of a spring morning. One ear flicked backwards. "I know, Mum, that was a special experience for me too."

Chelsea's first official show-jumping competition that year was held on a beautiful summer morning. As ever on such occasions, Braehead was 'en fete' with strings of flags bedecking the fences and fluttering merrily from the multitude of tents that had been erected the day before and now formed a small village that buzzed with activity and anticipation. The sellers of horseware enjoyed brisk business, and the fast food stands were all cluttered with chaotic lines of politely queuing customers. Chelsea looked fantastic. Lisa had brushed her glossy summer coat to a shiny copper sheen that flashed in the sunshine as, together with Sally, the three made their way excitedly down to the collecting ring. Chelsea strode purposefully, occasionally pulling ahead of Lisa and tugging the reins impatiently. She knew what lay ahead and was flighty with an excited anticipation that had grown steadily since Lisa's early morning appearance with her best show rug; the one that was only worn on special occasions …

… Chelsea had cooperated with the beautification routine, especially when Lisa murmured into an alert ear, "No plaits today, Chels. You know what that means – jumping, not dressage – so just a quick spray with conditioner and a good comb through the tail and mane. Doesn't take much to make you gorgeous." The mare positively preened with self-congratulation at her own beauty making Lisa laugh with joyous affection.

At precious moments like that Lisa often recited out aloud a favourite poem as she ran a comb through Chelsea's silken mane:

> *"Totally, for sure*
> *I've just had a manicure.*
> *The sun, I swear,*
> *Has bleached right through my gorgeous hair.*
> *24, 34, I don't know the stupid score.*
> *Run, run, fight, fight.*
> *Gee, I hope I look alright."*

Her lovely mare was behaving just like that precocious girl.

"Except that you'll be the competitive one in a couple of hours time. You minx!"

Lisa then strapped on the jumping boots and Chelsea smiled with delight, indicating her pleasure at this final confirmation of what lay ahead...

Sally went to declare Chelsea and Lisa for the first class of the day, requesting a place about half way through the field of thirty competitors. Today Lisa was riding and was a bundle of nerves. She was already an accomplished show jumper, but the long lay-off as a result of Chelsea's hocks, and then Foot and Mouth, had meant that she had only been able to compete in small evening events at Braehead. This had brought her along beautifully. At first she had used another horse – Susie – who belonged to the yard owners and who had been a gentle giant, nursing Lisa around the Minimus fences and then, with increasing confidence, up through Novice to Intermediate. Then Lisa's hours of practice, and participation in evening competitions with Chelsea, had paid off and the pair were now ready for this, their first full affiliated showjumping event.

Soon, Sally was back and set about adjusting the practice fences ready to offer Lisa support and advice. Lisa had already begun their warm up routine from walk to trot to canter and, with her beautifully supple horse, was now ready for the jumps. Chelsea simply flew over them, smiling broadly and tail flowing out behind, an image of relaxed, happy confidence. Clearly she was looking forward to the competition immensely. From her position behind her head Lisa saw two ears, pricked forward in attentive delight, and she knew that Chelsea had very quickly found her groove. Her eyes were fixed firmly on the fence and she judged her approaches to perfection. Ever since Lisa had watched Tony introduce Chelsea to cross-country, she knew from the mare's intent approach exactly where she'd place herself to make the jump. This was paying off now. Gradually her nerves diminished to a small, healthy flutter. Instead pleasure became the main feeling. Pleasure at the knowledge that Chelsea was having fun, enjoying the jumps and free to use her own brain and instincts – SO different from the regimentation of dressage.

"She's jumping for joy, Sally! Can you see it?"

"I can! She's happy and free-spirited, just as if she's joining the sun and the wind. Try popping her over a few uprights, now."

Sally changed the cross poles into a three-foot upright, which Chelsea swept over with disdain.

"Try a few more, Lisa. That's great. Now just walk her around quietly. I'll go and check on progress – see how many more to go before it's your turn."

After ten minutes Sally returned. "About four more to go before you. By the way, there are only a very few clear rounds so far. From what I've seen, most of the trouble is at fence six – the one close to the railings. Somebody has left a wheelbarrow on the outside of the ring. It's catching the horses' eyes and there have been quite a few run outs there."

"Thanks, but my guess is that Chelsea will be so focused on the jump that she won't notice it. A bit like me – I was concentrating so hard when I walked the course that I didn't spot it. So I certainly won't be worrying about it when I'm riding!"

The happy trio made their way to the entrance to the ring, ready for their round. Chelsea stood still, watching the competing horse complete its own round. Lisa observed Chelsea with interest and wondered, "Do you think she's actually following that horse and working out the best way round the course? I wouldn't be surprised. Sometimes she seems to turn for jumps so instinctively; so fast …"

The commentator interrupted her. "That's a clear round for 'Silver Ghost'. Three into the jump-off so far. Now, we have Lisa Graham riding her own Chelsea!"

The bell sounded for the start of their round and Lisa set Chelsea up for the first fence. They were on their way. They simply flew around the course.

"Not too fast, not too fast," Sally murmured her concern as she watched her friends approach the double. It was very slightly downhill – always a test for Chelsea because of her fused hocks where the loss of flexion, albeit only three degrees, could make a difference as she leapt away from the slope of the ground. "Easy, easy. Well done!"

Good athlete that she was, Chelsea had learned to cope and she surged over the double, meeting the second element on a perfect stride, all with such ease that Sally wondered if her concern was unnecessary. Then they turned for the fence by the wheelbarrow.

"Go, girl, go now."

And of course she did! The mare ignored the distraction and took the fence in her stride before turning gracefully to the final line of fences and popping over each one in grand style. Lisa brought her back to trot and turned towards the gate.

"That's the fourth clear round of the class. Well done to Lisa Graham on Chelsea."

Lisa never stopped patting the mare's neck as they walked out. After all the troubles of the past year, it was not surprising that both Lisa and Sally's eyes were misted with tears. Out of sight, Andrew had been taking a video of the event. He had not informed Lisa that he would do so, just in case it added pressure, but he swallowed hard before speaking to the owner of Braehead. Sheena had recognised the significance of the moment and her words of congratulation showed a deep perception.

"Brilliant, Andrew. You'll be so proud. To have brought Chelsea along after all those setbacks with her health is wonderful. But for Lisa to have brought her own riding up to this level so quickly is simply amazing. She looks as good as many of the lifetime jumpers out there. You'll be proud."

"Thanks, Sheena! I am. I can barely speak. It doesn't matter what happens in the jump-off. Her first affiliated show and she performs like that! It's beyond words. What a pair!"

In his joy and emotion, he forgot to turn off the video and the words were recorded forever, a fitting tribute to courage, determination and partnership. He joined the three 'girls' and hugged them all. But his words were lost in Lisa and Sally's excited chatter, so he surreptitiously slipped out a packet of Polo mints and began to peel back the silver foil.

Chelsea never missed a trick and immediately lost interest in the two ladies, instead pushing her nose cheekily against Andrew's chest.

"That's more like it, Dad. All this hooha and they forget who actually did the jumping."

"Time for a warm up before the jump-off." Lisa hopped back into the saddle. "Just in case we're drawn early."

Sally became businesslike again. "Right, I'll go and check on the fences. Be back soon."

There were only six clear rounds and Chelsea was drawn fourth. Sally returned to inform Lisa who was cantering around the collecting ring.

"You're fourth to go, Lisa and the fences are 1, 2, 4, 7, 8a, b and c."

Lisa brought Chelsea to a halt and reviewed the course, walking it through several times in her head, all the while tracing the path out in the air with her fingers.

"Hmm. What do you think, Sally? A safe double clear or shall we go for it?"

There was no doubt in Sally's mind. "You look so comfy; why not go for it? The going is perfect AND they've missed out that downhill combination."

"That clinches it!"

The strategy was agreed and the jump-off began. The first competitor went clear. A typical, safe leader's ploy – make those who follow face the pressure of a clear round. The next to go had a run out as they turned too tightly into fence 7 – the planks. So, four faults and a slow time. The third horse was just a youngster and the rider carefully took the long route, accepting the joy of a double clear in her attempt to build her mount's confidence for the future. And in no time, it was Chelsea's turn. They entered the arena and circled, waiting for the bell. Chelsea worked out the routine, just as she had done during the year of endurance rides when she had waited in the starting box for the countdown – '3, 2, 1, go and good luck!' So now she understood that, for showjumping, the bell meant 'Go'. She launched off, ears pricked and eyes bright and focused on Fence 1, cantering through the electronic beam that started the clock.

"Go, Chelsea, go," whispered Sally, squeezing her calf muscles as if it was she who was riding.

"Go on, girl," murmured Andrew as he 'zoomed-in' on the first fence.

Lisa had Chelsea in perfect balance as they soared over the first and turned sharply towards the second. They cleared it easily and managed the gentler turn to Fence 4. Again she jumped perfectly and turned on landing, with athleticism that belied her recent hock problems, making a smooth approach to the 'planks'. Andrew shook with anxiety and the image jumped crazily across his viewfinder. Sally held her breath. She knew Chelsea always found planks hard to judge. But not today! The horse was grooved in excellence and positively pinged over the obstacle, then on and through the final combination with a determined surge at the first element of the treble, taking out a stride between the final two fences and then racing to the finish. Double clear and easily the fastest time so far. Now, they could only wait for the last two competitors. The next horse made a determined effort to better their time but rolled a pole through the final combination. The last horse, an experienced stallion, pipped them by two tenths of a second, but only after rattling two poles in the final treble, accepting the good fortune that fell his way on the day.

Sally moaned in dismay. Andrew whispered, “Good girl,” and switched the video off. “Bloody thing. Ruins the occasion. Can’t see a thing.”

But Lisa, positive as ever, danced with delight as she hugged Chelsea and then Sally, and finally a somewhat ruffled Andrew.

“I can’t help but think of the day I sat on her after her steroid injection. If someone had told me she’d be jumping like this I’d not have believed it. It is her first affiliated competition after all.”

Everybody was caught up with the emotion. This time, even Andrew coughed with pleasure as a tear welled into his eye and threatened to embarrass him completely by rolling joyfully down his cheek.

“In you go, Lisa. Go and get your rosette.”

“And enjoy the lap of honour,” Sally shouted as the happiest partnership in the world went in to the prize giving ceremony. Joy had returned to Chelsea’s life.

Lisa and Chelsea continued to jump in all the competitions at Braehead, gaining in confidence with every outing and rarely being out of the ribbons. Then one day, as the summer gave way to autumn and a grey chill clamped a clammy blanket over Braehead, Lisa decided to join a small group of friends and fellow horse owners from the yard who had decided to take a lorry-full of horses to compete at a nearby agricultural show. The showground was only thirty miles away, not too far for a first big jumping event away from home. But Lisa was uncertain about how well Chelsea would cope with all the sights and sounds of an unfamiliar busy showground with animals other than horses, the ever present pipe band that always entertained such highland gatherings, and all the various displays and noises. Lisa was unaware of Chelsea’s former life in Ireland. Obviously she had jumped before, but what about travelling to large shows? Would she be able to concentrate on her jumping, or would the excitement of travel, and a strange venue, affect her in any way? There was only one way to find out.

The excited party congregated at the yard bright and early, and set about preparing their mounts – five horses and two delightful ponies, tough little grey-coloured creatures with shaggy manes and forelocks that flopped cheekily over intelligent brown eyes. The humans comprised six adults and two children. For several minutes the party was transformed into eight children, sharing with each other the air of excited anticipation that spilled out in a babble of giggles and laughter. But soon they set about their duties, the first task being to feed the animals and give them plenty of time to digest breakfast before the early departure.

As always at the start of a day, Lisa spent a few minutes of 'personal time' with Chelsea, standing in front of her gorgeous head, blowing up her nostrils and muttering sweet nothings towards intelligent brown eyes and receptive ears, and rubbing her white crescent. Then she left Chelsea to enjoy her feed and set about putting her saddle, bridle and other essentials into the lorry along with her own show clothes. Next she collected Chelsea's travel boots, a tail bandage and a light rug and placed them by the box ready for Chelsea to wear on the journey. Finally she went to fill three hay nets so that her companion would have something to nibble on the journey and during inevitable periods of waiting at the show. Although most of the group, including Chelsea, would be competing early in the day, two of the experienced horses were participating in the most advanced class and it was unlikely that the day would end before darkness. Lisa's stomach fluttered with a mixture of excited happiness and nerves. It would be a long day – a new challenge, but great fun – and she was relieved to have company, not simply because it would make the logistics at the showground easier, but because they all provided genuine moral support for one another. There was a unity of purpose within the team, and it was underpinned by a genuine concern, each for the others.

"How wonderful it is to be able to share closeness with animals and humans."

As ever, Chelsea was bright and alert, sensing what was afoot. She tucked into her breakfast with usual gusto, noisily slurping up the mix before licking every last drop from the feed bowl. "I'll never have to worry about you losing condition during the show season, Chels." Indeed, the mare positively thrived on the routine of competition and always made it perfectly clear that she enjoyed these occasions. "You just love the opportunity to show off, don't you?"

Once Chelsea had finished eating, Lisa began the familiar pre-show grooming routine, brushing her coat to its normal healthy copper sheen. This morning it was easy because Lisa had come up the previous afternoon and had bathed Chelsea, and had then covered her overnight with a light stable rug to give protection from chills, and to help keep her clean. This morning there were no stable stains, only a few pieces of straw in her mane and tail. These were removed easily before the comb did the rest. In no time Lisa and Chelsea were ready to go. On went the travel boots, tail guard and rug and the loading began. Chelsea was third on board – the horses were loaded in order of size, largest first to keep the lorry well balanced and easy to drive. The first two horses were experienced travellers and strode up the ramp quickly and without fuss. Chelsea watched with interest and, although she had never been on this lorry before, she was determined not to be outdone and walked pointedly up the ramp to join her companions. Lisa tied her lead rope securely in place and closed the partition across her stall, ready for the next horse. Soon all the animals were safely aboard, unlike the girls, who fussed and clucked like uncontrollable chickens, clambering across each other, 'forgetting' vital items and scrambling out again, vying for the best spots and then shrieking with laughter as they stumbled and fell over one another.

The driver, Dave, rolled his eyes in mock horror and the other two men shrugged knowingly, sitting patiently in the front seats pretending to be so very superior! At last Dave was able to switch the engine on and crunch the gears into life, like creaky limbs that had not been used for several days.

"Right, we're off. No more chances if you've forgotten anything. I reckon we'll be there in an hour."

There was little traffic on the main Inverness road as they headed north. The horses stood quietly, adjusting easily to the movement of the transporter. Some, including Chelsea, munched contentedly on hay nets; others dozed after the burst of early morning activity. The stretch of dual carriageway gave the human passengers an opportunity to pour tea from shared flasks and enjoy their own breakfasts of marmalade rolls, cholesterol-laden Aberdeen 'butteries' and toast. There would be little time to eat once they arrived at the showground, when they would be on 'all systems go'. They turned off the main road after about twenty miles and joined a small country road busy with vehicles heading for the showground. There were other horseboxes, floats bringing cattle, small trailers carrying sheep, and cars with spectators. Lisa loved these occasions and had always made a point of being amongst the early arrivers whenever she attended shows as a spectator, often enjoying an early breakfast with the stockmen before heading out to watch the judging. Today, she still felt the familiar rush of excitement – all the more so because, for the first time, she would be taking part. She was no longer a mere spectator.

Following the sign for 'Horse Boxes and Trailers', they soon found themselves in the Horse Park. Everyone jumped out and walked around the vehicle, stretching their legs and taking in the atmosphere. Lisa helped Dave to lower the back ramp so that the horses could look out as well and catch the smells and sounds of the showground. Then, leaving Dave in charge of the horses, they all strolled off to find the show ring, warm-up area and collecting ring. Finally, they found the secretary's tent and made their entries. Lisa concluded that she would be jumping with Chelsea in the early afternoon.

It is one of the challenges of show-jumping that, unlike endurance events, there is never a precise start time. Except for major competitions, for which riders have to pre-qualify, show-jumping competitions are normally open to any person who is eligible to compete and who turns up on the day and registers their entry. For the classes such as those in which Lisa was competing, it was not unusual to have at least 30 starters. Sometimes the field was as large as 60. Lisa always struggled to get used to this routine and also to the hanging around waiting for the jump-offs. The order of a jump-off is drawn just before it starts and competitors have to be ready to go first or, alternatively, to be able to switch off their horse if they are drawn later. In a sport that rewards skill and excellence, this is one aspect over which nobody has any control – all competitors are equally subject to the 'luck of the draw'. Each rider and horse combination always has its own preferred placing.

Lisa normally liked to have Chelsea well warmed up before they started a jump-off. However, the intelligent mare had grown wise over time and was able to switch off between rounds and conserve energy. Also, she rarely needed very much preparation time for subsequent rounds.

"She really does use her brain to work things out," Lisa had remarked to Andrew after one competition when Chelsea had finished the evening in a calm, cool state. "When we first started jumping her, she was as high as a kite for the whole evening. It took me ages to calm her down afterwards and get the sweat dried off so I could rug her up for the night. Now she's got it sussed and keeps her energy for the jumping. She's so smart. No wonder she hates dressage! She does like to use her brain and be an equal partner in whatever's going on. In fact I'm the one who hates all the hanging around and she's the one who can handle it better these days."

"But it was your patience that taught her in the first place, darling. Also, as you say, it's a team thing. She's calm because she knows she's with you. It's as clear as day."

Lisa remembered those words now and smiled happily, suppressing her feelings of impatience. At least she had arrived in plenty of time to prepare, and she would declare nice and early, aiming to start the first round by jumping fifth or sixth. Before heading back to the horses, she strolled through the cattle lines, admiring the stock and chatting companionably to the farmers. She enjoyed the banter, relishing their strange Doric expressions and the wry humour that was always evident behind their façade of dourness.

"If I'm ever in trouble, it's these folk I'd like to have as my neighbours. Wish I could have stayed longer," she thought as she slipped quickly away to prepare Chelsea, arriving just in time to help with the unloading. True to her nature, Chelsea stopped at the top of the ramp and looked around, not so much to familiarise herself with the new surroundings but to make sure that as many creatures as possible were on hand to greet her presence. Then, with an air of faint disappointment, she made her way imperiously down the ramp. "She certainly knows how to make an appearance." Soon all the horses had been unloaded and were tied to the sides of the lorry, munching contentedly on their hay nets until they were needed for competition. This was a familiar routine.

The two ponies were tacked up immediately and their riders, the youngsters Sue and Jane, excitedly changed into show clothes. They were scheduled to compete in the Working Hunter Pony class. This was the first event and would run through much of the morning. Lisa made a point of supporting the girls so she stayed with them for as long as possible, intent on watching at least the whole of the first phase, a jumping round of rustic fences. The small band of Braehead folk made their way together to the Working Hunter ring and watched with interest whilst Sue and Jane, one after the other, completed clear rounds. Their cheers and applause were distinctive, a small hub of enthusiasm and delight within the growing crowd of onlookers. Sue and Jane hugged each other and waved back to their supporters with youthful pride and a complete lack of self-consciousness. Lisa returned the happy wave and stuck her thumb in the air.

"That's a good start to the day," she thought. "Let's hope it augurs well for all of us."

Lisa could only stay long enough to watch a part of the second phase. Here the competition moved into a show phase where the animals were ridden by their owners in a group, then individually, before finally being trotted up in hand in front of the judges.

"I've got to go now," she called across to Sue. "Got to see to Chelsea. You're both doing wonderfully well. Keep it up and good luck!"

Lisa was genuinely sorry to leave the youngsters. She had become enthralled by the competition, with its mix of jumping ability, confirmation, manners and presence. Classes such as this could last most of a morning and both ponies and their riders needed utmost patience! All that now remained was the final phase, where the ponies were once again tacked up and ridden by their owners, en masse. But Lisa had stayed too long and simply had to look after Chelsea. It was frustrating to leave the girls, both of whom were well in contention. Already Lisa felt the addictive mixture – the buzz of competition and the thrill of achievement – and she was not yet even directly involved. She hummed happily to herself as she walked back to the horses.

"This is just the best. I feel good already about our own competition today."

Like Lisa, the other competitors from the Braehead contingent were all there for the show-jumping. Two had entered the Novice class, Lisa in the Intermediate class and two more were competing in the Open class. Lisa decided to take Chelsea for a short walk in hand to allow her to get used to the atmosphere. Her travel boots and tail guard had already been removed so she only had to take off the rug and put on her bridle. They strolled off together enjoying the companionship and ignoring the dankness of the autumn day. The show site was well organised and there were separate walkways and routes for horses which kept them separate from the general public. Many people thought that this was to protect them but Lisa had another theory! Chelsea, although interested in her surroundings, was not concerned by the hubbub. Lisa patted her. "You really have grown up, at last, haven't you?" They moved on to the warm up area, where Lisa simply walked the mare around a few times and let her have a pick of grass before the pair made their way back to the lorry. Lisa had another cup of tea. Then she went off for another wander round, leaving Chelsea happily tethered next to Jake and Ali, munching hay.

It was reassuring to know that Dave, their ever-patient driver, would keep an eye on the horses. He was inside the vehicle, equally happy, reading a newspaper, his legs stretched out across the front seats, being entertained by the music and chatter from Radio Northsound. Occasionally he would stop reading and, before turning a page, look out of his window at the animals. With a huge mug of tea and a hearty bacon roll, he was 'as happy as Larry'. "Don't you folk worry about me".

They were lucky to have Dave. He was invaluable, working at the yard during the week, always there when needed to fix things when they broke, as they inevitably did where horses were concerned. The last job he had done for Lisa was to nail rubber sheeting onto the dividing partition between Chelsea's box and her neighbour, Lilly. The two horses were normally great companions. But the pact of friendship would not hold on two occasions each day, morning and evening, when their hard feeds – the delicious mix of chaff, sugar beat and oats or barley – were scooped into their feed bowls. Then a flurry of irritation would prevail and the two mares would kick crossly at each other. Dave's idea to protect the partition had worked well and the wooden struts now needed minimal repairs. Not only was he competent, but also he loved horses and ungrudgingly shared a never-ending supply of Polo mints with the animals. Also, he never seemed to mind driving the large transporter to shows at the weekend. Once parked at a show, he was always content to stay with the horses who seemed to appreciate his steady presence just as much as the excellent driving skills that made their journey smooth and trouble-free.

There was a cheerful tap on the window. "Hello, Dave. Standing post as usual I see. Where's my better half?"

"Oh, hello Andrew. She's off for a stroll. Best wait for her here rather than go looking in the crowds. She'll be back any moment to begin tacking Chelsea up."

Andrew had made his own way to the show, realising that the lorry would be full of Braehead competitors. He had parked in the spectators' car park and then wandered across to the competitors' area. Finding the transporter had been easy. Now he was keen to help Lisa prepare for the biggest event of her showjumping career to date.

"That's fine. I'll just make myself useful and start the process."

Chelsea had already received a 'good morning' pat and had stopped eating to listen to the conversation between the two men. Now she nickered quietly as Andrew moved back towards her and rubbed her crescent. Lisa appeared, still humming happily.

Soon they were all ready to go. Andrew held Chelsea, and a stirrup, whilst Lisa mounted. As ever, he could not help but admire the handsome pair as his wife settled lightly onto Chelsea's back and took up the reins.

"I know I'm biased," he thought, "but they look as good as any horse/rider combination around. Just as good as those with years of experience." His pride and admiration shone from his face, reflecting genuine awe at what Lisa had achieved, both in bringing her own jumping skills along to this high level, and also in turning the corner with Chelsea, the 'problem' horse turned companion and star.

As a group, they walked to the warm-up area and started the usual routine of walk, trot and canter, first to the left and then to the right. To begin with Chelsea was distracted by the applause from the other show rings and the various tannoy announcements but she soon began to settle as Lisa circled her first one way, then the other, quietly demanding the mare's attention. So, very soon she too blocked out the distractions and worked up to the steady, consistent canter that she would need for jumping. Lisa had already declared for the class and was fifth into the ring. The prize giving for the previous class was taking place and she knew the stewards would not take long to build the course for her class, so she cantered round a few more times and then dismounted to go and walk the new course, leaving Andrew to look after Chelsea. She looked back and caught sight of him kissing the mare's nose yet again!

The Intermediate course looked imposing, not because the fences were any higher than usual, but because they were surrounded by floral decoration, sponsor's boards and bunting. This was certainly an important occasion. All the trappings and final touches of detail added to the atmosphere which was by now alive with tension and anticipation. The scale of everything seemed so huge and Lisa felt small and insignificant as she walked the course, carefully pacing out the lines between fences. Today she was alone but she remembered, with appreciation, all the previous courses she had walked with Sally. This helped her now as she paced steadily round the fences, planning the best route in her own mind. "…two and then three strides between the elements of the treble then keep straight out level with the flag pole before turning for the planks…" She was pleased to see that the recent weather had softened the ground which now had plenty of give in it, ideal for Chelsea who was never happy on hard courses, always preferring softer going.

"Better for her hocks. Great. This looks fine after all and I'm sure we can handle it all."

Gradually her sense of insignificance began to diminish and she welcomed the familiar flurry of butterflies in her stomach.

"It's a fair course," she remarked to Andrew, as she took Chelsea's reins and hopped back on board. "Could you put up some jumps for us now, please?"

They made their way back to the collecting ring and, after a brief canter around, they concentrated on the practice jumps. It never took Chelsea long to settle into her rhythm for jumping so Lisa did not start this phase of her warm-up too soon. It was more important that Chelsea was going well on the flat so that she was comfortably loose and supple. Although the mare seemed to have long forgotten about her hocks, Lisa still kept a close watch, running her hands over them before and after she rode, ever alert for any signs of heat or swelling that might indicate a problem.

Seeing the horse before her enter the ring, Lisa took a final practice jump and brought Chelsea back to walk. They made their way to the entrance to the main arena, Lisa checking the tightness of the girth as they went. As usual, Chelsea watched the current competitor intently. Soon it was their turn to canter into the ring. Lisa never tired of hearing the commentator's announcement – "Lisa Graham riding her own Chelsea" – she had dreamed of the experience for so long and would never take it for granted. The bell sounded and they set off towards the first fence, which they cleared comfortably. Now settled in to a steady canter, they cleared each fence with a smooth, flowing stride that allowed them to move effortlessly forward towards the next jump and so on through to the finish.

"Well done to Lisa Graham and Chelsea. Our first clear round of the day." Was that it? Over so soon?

With yet another pat, Lisa dismounted and ran up her stirrups. It was a big class and she estimated that it would take at least another hour before the jump-off – assuming, of course, that there was another clear round! The Braehead contingent arrived in the collecting area with pats for both horse and rider. While Andrew put a light rug over Chelsea's back, they clustered around Lisa, sharing news of their day so far.

"We had a great time. Sue was fourth and I was sixth." Jane, the youngest, was desperate to give their news of the Hunter Pony class.

"Wow! That's fantastic."

Lisa was genuinely pleased, and surprised. Both girls had performed well above expectations as the ponies were young and neither they nor their riders had much showing experience. They had only come to the show because there was space on the lorry and they thought it would be fun and good experience – oh the confidence of youth! Now, not only had they rosettes to show for their efforts, but each also had a voucher to spend on riding or horse equipment.

Walking back to the lorry, Angus and Alison reported on their event. They had thoroughly enjoyed the Novice show-jumping. Angus had one fence down and Alison a double clear but not fast enough to be in ribbons. Neither minded. Their young horses had gone well and had gained another notch of experience. Soon they were all back at the lorry, humans delving into lunch boxes and horses nonchalantly picking at hay nets. Lisa did not eat anything, but stayed on as long as possible so that she could chat to the others and share the excitement of their achievements.

Chelsea was content, resting a hind leg and totally relaxed, one ear pointing to the right listening to the chatter of the familiar voices beside her and the other straight ahead, scanning the activity that surrounded them.

"I wonder if she really is watching the goings-on and if she recognises the other horses. We meet them often enough on the competition circuit. Anyway, the important thing is that she's perfectly happy. That's what matters most."

Lisa would normally have stayed in the collecting ring, waiting to see how many competitors reached the jump-off. But with such a large field, and wanting to share the joys of her companions, she did not regret her decision to use the time to walk Chelsea back to the lorry with the others. But soon it was time to get back to the action.

As the first round was drawing to a close, Andrew removed Chelsea's rug and Lisa put on her own show jacket and hat again. With six clear rounds so far so there would definitely be a jump-off. In case she was drawn early, Lisa began to warm up, slowly and gently, listening out for the draw as she did so. She heard the tannoy announcement – they were fourth in out of eight. Perfect – no great rush. She visualised the jump-off course, bringing to mind the optimum route through the reduced course of five fences. Competitors are never allowed to walk a jump-off course. When it came to their turn, Lisa knew that there were already two double clears but, as neither time was unbeatable, she planned to take it steady and simply go clear at Chelsea's normal pace. That should be sufficient to take the lead and put the pressure on the last four competitors.

"Right, off I go. Wish me luck."

"I do, Lisa. Go for it."

But Andrew was convinced that, together with wise Chelsea, Lisa would not need any luck. He was wrong. And, as a reminder of his presumption, Lady Fortune withdrew her favour. A hundred yards away, in the livestock section of the showground, two sheep escaped from their show ring and, in a panic, sought desperately the refuge of their pen and their companions.

The bell sounded and Lisa completed a gentle arc before urging Chelsea through the timing beam. They cleared the first easily, turned naturally into the second and jumped it smoothly. All was going well as she turned for the third fence, approaching it with steady confidence. Then, nearby, the shouts and a ruffle of movement amongst the large crowd, disturbed by the loose sheep, distracted the mare's concentration momentarily. The fence loomed and she recovered instinctively, concentrating on the obstacle, but not soon enough to clear the fence which she clattered in an ungainly mess of poles. Lisa felt her body fall forward, almost beyond the point of no return, but she grasped the silken mane just in time to prevent a fall, steadied herself back into the saddle, and patted Chelsea's neck.

"Easy, girl. Well done lass."

Back in control, the pair jumped the remaining fences safely, completing the disappointing round on a note of confidence. In the end, they finished with four faults – but with a fast enough time for what would eventually be sixth place. The tannoy blared its sympathy: "What bad luck for Lisa Graham. Those faults are surely not deserved. Everybody, give her a good round of applause."

"That was a nasty moment." A breathless Lisa dismounted. "I was worried there had been some terrible accident. I heard the shouting and could see people running hither and yon out of the corner of my eye. Chelsea was good to keep going and we got it back together again quite well. Another bit of experience, I guess – and I did manage to stay on board!"

"You both did really well, Lisa." Andrew meant every word. He had seen how close a rider could come to disaster and potential injury and his relief at knowing that nobody was hurt was as intense as any pleasure in winning. "Chelsea didn't let you down. Many horses would have refused the fence, or run out, but she was determined to keep going. What guts and trust! AND she was determined to stay under you when she felt you going. Great riding, and what a horse!"

They both patted their friend, forgetting completely the poor placing. Lisa summed it up perfectly.

"Every time Chelsea is put to the test, she never lets me down. A star, a real star. We're even in the ribbons."

After the prize-giving, during which sixth place received the loudest cheer, and an emotional lap of honour, they returned to the lorry. Faithful Dave was still there – on his umpteenth cup of tea, now using it to wash down a massive slab of fruitcake. The news had travelled on ahead and he welcomed Chelsea as a heroine, delighted for them both. Dipping into his Polo-filled pockets, he slipped several treats into her mouth, fussing her all the while. Lisa untacked Chelsea and sponged her off. She was warm from her exertions, and the fright! Lisa put a fresh cooler on the brave mare and offered her a few mouthfuls of water. Then, once she herself had changed, she allowed Chelsea some more to drink. When Chelsea was cool again, Lisa left a full bucket with her so that the mare could slake her thirst, as she wanted. Then, with a final pat, Lisa slipped off leaving her in peace to enjoy a pick of hay. She joined the others supporting the final two Braehead competitors, Ian and Karen, in the Open Class. Both were very experienced riders and each had one eye on qualifying for the annual Festival of Showjumping, scheduled for the next month down in the west of England. The riders were in good form and teased the others.

"Someone has to go home with a red rosette!" Sure enough, Ian did just that; and with Karen second, they had taken the only two qualifying spots on offer for the Festival. Naturally, everybody was thrilled, none more so than the two local heroes who had worked hard over the previous months to bring on their horses. Lisa was delighted, but suddenly became thoughtful as she saw how much it meant to the two ordinary, decent folk. The prospect of a trip south to mingle with the cream of British show-jumping meant everything to them. For the first time, Lisa knew that it was no pipedream to be thinking, for herself, that an achievement of that magnitude was now within her grasp. So, although Ian and Karen's success was now a great excuse to enjoy a few beers in the lorry on the way home, to sing nonsense songs, and to laugh and joke boisterously, Lisa began to plan her own future. In the middle of one celebration, the seeds were being sown for her own challenge – the biggest challenge of her life.

It seemed no time at all before they turned into Braehead. They gently woke Jane, who had fallen fast asleep stretched out on a duvet in the Luton. At just ten years of age, it had been a long eventful day for her but the smile on her sleeping face said it all – and for all of them. Together, they shared the tasks, unloading the horses, removing their travel boots and rugs and settling them for the night. Chelsea's evening meal had been left in a bucket by her box and, as ever, the mare tucked in as if she had spent the day lazing around the field. Lisa quickly sorted out her equipment and was soon ready to leave. She gave Chelsea a final check over and a pat and hug, ready now to make her own way home – tired but happy. But there was just one more thing to do.

"OK, everybody. Before we go, how about a whip round for our driver and number one support man?"

The adults all contributed generously towards Dave's 'thank you' present and the final honour was left to the youngsters to hand over the envelope. Behind their kisses and embarrassed giggles, and the polite laughter of the adults, there was a realisation amongst everybody that theirs was an expensive sport, one in which money was always short. Only the elite enjoyed sponsorship, leaving the ordinary competitors to beg favours and to scrabble around for even the most basic support. Dave was an angel, a quiet, behind the scenes hero, who did so much out of his love of horses and his fellow humans.

"I'm grateful to you all," he murmured, delighted and embarrassed. "Speakin's nae my thing. Believe me, I'm thankful for your gift. It'll be used wisely, but I will use part of it to have a dram or two. Most of all thank you for the friendship that you all give so freely. It's a grand thing."

Chapter 12

The Turning Point

"Wake up, darling James."

Love and gratitude welled up within Harriet. Lightly, with the back of her hand, she stroked the wonderful forehead and watched the eyelids flutter. His nose was burned raw-red; on the side of one nostril, small blisters oozed clear white liquid. She still could not believe that here he was again, alive and well, waking up in their bed and about to share another day of his life with her. In her mind, the previous three days now blurred into a single confused nightmare from which she had awoken minutes before.

"Thank you, God," she prayed silently waiting for James to join her in the joy of normality.

He opened his eyes and saw her tousled beauty, wisps of blonde hair hanging across strong cheekbones. A single strand of hair lay unnoticed, caught between her lips.

"Hello, gorgeous, am I glad to see you."

Now it was his turn to savour the moment, knowing that he had never expected to see his beloved wife again. The previous evening he had collapsed into bed, drugged by exhaustion and a painkiller. Sleep had enveloped him quickly, stealing from him all but a moment to relish the feeling of relief and happiness.

"How do you feel, darling?" The velvet of her cheek rubbed his stubble and then a kiss played across his lips like a butterfly alighting on a frond. "How's the sunburn and blisters?"

"Sore, but that's not important. Let me enjoy this moment for as long as I can. I want it in my memory for ever, a reminder never to take you for granted."

Eventually, they were forced to break the spell. He eased himself gingerly into a seated position and touched a shoulder, chafed raw-red and still seeping blood where a vivid sore had been rubbed open by the straps that had supported Gideon's litter. That was his only injury. However, he moaned with exaggerated self-pity as he felt his aching back smart with the pain of sunburn.

"Wish I didn't have quite such a white body. This is going to peel off and I can't even say that at least I'll have a good tan." Last night's application of Calamine Lotion by Sister Antonia had worn off and he needed another. "Rub some more of that ointment onto my back please, Harri."

Harriet took great care as she spread the cooling salve.

"Neil says take the rest of the week off. You'll need to go back to the clinic anyway to have your shoulder seen to. God, I'm happy to have you back again. The last two days have been the worst in my life."

"I know. It must have been worse for you. At least I knew what was happening." James decided to keep quiet, at least for a while, about his brush with death. He had promised the bandits that he would say nothing about their decision to kill him, nor would he describe the location of their hideout for two more days. That would give them time to disperse to safety. And he intended to honour his promise. He was certain Gideon would too. Even the driver's hatred of the tormentors was not enough to break the undertaking James had made on both their behalves. What James did not fully appreciate was the extent to which Gideon's gratitude was boundless. He could have asked for anything and Gideon would have gone the ends of the earth to provide it. Such was the bond that had developed between these two humans, sharing the certainty of death together.

Azenzio and his mother had argued tirelessly on their behalf. They had been harangued mercilessly, ridiculed for the trust that they were asking for. But slowly a realisation had grown that the amazing story of James and Azenzio's friendship was not only true, but was visible, there before them all, in its intensity. The energy and empathy between the two young men was so powerful in its gentleness that it calmed the whole group. The breakthrough had come when one of the men in the execution squad laid his gun at the feet of his leader.

"These men will not die by my hand. We are not evil. We are not outlaws – it is Amin who has driven us to killing. Let it stop."

A stunned silence had followed. Then, one by one the others had laid their guns symbolically at their leader's feet, not as an act of surrender, but as a token of rejection of his command to execute his prisoners. The bandit leader had then shown his own magnificence.

"So be it. Let us be men again. You, bwana will carry your wounded friend back to the road and I will help you."

Ten days later, James was struggling to keep his attention on the endless columns of figures – yet another monthly measurement was required! Edward appeared at the door.

"Bwana, there is a man to see you."

James groaned. "Oh God, not the police again. How many times do I have to …", but then he saw, beyond Edward's anxious face, a familiar figure supported by crutches. "Azenzio!" James' instinctive pleasure was quickly suppressed. He did not want to compromise his friend's safety. Even good, faithful Edward should not know that one of the bandits was here.

"Come in, Azenzio. Tell me, how are you since we last met? How long has it been, three months, four months? How is your mother? Thank you Edward, I will speak to Azenzio alone. I met him in a duka on the way to Kampala many weeks ago and we spoke together." James felt feeble. His rushed explanation seemed so false, so inadequate, but it was the best he could do.

Edward showed no outward emotion. Only the tiniest smile creased the corner of his mouth.

"It is good, bwana. Azenzio has visited Gideon in the clinic. All is well." The tea boy bowed imperceptibly and slipped quietly back to his photocopying duties.

The men hugged and then shook hands – in the African way.

"It is good to see you, Azenzio, but why? Why have you risked yourself to visit me?"

"It is my mother. When you were released, our leader told us to return, each to our own villages. But we had nowhere to go. My father will not allow her to return. Now I must find work otherwise we shall both starve. I cannot work in the fields. Can you give me work, my friend? I have two strong arms and will learn quickly."

"I must think, Azenzio. You have no education so you cannot do office work, but I owe you my life. Above all, you were my first friend. Whatever I can do will be done. I promise. Where are you staying now? Is your mother with you?"

When James allowed a filthy black cripple and his mother to stay in his house for a week, he incurred the disapproval of his white colleagues. It was just not done. Neil's geniality slipped for the first time.

"Get them out immediately. We are not hostels for every vagrant who passes."

James' brush with death had changed him – into a tougher yet more humane person. This was the moment when that change manifested itself. No longer was he beset with self doubt. He was completely unperturbed by Neil's brusqueness and, right then, he began to make his own decisions, based on a newfound inner certainty. Politely but assertively, a new man spoke.

"I am not concerned with colour. And my home is not a hostel. I have invited a friend, the one person in my entire life who has known me longer than my parents, into my home as my guest." The words were spoken with such calmness that Neil sensed immediately that his young charge was not attempting to be confrontational. James repeated, "It is my home and I choose my guests. Neil, it only seems strange because he's black and filthy. But we've all had guests and nobody's complained in the past. I do recognise that the house is provided to me free, as part of my contract. But, I do request that I be allowed to choose my own guests."

The Scots are amongst the most fair-minded people in the world. Neil had been born in poverty. He remembered the Glasgow tenements in which he had been brought up, with their generous community spirit – a spirit that loved to mock the establishment with a wonderful wry, Glaswegian humour, and a spirit that always ensured that neighbours were cared for. He remembered his mother uncomplainingly offering jam 'pieces' to the bairns next door when their father hit hard times. He remembered her cheerful refusal to accept money from their mother, day after day. "Nae bother, nae bother."

Neil rediscovered his humanity in that moment.

"OK, James. I won't interfere. As long as they are guests and not permanent fixtures, then I'm sure the firm can't object. How long will it be?"

"Actually, you can help there. Harriet wants to ask the old lady to work as our servant. I know most people have houseboys, but we'd like a 'house lady'. So she'll get a room in the shared servants' quarters. Then I was thinking; Azenzio could share his mother's room, and may want to, but isn't there a job in the laboratory that he could have? I guarantee no more trustworthy a person exists. He'll do his absolute best and testing concrete samples doesn't require two legs or much strength. He'll learn quickly. I know it."

Neil sighed. What was it about this gentle young man with whom it was so difficult to be angry?

"Alright, alright. Malcolm does need more lab staff now that the project's in full swing. If you clear it with him I'll be quite happy. Is that all?" The twinkle in his eye showed that the question was made in jest.

"More or less. That does mean, of course, that Azenzio gets his own room in the bachelors' quarters; if he wants, that is?"

"You know it does. Now hop it. Oh by the way, before you go, all this is subject to one condition."

James' elation was short lived. Where was the trick?

"What's that?"

"Just that you and Harriet come and have dinner tonight. I want to hear the story of your longest and best friend."

"You simply won't believe it."

"Don't be so sure. With you, I'd believe anything."

His three-year contract in Uganda was soon at an end. Naturally James was asked to renew it. Arthur Garland knew that he was worth his weight in gold, having received glowing reports from Neil about their impressive young employee. After his escape from the bandits, everyone had expected James to request relief from his office manager's duties, especially the monthly trip to Kampala. They had been wrong – he had simply said, "Lightning never strikes twice and anyway, it's too much fun." So he had continued with his duties as if the incident had never occurred, accepting, for a few months, the presence of an armed policeman in his Landrover. He knew that the hail of bullets that had peppered their vehicle last time would almost certainly kill them all if it happened again. The presence of a guard had been a gesture from Arthur Garland that was simply psychological. In practice, it was an irrelevance – just another life in danger. But, somehow, James knew that the incident would never happen again. And yet, having another person to talk to had added an extra element of interest, even though the conversation had never been free flowing – James knew that he could not speak openly about certain things. One advantage had been that his reputation amongst the regulars at the army checkpoints had now reached heroic proportions and their vehicle was seldom asked to stop. 'The Good' always made sure that the young white bwana received special treatment and saluted him with exaggerated formality.

James rejected the offer of an extended contract.

"It's been three good years, Neil, and I've worked here on several different road building projects under you now. All good fun and with great people. But Harriet and I want to spend some time in the U.K., buy a house and give her a chance to start a career."

He did not say how much he hated the clerical aspects of his job, especially those dreaded monthly measurements. But he had enjoyed the more complex areas of contract administration and his new self-confidence had made him a competent negotiator when dealing with claims. He was liked by all the contractors who knew that his driving force was always 'fairness under the contract' and a ready acceptance that the written word could never cater for every circumstance, particularly in a corrupt country under the heel of an insane dictator.

His contribution to the projects had been powerful, but behind the scenes. What 'Head Office' never realised was the positive effect on efficiency of harmony and trust between traditionally vehement antagonists. Occasionally, belated telexes had come through, via John Hare's office in Kampala, questioning some of his decisions and reminding him of the firm's position as consultants to the Client. Neil had always supported his young star, reminding their remote bosses, "The Client is getting projects delivered on time and at high quality. If the budgets are not always met, ask them to first take a close look at their own house!"

"I understand, James." Neil regretted the loss of his likeable companion but did not want to stand in his way. He'd miss the quiet, supportive presence, his affinity for the locals and ability to make them all feel valued. "We'll all be sad that you're going, but I think Azenzio, Edward and Gideon will feel it the most. I've enjoyed watching the family spirit that you've engendered here with our black staff and I hope that your replacement will be able to keep it going. Changing the subject, it's Burns Night at the end of the month. I'm going to hold a party for the Yugoslavs and show them some typical Scottish tradition. I'll give the address to the Haggis. We've got good old George to play the pipes and give the 'Immortal Memory'. Will you toast the lassies?"

The Burns Night was going well mainly because of their guests – twelve Yugoslavs, selected senior managers from the current contractors' staff who threw themselves into the experience with their typical Balkan liking of a party, loving the ceremony, the gut-wrenching wail of the pipes, and the huge platter of steaming haggis, sliced open ferociously by Neil in mid flow during his address to the 'great chieftain o' the puddin race'. They loved George's wry observations on Burns, famous for his socialist views and for being a man of the people, striking a perfect chord for the guests whose own country's politics, although non-aligned with the Soviet communist bloc, were nonetheless based on Tito's more open brand of state socialism. But most of all, they loved the removal of the barriers between themselves and their British counterparts, made all the more marked by free-flowing whisky. James waited his turn to speak, feeling the familiar butterflies but also eager to play his own part. He stood up.

"Ladies and Gents. Before I start, I want to share with you the result of today's international between Scotland and England at Murrayfield."

There was an immediate hush. Nobody had heard the result of this annual needle fixture between two rival nations – the final whistle had only blown a few hours ago.

"I know our Yugoslav friends do not play rugby so this may not mean a great deal, but I hope they will share with me now a toast to the new holders of the Calcutta Cup. Today, Scotland beat England by twelve points to six. I give you Scotland."

A huge cheer thundered from the table and, to a man, the Yugoslavs rose and applauded vigorously before putting glasses to their lips and swallowing, in a single draught, their glassfuls of whisky.

The tone was set beautifully for a fun-filled speech that caught the essence of Burn's genuine affinity for women. James played it perfectly, finding the appropriate balance between the raunchy coarseness of the poet's lesser-quoted, sometimes censored works, and those genuine love poems that captured the beauty and allure of the gentle sex. To James, this was one of those moments when the bond between humans was palpable and everything flowed with a perfect ease, his audience both enthralled and involved, laughing at the humour and quietly acknowledging James' words as he stood in gratitude and wonder at the gender that always brought so much comfort, gentleness and delight to its menfolk.

"Especially as we work here, in this beautiful, strange, harsh land so far from our own home countries and, for some of us, so far from our loved ones." The witty, laughter-filled speech ended perfectly. The context for the unusually thoughtful ending was exactly right as everyone recognised, in the tough macho world of construction, the value of female support. "I now ask you raise your glasses as, together, we toast the health, wellbeing and continual companionship of our strongest partners in life – the lassies."

The party applauded loudly showing genuine appreciation of the words. Later, once they had all risen from their tables and the dancing had begun, James stood with four Yugoslav engineers, enjoying yet another dram of Neil's cherished Lagavulin malt.

"Strbac, thank you for applauding so strongly when you heard that Scotland had won its rugby match. But can I ask, why? Were you just being polite because this is an evening of Scottish culture? Were you all just joining in the spirit of the party?"

Strbac Slavco was a Bosnian. He looked at his three Yugoslav companions and spoke, suddenly changing mood, his voice reflecting now a deep sadness, loosened by the warmth of the evening's whisky.

"We know there is much rivalry between England and Scotland. We know of it in football, so we understand it is also for your rugby. And we know why it is important for Scottish people to win over their historical enemy. You are a nation that is small and has been controlled by the larger nation. It is your way of expressing your freedom. But you do it on the field of sport. Otherwise you live in peace and friendship with England. And this is where it is different for us. We also are a country of many parts, dominated by the largest group – Serbia. Our leader, Tito, is holding us together – today. One day he will die and there will be fighting, not on the sports fields, but in a war where the defeated will be killed."

James was stunned. Strbac's three compatriots nodded in agreement, their own acceptance of this awful prediction. Ivan Milosevic, the senior engineer added sombrely, "I am Serbian, the largest and strongest group. It is we who are your England. Strbac speaks the truth. We stand beside each other here today, but one day we will be enemies and there will be much killing." Then, with typically enigmatic Balkan perversity, he raised his glass once more. "But today, it is a day for Scottish Land", and the five men touched glasses and tipped their heads backwards, emptying the contents in single gulps.

Ten days later, James and Harriet said their final farewells to all their friends at the office. His head throbbed its constant reminder that last night's party had been a real humdinger. He walked into each office separately and shook hands with good friends and respected colleagues. Everybody reciprocated. Harriet hugged them all – she had been the site darling, pretty, vivacious and great fun, full of typical American openness and generosity of spirit. A little bit of sunshine was leaving Fort Portal.

They left the final office – Neil's.

"I'd come with you to the car, but I think there a few more folk who want to say 'goodbye', so I'll leave you in peace. Once again, thanks for all your efforts and I look forward to hearing all your news."

He gave Harriet a huge hug and waved them off. They walked down the stone steps, into the car park where they saw Gideon buffing the vehicle in readiness for its important passengers. Then they caught sight of the others – all the African staff were waiting at the other end of the car park. Edward had been on lookout. He emerged from his small office.

"Bwana, we wish to say farewell. Please come with me."

He led the pair towards the small group who immediately began to sing. James did not understand the words. It was an ancient tribal chant; sung now in an unfamiliar dialect of Swahili. But he sensed its meaning, closing his eyes and living the song in his imagination, visualising a time long passed when rhythmic, pulsing masculine tones had carried over still evening air, gracefully and slowly across villages, borne only on the lazily swirling blue smoke of open fires:

"Today, this night, a great leader leaves the land of his brothers.
As the winds blow the last smoke from the dying fire,
As the evening sun falls into the earth
And sinks into its place of sleep within the heart of the world,
A brave man starts his own journey to a place that is unknown.
Some call this place Death.
He goes to meet his ancestors.
He goes to prepare the place so that his brothers may follow.
He goes in honour, for he is mighty of spirit."

Tears welled into James' eyes. The song died away but they continued to hum, softly, deeply, continuing to reflect the essence of Africa. Azenzio moved quietly from the group, swinging slowly on his crutches, and stood by his side. They laid their arms on each other's shoulders. Azenzio spoke aloud, "They are saying farewell to a mighty spirit. It is you, my brother James. You leave us now, but we will all meet again one day, in a good place."

"I know. I absorbed every word of the song. I did not know the words, but I understood each one. To me, it was a common language, that of love. Harriet and I want you all to know that our love for you will never die. The vibrations of your song entered every cell of my body and they are now a part of me. I am filled with it and I will use its energy when I think of you every day. That energy will carry across the lands back to your hearts. When you feel it, as you will, remember that my love for you is alive." He heard a sob and looked at Harriet. She was weeping, giving herself entirely to that precious moment. James placed his free arm around her waist and corrected himself: "remember that OUR love for you is alive."

Not surprisingly, it took James a long time to adjust himself to life in Britain. He and Harriet enjoyed their three-month break, visiting Harriet's parents and using their trip to America to take a holiday in the Rockies. But all too soon he was back at work, commuting through the drudgery of traffic and people, masses and masses of people, all in their own worlds, impervious to their fellows, irritated by each other's thoughtlessness, edging and jostling themselves through day after day of uncaring sameness.

James reported to the head of the Contracts Department, Terence Nebworth. They knew each other as Terence had visited Fort Portal on two occasions, to 'put to bed' two particularly difficult projects whose claims had been unresolved. Terence was in his late fifties and of the old school, respectful of authority and now expecting the same respect for himself. On both his visits, James and Harriet had put him up in their spare room and he had been an amenable, if unexciting guest.

"Punctilious and proper, a typical cool Brit", as Harriet said after enduring a week of clipped and humourless good manners. "One day, he'll find something funny about life. I hope I'm there because, actually, he's not such a bad old buffer."

James had laughed. "You'll probably be the cause of that funny moment, Harri. With you, every moment is fruitful territory for a good laugh!"

On his home ground, Terence was even more punctilious!

"Five times worse," James reported gloomily. "How AM I going to cope?"

James was by far the youngest and most junior member of the Department. So he was given the mindless tasks, just as if he was living one permanent flow of monthly certificates, a nightmare of never-ending sameness. After three months he was in despair, but resolved to stick with it, knowing that Harriet was doing well with her own career aspirations, having found work as a geologist with an oil company. Like James, she was based in London, so they had bought a house in Maidenhead. With the millstone of a mortgage around their necks, it was now essential that they both worked. Even after three years with Arthur Garland, James' salary was paltry, a reflection of the engineering industry and of Arthur Garland's paternalistic approach to its employees – "We cannot pay you well but we will look after you; offer you a job for life." How often had he heard those words? Harriet's job was better paid, but she was serving a probation period and had no certainty, as yet, of a long-term career. So, until a clearer picture of their prospects emerged, they accepted the short-term misery, joining the multitude of 'first time' home buyers for whom the initial years were painful as the anchor of financial necessity was dropped into a glutinous sea of drudgery.

One day, Terence ordered the whole Department into his office. Eight senior engineers, most of whom were in their middle years, and James walked meekly in wondering what was about to happen. Terence's face was thunderous.

"Close the door, James." Without any niceties, he moved straight to business. "I've called you all here to make my disappointment clear. Standards have been falling away for some weeks now and I have made a list of issues that I want resolved. Some of these issues apply only to individuals; others are more general. You will recognise who you are as I speak. If you do not do so, listen nonetheless because if these failings are repeated, even if it is your first time, I will regard the warning as having been given. Firstly, on the matter of timesheets, you all know that …"

The harangue continued for twenty minutes as, topic by topic, their boss drew their attention to a multitude of failings and insisted that the issues be 'rectified, not repeated'.

It was a staggering display, reminding James of his humiliation at the hands of Miles Penham. He was sure that not one of the issues could be directed at him, so he watched the faces of his older colleagues, looking for a spark of outrage, waiting for some form of reaction, some indication that, as adults, they were all past the need for such a schoolmasterish reprimand. Was this really the culture of life within the Arthur Garland Partnership? He looked again and his heart sank.

"My God, it is!" The thought chilled him. "It's just like the Japanese. They sell their souls to their masters and accept everything that is thrown at them, happy in the knowledge that they are being faithful to the organisation, looking only to the day when a pension offers them freedom of thought and action."

Terence was summing up and James returned to the present. Nobody other than Terence had spoken since they entered the room, and nobody offered any words as they stood up to leave. So James took it upon himself.

"Terence, I think you've been a little harsh on us. Shouldn't these issues have been raised on an 'as and when' basis, quietly with the individuals concerned. Then it needn't have been so, well, quite so serious. I'm not saying we can't do better but, somehow, I feel quite demoralised. Which I wasn't before I came into the meeting."

Silence crackled through the room.

"Stay behind, James. Thank you, gentlemen. That is all."

"That was bad enough," James reported to Harriet later that evening, "but then he told me that, whilst in Uganda, he regarded me as a maverick, soft on the contractors and not experienced enough to see the larger picture, that I had ground to make up as an 'Arthur Garland team player' and that my father's position as a Partner was being used 'most inappropriately' by me to indulge my whims. It was awful. Is this really how business works in Britain? If so, give me Africa any day."

"The atmosphere there must be pretty toxic if what happened today is normal, James. Why don't you look for another job?"

"There's talk of changes. I think I'll hang in there and see what happens. Apparently the work isn't coming in like it used to in the old days. The primacy of British Consulting Engineers is definitely fading now that all the former colonies are beginning to realise that there's more than one source of expertise in the world. We've just lost another big contract – this time in Lesotho. Looks like the old Motherland has been complacent for too long. The French are the worst at muscling in on our territory. They pinched the Lesotho contract from under John Clarke's nose. They're definitely not so squeamish about bribery either. Looks like the old gentlemanly British days are over. Actually I feel sorry for John. He's a real gent, one of the nicest Partners, and I was enjoying helping him put together the proposal. He'd never stoop to shady dealings, but the French would. They'd eat him for breakfast. In fact, they've just done so."

So James stayed on, and time passed inexorably; years that he would later look back on as wasted, wilderness years. He was neither stimulated nor bored, neither miserable nor happy, neither stressed nor demotivated. He simply coasted, concentrating on his life with Harriet, their home and their families. How easy it was to lose sight of the ball. The early rumours of change were correct in fact, if not in timing so, for the first eighteen months, life at Arthur Garland continued as normal. The first round of redundancies occurred two years after James began his spell in London. Twenty members of staff were made redundant, and for the first time in the firm's history, the perceived certainty of a job for life was shown to be baseless. The same pattern was repeated as time passed.

Britain of the 1980s was changing quickly. Under Margaret Thatcher's new style of Leadership, the free market prevailed and industry, a caged dinosaur, at last felt the breath of deregulation and flexed its muscles, following Thatcher's lead. Michael Edwardes was the first, making the ailing car giant, British Leyland, face up to reality. The coal industry followed shortly afterwards, but only after a bitter strike that was crushed by the relentless certainty of purpose of the politicians and the toughness of the chairman of British Coal, Ian Macgregor. In the face of this changing world, Arthur Garland resisted to the end. The Partners talked of holding to the old values and weathering the storm of competition until the halcyon days of old returned. Instead, they lost further contracts until at last, their overseas work dwindled to almost nothing and they were left with the scraps that were offered by the 'old fashioned' British market.

One day, Mike Brainwood, Garland's youngest Partner and the great hope for the future, announced that changes would be made. The firm had agreed with a major investment company to invite in their expertise in exchange for huge injections of cash. In a written circular to all department heads he stated, "We have six months to carry out their recommendations; thereafter we either survive or face more radical intervention. This is a time of hope and possibilities. Let us grasp the opportunity." The first action was a major restructuring of the various departments, into profit centres that would have to prove their own worth. The Contracts Department was to merge with others into a new division, comprising a total of one hundred and fifty staff, all of whom were called together one Friday afternoon to be informed of the way forward.

The atmosphere was tense in the huge meeting room. Friends and colleagues gathered into small groups, whispering their shared conjectures and fearing the worst even though everybody had been assured that there would be no further layoffs. There had already been several rounds of redundancies so trust had dissolved leaving an air of cynicism that had, in itself, become self-defeating. Their enthusiasm for meeting yet more demands for increased productivity soon dissolved within the same cup of despair. Mike sensed the air of gloom and was determined to 'shake them all out of it'. He strode confidently into the room, which immediately became hushed.

"Good afternoon, ladies and gentlemen. Let me begin by outlining what has been happening in the worldwide civil engineering industry over the past few years ..."

The audience remained politely hushed as they listened to what was, by now, a well-known resume of recent history. But Mike played it cleverly, making an excellent case, absolving the Partners for the firm's misfortune. He described the measures they had taken, including the lay-offs, as 'regrettable but necessary early action, in anticipation of the downward slide in business'. He thus justified the past harsh decisions 'for the benefit of those who now remain' and he set a tone of fear, in the guise of an impressive argument laying blame for it all at the door of external factors.

He now had their attention! Pleased with himself, and satisfied that they were suitably shaken, he continued:

"So what do we do now? Firstly, I want to say that there will be no further lay-offs." He stressed the point and allowed a moment of silence for it to sink in. "The past has been difficult and some excellent people have been forced to go. But no more. I want you all to know that the Partners regard their staff as their greatest asset. The success of the firm is rooted in its people." Mike leaned forward, resting a forearm on the lectern as if he now wanted to share a valuable confidence. "So let me share with you how each one of you can help us to succeed in these difficult times. Before I do, I'd like to explain something of our financing arrangement with FFI. This is the organisation that is going to provide funding to Arthur Garland so that we can return to our former predominant position in the industry. Basically, what they are doing is …"

The funding conditions were presented by Mike in a generally positive light but also in a way that made it quite clear that radical changes were about to take place without any guarantee of success.

"So you see why I say how important our staff is. Without you, without your cooperation and shared determination to increase your productivity to meet the demand of this increasingly competitive world, FFI will withdraw the longer-term investment. That is why we have restructured the various smaller departments into this new division, the CATS – Contracts and Technical Services – Division. This will enable us to monitor more effectively … to ensure that we can identify … to provide a benchmark of performance … ensuring a strategic fit …providing us with a results-driven focus …utilising our core competencies such that best practice …"

The words flowed with impressive authority as Mike painted a picture. In his own mind he described that picture, embellishing it with business jargon – his adoption of FFI's language.

The performance was highly professional showing a man determined to take control and to drive Arthur Garland back into a position of pre-eminence, a position in which rewards would be available for the committed and possibilities were endless. The foreground of the picture, the main focus on the subject, was received by the staff clearly and they could only accept the logic, some even admiring the force and charisma of the speaker. So powerful was the performance. But to each individual in the room, the background to the image was seen through their own perspectives and each person saw a difference, reading his and her own nuances. James saw a backdrop of dark clouds, ominous and foreboding, full of implied consequences, of unanswered questions and of impending storms. The darkest cloud, glowering behind the main picture, was contradiction. If we, the staff, are the firm's most valued assets, then why are we being given what appears to be an ultimatum? Why, if as Mike says we have six months to turn things around, are our futures so clearly being put on the line? Didn't Mike start out by saying that there would be no more redundancies? If he really meant that, then what happens if things do not work out after six months? And is six months really long enough to recover from a steady decline over the years? The questions built in his mind, one leading another, until his head was filled with despair. The black towering cumulus began to fill the picture completely.

"Are there any questions or comments? I value what you all have to offer."

Mike had concluded with exactly the words that so perfectly described James' mind. It was filled with questions and comments.

A hand went up, in the row in front of James.

"Yes, Giles. Please feel free to speak."

Giles Marsden was deputy head of the Contracts department. He was ten years younger than Terence, a shining light within Arthur Garland and a highly ambitious individual. He saw, in the impending restructuring exercise, an opportunity to accelerate his climb to the heights of Partnership. Terence was absent through illness; an attack of angina, stress related, had resulted in his admission to hospital two days earlier. So Giles took it upon himself, as stand-in, to speak on behalf the 'former' Contracts Department. He stressed the word, giving a clear message that new days lay ahead.

"Mike, in Terence's absence, I think I speak for the former Contracts Department, knowing that as of now it is a part of the CATS Division. What you have said gives me great confidence that the Partners are heading in the right direction. It is in uncertain times like these that people look for leadership. Firm leadership. We are all looking for a steady hand at the wheel. In your presentation this afternoon, I saw that. On behalf of those for whom I am currently responsible, may I thank you and say that it is now up to us to repay the confidence that you have placed in us. I would like to suggest that we all show our appreciation in the customary manner." Giles began to applaud and was followed, falteringly, by most people in the room.

"Thank you, Giles. It is that sort of positive 'can do/will do' attitude that will turn the firm around. However, as we still have a few moments, and as I do not wish to ignore the concerns that people may have, let me ask for any more questions or feedback."

Mike beamed at Giles, who sat down glowing with pleasure at the impact he had made, and impervious to the fact that he had given a vote of thanks before the proceedings had ended. In doing so, he had closed the door on many people whose genuine worries and issues might have been aired. Now, with the impression that they were in the minority, and cowed by the importance of the occasion, nobody spoke. An air of fear and embarrassment pervaded the room. Nobody wished to be seen as negative, let alone raise objections. The silence continued to hang heavily.

James felt for everybody whose thoughts, like his own at that moment, were racing with issues and deep concerns. He knew by their faces but he also felt the mood of anxiety in his body, in the same way as he had been able to absorb the love of his African staff and had 'understood' the words of their farewell song. But this time the feeling was of dread and it did not permeate his whole body but sat, leaden and gnawing, deep in the pit of his stomach. The contrast was unimaginable. Then he felt something else – the gentle warmth of Azenzio's arm on his shoulder, his friend's last moment of contact before James had climbed into the Landrover for the journey away from Fort Portal. And he remembered Azenzio's words as he explained the song. "They are saying farewell to a mighty spirit." James was afraid. He feared the future, and he feared the present, particularly ridicule. But he also found courage and the young man with 'the mighty spirit' raised his hand.

"Ah yes, James Anderson – am I right? Please feel free to speak."

"Mr. Brainwood." All Partners were addressed as 'Mister.' by junior members of staff, a custom that had been passed on from a different era. "I do not really have a question but, given that we are moving into new times, I wonder if I could share my thoughts with people here about what it is that would allow me to perform to my full potential." A low murmur of concern rippled across the room. James immediately corrected himself. "Oh, please don't get me wrong. I'm not making demands. Nor do I want to be critical of what has been proposed here today. I'm simply responding to your request for feedback, in a way I think that adds another dimension that could be magnificent." Now the room hushed with interest. That last word had caught people's imagination. Faces now peered intently. Only Mike's eyebrows furrowed with alarm. He sensed they were moving into the unknown and that was dangerous. James continued. He was now committed and his fear dissipated, partly due to fatalism – he had taken the first step – and partly because he still felt a friendly presence, an arm across his shoulders. So, with courage, he spoke the words that had been in his mind for the past hour.

"I wonder what it would be like to work for a firm that I love alongside people that I love."

The stunned silence was broken by a snigger. This precipitated a rush of mirth from a small minority.

"I don't think everybody understands what I mean by 'love'. Will you allow me to explain?"

Giles stood up. He spoke directly to Mike.

"I'm sure James has the best intentions, but as his acting manager, could I apologise for his contribution. It does not deal with the purpose of this meeting which is, as we all know, to see how a restructured organisation can better meet the needs of the future. Perhaps James could raise his ideas, dare I say – his own brand of management – with either myself or Terence, or yourself if you wish Mike, on another occasion. Those of us who have had any responsibility for managing people will be able to give him guidance."

At first James was shocked, conscious of the sharpness of rejection and humiliation. He also felt a deep and painful sadness. But the intensity of these feelings sent a spark through every cell of his body and that spark galvanised healthy, strong, deep-seated memories. Like a wave of peace, an unimaginably beautiful force of goodness washed through him. James knew that it was the love that his African friends had placed there, deep within every cell, and he remembered the simple, decent people that he had once had 'responsibility for managing'. Now he felt a wonderful calmness. James drew upon the strength of their love and, before taking his seat, he replied simply, "If that is what you wish, I'd be more than happy to do so."

He remained in his chair as the meeting closed and the room cleared. He waited, calmly, unperturbed, thinking about his future and knowing that his days at Arthur Garland had come to an end. There was too great a mismatch between their values and his own growing belief that the purpose of work was more than simply a means of earning money. How wonderful it felt to have absolute certainty of purpose, but how important it was too for that certainty to be grounded in love. For it was that oneness with love that ensured that he could not bring himself to be angry nor be concerned that his voice had not been heard and even that he had been humiliated. In fact he felt wonderful, proud that he had shown the courage to let his fellow beings see his authentic self. At last, he truly liked himself. The moment of his greatest humiliation had also been the moment of his highest self-esteem. Without one, the other could never have been experienced.

It was time to move on. "Something will crop up." The thought reflected his inner certainty.

"Hello, there. My name is Andrew Graham. We don't know each other but I'm an Associate. You may have seen me around – my office is on the second floor. It is a great pleasure to meet you James. I admire your father, but I was filled with admiration with what you did this afternoon. Do not feel that your message was lost on everybody. I understand exactly what you were trying to say, as did more people in the room than you may appreciate. I can't stay for long but would you be kind enough to drop into my office on Monday morning for a chat? Oh, and by the way, enjoy the weekend – don't let things get you down. I think that your single contribution today was the most valuable one of the entire meeting. Look forward to seeing you on Monday then. Pop in whenever it's convenient. Cheerio!" As he slipped out of the room, Andrew turned again to James. His smile reflected genuine friendship and encouragement.

"So soon?"

"Come in, come in!"

The cheery welcome lifted James' spirits even higher. Andrew's office reflected the man himself. It was a place into which the sun chose to shine, to offer its cheerfulness and to highlight the world's beauty. James had just left Giles' office. What a contrast! Although it had the same aspect as Andrew's, there the sun had cast fierce crisp shadows, straight lines reflecting each bar of the venetian blinds, each edge of the filing cabinets and the desk surface, piled tidily and symmetrically with contract documents. It was as if the sun preferred to leave space for the shadows, to draw its own hard lines of delineation. But now James saw softer, less stark shadows – the umbrella plant's halos of leaves shimmering on the wall as a gentle breeze wafted through the wide open window, the curtains flapping lazily across a cheerful green carpet and, low in one corner, the fuzzy outline of a dream-catcher reminding James of a human head, dreadlocks hanging loosely downwards and a smile breaking across the circle of its face. Here the sun shone through the objects, becoming a part of them and infusing them with its energy. Here the sun shared the office's space with its friends, the shadows. Here there was wholeness.

"I'm gasping for a cuppa. Let's get ourselves sorted out first. What'll you have?"

Soon, Andrew placed a mug in front of James, who sat on the far side of the desk. The mug, so different from the firm's standard white crockery, was simply inscribed 'Me too!' which momentarily puzzled James. Andrew sat beside him in the second free chair and took a sip from his own mug. On it were the words 'Ouch! I'm Hot Stuff.'

"Right ho, James. Let me do the talking for a moment. As you know, Arthur Garland is going through some major changes, much of it imposed by our friends from FFI. I have been asked by John Clarke – he's the Partner who's going to lead the Finance and Business Development Division – to help make the change as effective as possible. John believes strongly that the staff should genuinely buy into the future, but he knows that many of them are shell shocked by what has happened over the past few years. He knows that this will be no easy challenge. Last week, he asked Mike Brainwood if I could attend his launch of the CATS Division, simply as an observer, to test the atmosphere and to see whether Mike's no-nonsense approach would work for us. As a guest at the meeting, I did not feel it appropriate for me to speak. But believe me, James, I wanted to support you in what you had to say." Andrew paused, looked at James' intent face, and took another sip. "Can I ask you, if you had been allowed to, how would you have elaborated on your comment about loving the people you work for and with?"

James relaxed knowing that for many months he had been desperate to share his views with somebody. Here was his chance. The words flowed easily, even though he had not prepared the speech.

"First of all, can I thank you for your kind support at the end of the meeting? It made my day and, as you pointed out then, my weekend was really enjoyable. I was completely untroubled about my humiliation. Do you know that, before I left the building on Friday, two other people went out of their way to say that they understood what I was trying to say? One of them even apologised for not having the courage to support me in public. Anyway, to answer your question – I think that work should inspire people. Beyond working, their jobs should involve friendship and fun. Being the sort of person I am, I'd even go so far as to say 'love', but I quite understand if that word is too emotive for many people. You've got to make it clear what you mean by 'love' before you use the word too freely. Maybe that's where I went wrong on Friday."

"Then, what is your definition?"

"Love is the absence of fear. Love is what makes people behave in a way that moves their values from a fixation on self to an appreciation of others. Love in the workplace is putting the human spirit above financial performance."

"How would you engender that philosophy within an organisation like ours, AND still be a viable business?"

"To be honest, I don't know. Telling people to change certainly won't do it. Is it something you teach? I don't think so. Sorry, Andrew, you've caught me a bit by surprise here. I need time to think."

"Don't worry. This is an exploration into possibilities. A chance to see if we're on the same wavelength. The answer won't necessarily fall into our laps. I guess success is only ever moulded out of hours of toil. But let me take some of this from your shoulders and share some of my own ideas – an insight for you now into where I am with my thinking. As an Associate here, I feel responsible for what has happened in the past. I know John Clarke does too. So the first things I believe in are integrity and trust. I am trusting you now with my thoughts because I believe in your integrity – not just from Friday. I've heard a little more about you than you may realise. Your old boss, Neil, is a good friend of mine. We joined Arthur Garland as part of the same intake of graduates. Anyway, to continue – as a part of the firm's senior management team, I believe that it is we, the leaders, who are responsible for our demise and things will not be put right simply by asking for more and more from our staff. In fact, it is the other way around. As leaders we should serve. In this time of change within the firm we should be asking our people, as I am doing now with you, 'How may we serve you?' and then we should listen; and I really do mean listen We should not fit what we hear around our own perceptions, but we should be open to everything, even the unpalatable, even what our egos are most hurt by. This is how I propose to manage our own divisional meeting this week. I intend to ask our folk what is it they want of us, so that they feel properly 'enabled' to work magnificently. That is why, when I heard your comment on Friday, I was greatly encouraged. John and I had wondered whether people's answers would be based on materialism – increased pay, guarantees of employment, that sort of thing. Important as these are, they deal with the personality only – the outer shell that houses us as humans. I am convinced, as I suspect you do too, that what really matters is what nourishes the soul."

James warmed to the other's words. He could not help feeling that he'd come home at last. He replied, "I guess it'll be a mixture of both things, materialistic and spiritual, if that's the right word. We can't ignore the fact that people still have mortgages and so, for that matter, does the firm have business debts. You know what I feel – take the chance and go for it. It's what I was asking for on Friday – a chance to add my own dimension."

James paused. He wondered where he fitted into all of this. Without diffidence he asked, "What do want me to do, Andrew? Am I just a sounding board? I want to be more than that."

"Will you work with me, James? Part of my brief is to review the division's training needs and I'd like to ask you to become my assistant. I'd like you not just to work with me putting together a training strategy but to also consider running some of the stuff in-house. You have a presence about you that people like, an easy-going style of communicating. Think about it. I'll make sure you receive any type of training and support that you think you need for yourself to equip you for the job."

"The answer's 'Yes'. It's just the sort of thing I've been wanting to do. I genuinely want to do something that will help others. This could be it."

"OK then, that's wonderful. I'll speak to Giles, or Terence if need be, and ask for their agreement for you to be transferred here. There will be no problems with John Clarke – he saw you in action on the Lesotho proposal and appreciates your qualities. Nor will Mike Brainwood be a problem. If it were all cleared by Wednesday, would you be kind enough to come to John's and my presentation to the new FAB Division. Hope we can live up to the acronym. In any case, I'd like to bounce more ideas off you later today. Can you stay on a wee bit longer this evening? I'd be most appreciative. We'll order in a pizza and work in peace. Clear it with your family. If there are any problems, we'll find some time tomorrow instead."

"Harri! It's me. Something fabulous has happened. I'll be late home tonight, but it's a great reason. Tell you all about it when I get home. I won't need feeding – just prepare something for yourself and be ready to hear my news. Look forward to seeing you later. Love you lots. Bye!"

Answering machines were wonderfully convenient, but James wished he could have shared more of his joy with Harriet in person.

Their evening session went brilliantly. Andrew had already got clearance from the others to transfer James to the FAB Division so they set about, with clear minds, planning for Wednesday's meeting, and beyond. Andrew bounced his ideas for the meeting off James, who was hugely impressed, and encouraged, by the Associate's energy and intelligence.

"Right, James. We won't go in too much with the touch-feely stuff. I like your word 'love' because I know what you mean. However, I'm going to lead into that slowly – call our new approach one of 'Values Centred Leadership'. Out of that will emerge the full spectrum of meanings and issues."

Andrew was equally impressed with James' thoughtfulness and commitment.

"I don't like the idea of being responsible for a 'Training Programme'. It's sounds so dry and, anyway, it has connotations of being programmed with facts and moulded into the clone of somebody else's image of an ideal person. Why not call it the division's 'Opportunity for Personal Growth'? I've got some ideas for in-house sessions, but there's things we'll have to go outside for, for example some people will always want training of the traditional kind. You know, technical skills like project management and computers are big these days; also there's psychometric stuff. I could do that in due course but in the meantime …"

At ten o'clock, they reluctantly called it a day. Then James had the pleasure of rushing home and sharing his joy and excitement with Harriet.

"Hello, folk. Just get comfortable? There's tea and coffee at the back. I'll start in five minutes, so please grab yourself a refreshment whilst I get my head around this overhead projector." Andrew had chosen not to walk dramatically into a room packed with nervous, gossiping and possibly demoralised individuals. Instead he ensured that he was there to greet his new contingent of staff, to make them feel at home and, had it not been for this damned overhead projector, to mix and chat with them.

"I can help, Mr. Graham." A young clerk from the Accounts Department stepped forward, munching a tea biscuit. "It played up for us yesterday when we had our team meeting. All you've got to do is …"

Soon the technology was sorted out. "Thanks, Davie. You're a star."

Andrew saw that the room had nearly filled and there was a babble of excitement, interspersed with a few laughs. He saw James, chatting with John Clarke, and raised a hand to catch his eye.

"Ready to go now, James. Would you mind asking those people at the back to find a seat?"

John Clarke made the introductions. He was a brilliant engineer and a charming gentleman, out of the best of the old school. But he also knew where his weaknesses lay so he had delegated all of the presentational aspects of the divisional launch to Andrew.

"So, without further ado, I'd like to hand over to Andrew Graham, who will be my right hand man in this move into a new and, I'm certain, happy future."

"Thanks, John. Well now, where do I start? Who here has yet to hear of FFI?" No hands were raised and a few people laughed. "Put it another way – who here is sick of hearing about FFI?" A forest of hands shot upwards. "So you've answered my first question. I'll just say that there are serious aspects of their funding of our firm that should not be taken lightly. John and I will deal with questions that are worrying folk in a short while. Meanwhile, can I ask you all another question? Who here doesn't know what you will be doing tomorrow when the new division has been properly launched?"

Again, no hands were raised. "That's fantastic. Can I thank all those managers who have briefed their staff. Next question. Who knows what they will be doing in six months time?" This time there was a collective, silent, intake of breath as interest was caught. No hands were raised. "I'm going to suggest that nor do I know and that, actually, it IS you who knows because, as a result of today, you will be deciding what it is you intend to do with your lives here at Arthur Garland."

Andrew painted a picture of a workplace where people took responsibility for their own destinies, where problems were solved proactively and where individuals mapped out their own career paths and, in conjunction with their managers, turned those maps into living reality.

Soon it was time for open questions. The first one went straight to the point.

"How can we map our own futures when, in six months time we may be out of a job? Only if you can give us any guarantees, Andrew, can we have some element of certainty about drawing our own maps."

"Before I answer that, does anyone else have a question related to it in any way, because we are getting to the heart of the issue here and others may want to make their own comments."

Another hand was raised. "You've already mentioned how much you value us. Can we trust your words when in a few months time we may be out of a job?"

Andrew took a deep breath. "You know, you are quite correct. It must be hard to trust. Let me explain my standpoint on the implied promise of 'jobs for life', which we all know has been broken several times over the past years. You are asking for truth. I have to say – I cannot give that absolute guarantee. But will this do? John and I guarantee that, whilst you are with the FAB Division of Arthur Garland you WILL be valued and we WILL do our best, in conjunction with yourselves, to make you EMPLOYABLE for life. That means that we will invest in you as individuals so that, if the day does come when you are forced to leave us, you will be a marketable human being. This ties in with your own responsibility to map out your own lives. The FAB Division will work with you, will even positively encourage you, to find in yourselves what it is you really want to do with your lives. Then, we will invest in you so that you can make that dream or calling come about. Even, by the way, if that means that you choose, of your own volition, to move on."

"Isn't that being altruistic and therefore naïve? A business has to survive."

"Yes, it is altruistic. It is also naïve if you believe that a business should exist solely to make a profit and that profit making and altruism are mutually exclusive. But what about other reasons for a business to exist? We are all interdependent entities. I affect you. You affect your supermarket with your spending choices. Your supermarket affects its suppliers, its suppliers their suppliers, and so on, down to the very materials that the world provides, and the people who provide them. Change your purchasing habits and you change a human being's life somewhere, or the environment, even the course of history. Look at it another way; maybe a more obvious way. We at Arthur Garland have been involved with nuclear installations, and some people find it hard to balance their employment here with what could be seen as support for an industry that directly threatens the environment. Those people see the interdependency link. My view is the same. It may surprise you to hear this from an Associate but, if I had my way, I would avoid, at all costs, contact with the nuclear industry. Not very good for our profits, but worth it because of interdependency. Think of Chernobyl – it only needs a single mistake, just one. But before we get lost on that track, can I get back to your point? Organisations ARE more than job and money generating entities. They allow us to express ourselves by making our own contributions to life, the country, yes even the environment and, most of all, each other. If you accept that is the case, then can I suggest that we live it by showing true respect for each other? If we can do that, then the issues of profit and job security become shared challenges for which there will be solutions. There will always be solutions."

And suddenly the meeting flowed. Views and questions were aired without rancour as people sought genuinely to fully understand the amazing concept.

"Are you suggesting that we respect each other and is it two-way? In other words, will you also respect us?"

"It is time for the leaders to show their respect of everybody. To show what I mean, I'd like to start by moving on to addressing another question – what can we, John and I, do to help you feel that Arthur Garland is a place that you'd love to work?"

"Guarantee us a job."

"Remember, we guarantee you employability."

"How?"

"We will help you find 'opportunity for personal growth'. It's our new expression for 'training'. Please understand how this ties in better with what I've been saying already. If you identify something that you need to do to make yourself better at your job, more self-confident, happier in yourself, whatever, then take responsibility for making that thing happen by speaking to us and working with us. If it makes you better, or even just happier, I'm sure you'll enjoy working here all the more and we'll all benefit from your improvement."

"You say happier, Andrew. Can I say something; give my own example, of being unhappy? Some time ago, I got a telephone call at work to say that my daughter had passed away – leukaemia. It was sooner than expected and I felt so guilty about not being with her at the end. I needed a place to go whilst I waited an hour for my husband to collect me and take us on to the hospital. There was nowhere to sit in peace and quiet. I could only go the ladies loo and the atmosphere there was crushing. Later, when I began to speak to others about this, many of them had their own stories of sadness. In a company this size, at any one time, there will be several people experiencing deep pain. Can we recognise this somehow, like by providing a quiet room, a sort of sanctuary. Right now, that's how I see respect for others."

"Marita, that's a fantastic suggestion. Thanks for your bravery in speaking up. It's exactly the sort of thing I mean. Can I take a chance here and pick up on your concept of a sanctuary? Shouldn't the whole workplace be a sanctuary? John and I would like to make it so – treat every individual as sacred. If the soul is nourished, won't other things fall into place? Marita, would you volunteer to work with me to find a place, a soulful, peaceful room, one that we can turn into a place of retreat for anybody in pain. Thank you for a specific example."

That was the turning point. A wonderful moment when people genuinely began to understand what Andrew was driving at. His offer to help them be more magnificent and at peace with their employment opened their minds beyond simply a desire for material 'things' into a consideration of more abstract, holistic concepts. Soon the word 'love' was introduced, naturally and in context, such that everyone was completely at ease with its use. Together, as a team in harmony, they discussed issues such as their desire for learning and self-betterment, of bringing 'soul' to the workplace, of the removal of the fear of failure, of how by simply bringing flowers and plants into the office the atmosphere would change and, above all, how once again they could begin to trust each other and the Partners of Arthur Garland.

Andrew allowed the discussion to run its course. At one moment he looked at James' face and saw eyes alight with pleasure, and a smile of contentment that was so serene and full of peace that Andrew was convinced he saw an aura of light surround the young man. He continued to look at James, recognising the catalyst that had caused this amazing event to occur; an event that he had, just one week ago, considered only as a dream and had all but dismissed until he had heard a lone voice standing up and, with such incredible courage in the face of ridicule, putting into words what so many people felt. He continued to look at James, enjoying the glow that enveloped him until inevitably, his new assistant sensed the eyes watching him and looked towards Andrew, who simply winked. James' face shone even more.

"Thank you everyone for your contributions. This has been an incredible moment but also a reminder that we, John and I, have much to do to take forward your ideas, to repay your trust by serving each one of you. I feel humbled and, yes, a little bit awed by the enormity of what lies ahead. But, isn't it going to be a wonderful and interesting journey? It goes without saying that we all need to take responsibility for our own part of that shared journey, and mistakes will be made. But let's acknowledge the mistakes as learning experiences. Let us never allow fear of failure to stultify our efforts. Now, the first concrete thing we can talk about is your 'opportunities for personal growth'. I'd like to ask James to say a few words about where our thinking has reached in that respect. Remember, this is about making each one of us not just 'employable' but also happier with our lives generally. We would not be here this afternoon, doing what we are doing, were it not for James and his courage to speak openly about his vision of what a workplace could be like."

James stood to speak, proud that he had been entrusted with this part of the event. He outlined their plans for investment in human beings, how personal development time would be set aside each year for individuals to identify and follow through whatever form of learning they felt drawn to.

"It may be directly work-related, for example experience of computer software is now a big part of people's jobs. It may be 'you' related, for example some of you may want to go on leadership training, or may wish to work on your 'people' skills beyond simply those required in the workplace. I know I'll want to go on a mixture of things, especially as I'm going to give some of the in-house stuff myself. And here's the amazing bit, credit for which goes to Mr., sorry that is John, Clarke. Some of you may wish to go on vocational training that has nothing to do with Arthur Garland or civil engineering. I know Marita has talked to me of her love of painting. Well, why not discuss this with Andrew or your boss? You identify the course, you research the market and, with you, they will see how it can be made possible – like fitting it in to the work calendar or finding the budget for evening classes, whatever. But, WE have to make it happen. It's not going to be like the old days when you are told what you ought to do in order to progress your career. Obviously a lot of the old stuff will still apply, but think it through for yourself and work together with Arthur Garland."

When James had rounded off his presentation, Andrew added with a wry smile. "I can see how some minds are working. Clearly, some people are thinking, "What if I train to become, let's say for the sake of argument – a farrier, so I can start my own dream business? Will Arthur Garland pay for me to learn something that results in me moving on?" The answer's 'Yes'. How else can we truly say that we are making the workplace a sanctuary for everybody, to work in joy and without fear? If it were your heart's desire to do something else, you would not have been fulfilled here anyway. But if you are happy while you are here, I hope you will perform magnificently, but magnificently through inspiration of self, if that's the right word, rather than as a result of the coercion of others."

The meeting ended with a round of applause. The clapping was not just polite; it was a response from people who genuinely felt appreciated and who wanted to return, with warmth, their own appreciation of the vision that had so wonderfully been laid before them.

Later, in John Clarke's office, Andrew was filled with elation.

"But now it's up to us. There's a long road ahead. Thank goodness for our staff's buy-in. I suspect the objections will come from other quarters. But it's a great road that we've embarked on."

Chapter 13

Towards the Goal

"When you set goals, especially a big one, time seems to move so fast."

Lisa sliced the top off a boiled egg and stuck a finger of toast into the delicious orange-yellow well of soft yolk. Normally, she never had a cooked breakfast but today she would be busy and was not sure when there would be another chance to eat.

"Is that a general observation, or are you building up to something specific?" Andrew knew the answer to his own question; he was just having fun.

"Look outside. It's barely light. The autumn days have shortened and we've hardly noticed the passing of another season. It'll be winter soon and the showjumping competition circuit moves indoors. Indoors again – I just don't believe it."

Lisa was not entirely happy. She was never totally at ease jumping in enclosed areas. It seemed like only yesterday that she had been nervous just cantering indoors, let alone feeling confident enough to jump. Now here she was planning her competition schedule with meticulous determination, all with a view to an ultimate, exciting challenge. This meant working her way through a constant series of showjumping events, even the indoor ones, building up to a level of competition experience that would allow her to mix with the elite.

"When you set a goal, it's amazing what happens. I used to think it was nonsense but now I'm open minded about these things – simply having the intention to do something really does cause circumstances to bring it about."

"As long as the intention is genuine; from the heart."

Andrew's mind went back to a day, years ago, when he had once experienced exactly what Lisa was talking about. He smiled to himself, feelings of pride mixing with affection as he remembered how his own intention, clear of vision but oh, so uncertain of method, had been nudged forward by the courageous words of another person, and how so many lives had been affected by one simple moment – when the 'how' was offered to him simply because the 'what' was so clear in his mind.

"Tell me what you're thinking about."

"As you know, during the summer, I began to realise that Chelsea and I really do have the ability to take a quantum leap forwards. So many things limit people's horizons, but I can pinpoint the very moment when mine broadened in an amazing way. You know what I mean, we've spoken about it often enough. Sitting in that transporter on my way back from the summer show at Balbegie, I saw such joy and pride in the faces of Ian and Karen. They had qualified for the Festival of Showjumping and had moved into the big time. There they were – without sponsorship, unknown, ordinary folk who had used their talents to the full. And I thought of myself, not that far short of them in skill but with that magic extra ingredient – Chelsea, my brilliant mare who is the equal of any other horse. And I had an image of myself as a child, going with Dad to the Royal Highland Show in Edinburgh, an agricultural show just like Balbegie, but the biggest one in Scotland. I've told you all this before."

"Keep going, Lisa. I love hearing these stories."

"Dad had to attend the Highland Show as part of his job. So we spent most of the day looking at the cattle and sheep. But there was always time to watch the showjumping. And that was my highlight. That was where my childhood dreams of being with horses began, some forty years ago. Well, the Highland Show is no more impossible for me than the Festival of Showjumping was for Ian and Karen. And yet I had doubts too. I couldn't help thinking, "No way. The effort required to qualify means total commitment. Where will I find the time? Can we afford all the expense? Am I really so conceited as to think that I, Lisa Graham who only began riding seven years ago, can aspire to that?" But something deep inside me said, "Go for it." So what happens? A few weeks later we hear that in March Braehead is to host next year's Indoor Champions of Scotland AND that one of the classes will be the final winter qualifier for the Highland Show. There, on our doorstep. No expense in travelling. No need to find time and a support team to go away for several days, no need for Chelsea to worry about a strange venue, and so on and so on. And you know the rest, because you're a part of it all. Here we are entering every indoor event we can, building up to the Champions of Scotland, not just because I'd quite like to have a go, but because something out there in the Universe has responded to my dreams and has offered me the 'how'. So now I can't be half-hearted and just dream. I've got a responsibility to make it happen."

"And you will."

Andrew's belief in his wonderful wife was as unshakable as ever.

Normally, Lisa never took the indoor season too seriously and competed only once a month through the winter. "Just to keep Chelsea interested." This year was different as she set about her busy schedule. But one routine never changed. Whenever a competition took place in Braehead, she always allowed Chelsea to warm up on the day with a hack in the woods. Happy to practise in the open countryside, Lisa tolerated, with her usual good nature, the constant teasing from bewildered friends and fellow jumpers. In fact she was surprised at how many show jumpers were apprehensive about hacking, just as she was never entirely happy with the enclosed atmosphere of an indoor arena. In truth, it all made perfect sense – Lisa had learned to ride outside, rather than in a conventional riding school. But now, her dislike of being indoors was diminishing the more she participated and even her 'weather vane on the acceptable' – Madam Chelsea – had begun to accept that, in the end, the fun was in the jumping and she would do it anywhere as long as her wonderful mistress was also involved.

After Christmas, Lisa gave Chelsea a break from competition for a whole month, planning to return to action in February, in time to bring her back to competition fitness for March and the Champions of Scotland – the last indoor show of the season. She never rested Chelsea completely, as many riders did with their mounts, simply because she felt that if Chelsea had too long a lay off, her hocks would stiffen. Equally, she knew that the mare needed a mental break – as she herself did! So instead, she rode Chelsea twice a week in the forest if the conditions were fine; otherwise, if the indoor arena was free, she loose schooled her simply ensuring, at these times, that they were just two best friends enjoying each other's company, with little emphasis on training and discipline.

It was on one of their 'fun-only' forest hacks that Chelsea met her first skier. Hacking in snow had always been a joy for Lisa, a chance to enjoy the muffled atmosphere and the 'clean' feel of pristine whiteness. "But today we discovered a strange new phenomenon." Lisa accepted the glass of whisky from Andrew and paused to savour the first sip before continuing her story. Their pre-dinner drink and chat had become a much-loved tradition, begun many years ago by Andrew's wonderfully hospitable father and continued faithfully since his death, often providing an opportunity to invite his gentle presence into their lives.

"We were taking the route beyond the farm, where the people track runs parallel to the horse track. Suddenly Chelsea stopped for no reason. I couldn't see anything untoward so I nudged her forward. Still she refused to budge! So I looked again – she's never wrong. And sure enough, there WAS somebody coming along the people path. All I could see was his head in the distance. "Come on, Chels" I said, "It's just a person."

"Chelsea was having none of it. "Oh no it's not," she replied, staying put, "It's a Martian." Then I heard a 'shush, shushing' noise and this cross-country skier emerged from the trees, his head and shoulders seeming to glide through the air. No wonder she thought it was a strange creature!"

"As he approached, I called out, 'Good Morning', and he made some normal comment like, "Great day to be out." That was enough to convince Chels that he was human after all and she was happy to move forward again, but seemed bemused by his funny walk. When you think about it, she was right all along – humans don't slide along, they walk. She misses nothing!"

By early February, a wave of excitement was sweeping the yard. The atmosphere was already building and, together with three other Braehead folk, Lisa turned her mind to the qualifier for the Royal Highland Show. They calmed one another's nerves, stressing the 'it's just another event' philosophy. The course would not be any bigger than others that Lisa and Chelsea had tackled. Even so, the format would be imposing, not run of the mill, and the track would be demanding with tricky combinations and accurate strides needed between fences. Lisa learned to welcome the nerves. She was convinced that she would enjoy the challenge and, just as important, so would Chelsea. They had nothing to lose and much to gain – one of the two places on offer at the Highland Show.

"I know I won't be distraught if we don't make it. But I can't get out of my mind the feeling that we will succeed, that this time it is our turn and that the Universe is with us. Chelsea has no fitness problems. Her jumping is peaking. I'm a better rider than I've ever been. And I have this vision of a future history, of us riding a double clear in Edinburgh. It's all so strong."

With these positive thoughts, Lisa brought Chelsea back into full work in the second week of February, a little sooner than she had originally planned; but Chelsea asked her to. The mare had picked up the air of excitement and had begun to fidget, especially in the school when she saw the arrival of newly painted uprights, cross poles and planks, all stacked neatly at one end. So back to work.

They started on fitness. Fortunately the worst of the snow had cleared and they were able to put in plenty of miles on the soft forest tracks. Gradually Lisa increased the schoolwork and then moved on to the serious sessions – jumping. She knew that it would be essential to improve Chelsea's response to requests to extend or shorten her stride between fences, adjusting in time to hit the optimum take-off spot in front of each jump. Chelsea was naturally adept but, with the more challenging courses, they would be faced with a large twisting track and accuracy was essential. Chelsea responded well to the new learning partly because Lisa approached the sessions in her normal unconcerned manner, intent on making the experience fun using lots of grids and small jumps. They also practised at jumping a class ahead of their normal level, and never fussed when fences were knocked down, although Lisa always made sure that they ended on a successful note and that Chelsea's last thoughts were of a smooth and enjoyable jump.

It was good experience for both of them, although Lisa confessed afterwards to Andrew, "I sometimes feel quite sick walking these courses. For the first time ever, I actually feel small as I pace out the strides between larger fences. Up to now, I've always joked that height doesn't bother me – just as long as it is something I could have jumped as an athlete in my student days! But these fences are definitely out of my league – all the more so, at least psychologically, because they're in the confined space of an indoor arena."

"Remember, you're practising beyond the heights you'll be jumping in competition. Everything will seem less daunting, come the day." Andrew continued to be supportive, but this time the words seemed inadequate. He was also beginning to feel the tension and was trying not to show it.

"I'm not the one doing the jumping," he thought ruefully, looking in horror at the seemingly massive fences that Lisa had set herself. "Look after my Lisa, please Chelsea."

Show day dawned and Lisa rose after a sleepless night. With nothing to occupy her mind other than the day ahead, she set off for Braehead bright and early. To help inspire herself, Lisa had bought a tape containing the BBC Showjumping theme tune. It was often used at competitions as the music for the lap of honour, an uplifting way of congratulating the rosette winners as they exited the arena. Humming the tune, Lisa visualised herself on Chelsea completing a perfect round and enjoying the lap of honour! As usual, Andrew decided to follow later – Lisa would phone him from the yard when she had some idea of the schedule and had an indication of when she would be jumping. Raindrops spattered the windscreen, increasing steadily as the journey progressed so, by the time she arrived at the yard, a steady drizzle had set in. Already puddles filled the outside paddock and a few early risers had begun to practise for the first events, churning up the earth into a muddy morass. Lisa knew from experience that, although sodden, it was perfectly safe, if far from ideal.

Half an hour later Lisa emerged with Chelsea, intent on a warm-up session. She turned to enter the paddock, but changed her mind. Why not go for that hack in the woods instead? Why change a routine just because this was the big day? They had plenty of time to do the short loop and Chelsea would find it relaxing, as well as being so much more fun.

"So what if we come back covered in mud? By the time we've popped over a few practice fences, her legs will be filthy anyway."

So they set off around the forest track. Chelsea's early morning stiffness, and her nerves – she had picked up the atmosphere of the occasion immediately – soon disappeared as the pair concentrated on fun. They enjoyed an exhilarating gallop on a short stretch of good going on the way home.

When they reappeared at the yard, the inevitable questions were asked: "Have you changed your plans? Is all well?"

"No, and yes, we're fine," smiled Lisa. "Just thought the woods would be better for warming up than the paddock."

Not for the first time did a few of the more traditional Braehead riders laugh at Lisa, but these days, they all knew about her quirks and everybody admired her willingness to follow her instincts without being concerned about image. Some even secretly wished that they were less hidebound by their own straightjackets of conventional horse wisdom. It can be so hard to change a mindset, especially after years of fixed beliefs. Yet nobody could deny that Lisa had worked her own brand of caring magic with Chelsea and the results could not be questioned. "Each to their own," Lisa responded cheerfully to the good-natured jibes.

Lisa proceeded to give Chelsea a final brush over.

"You never need much to look beautiful, do you? Totally, for sure, you don't need a manicure."

She groomed herself too and changed into her show jacket and long boots. Then she strode purposefully to the indoor arena to check progress. Her timing was perfect, declarations for her class were being taken and the course would be ready for walking in a few moments. Some fifty entries were expected and Lisa opted to go tenth. That would give her time to warm up again, this time conventionally with some practice jumps. Lisa walked the course thoughtfully. The competition was in two concurrent phases. The first six fences comprised Phase 1. If these were jumped without any faults, the rider proceeded immediately to Phase 2 – five more fences but this time against the clock. It was a sensible format that avoided the need for long waits by those horses who had won through to a jump-off.

With so many jumps, the indoor arena looked more cluttered than it had ever been. Lisa walked round carefully, planning her route in the normal way. At times like these, she liked to remember Sally, now living in Canada, whose advice had always been given so freely.

"I wouldn't be here now if it wasn't for you, Sally. Wish me luck." Feeling a build-up of nerves, almost a near panic, Lisa took a deep breath. "Remember, you're doing this for fun. Just relax and enjoy it. If you're calm, Chelsea will be fine too." But she was not entirely convinced and it was nice to think that Sally was with her in spirit, right now aware of the moment. Her e-mailed message of encouragement, 'I'll be thinking of you all day', was the final thing Lisa had read before going to bed last night. Her thoughts ran on, speaking silently to her own alter ego. "At least it's a soft landing in here, if you fall off. Hey, cut it out. Sideline those negative thoughts. You're being daft today. It's only fun. Remember – your original ambition with Chelsea was just to hack her out by yourself. You've come a long way beyond that." The smile returned to her face as she walked out of the arena. "That's better."

"Hi there, you look happy." Andrew had arrived at last.

Lisa realised that indeed she was.

"Hi! Yes, I am. Nice to have your support too. That helps a lot. Walk back with me and I'll fill you in on what's been happening and also, what I'd like you to do. We're going tenth and …"

They arrived back at the boxes to find Chelsea waiting contentedly – a picture of relaxation as she dozed amid a flurry of activity. What a difference to the old days!

"Time to go, Chels."

Lisa stroked the powerful neck and gently allowed the mare to wake up. Chelsea's ears pricked as soon as she saw Lisa's jacket. "Almost as if she'd forgotten about the show and has just remembered."

Andrew led her into the paddock and helped Lisa to mount – an easy swing up to the saddle. The rain was now pouring down and a biting wind had started to gust across the open expanse of the paddock. Lisa was glad that she had put on a warm winter Musto over her show jacket. Andrew stood to one side, happy just to watch and offer supportive chatter. There were several helpers standing inside the paddock, ready to make adjustments to the fences for Lisa.

She began with a brisk warm up on the flat. Then she jumped over a smallish cross pole to let Chelsea get her eye in. And gradually she progressed in height. With a fluent rhythm established, they once again cleared the cross pole and, for the first time, continued on to the second practice fence – a bigger spread. Chelsea cantered in confidently but was faced with a large puddle that had developed over her chosen take-off point. As she dipped her head in preparation for the jump, her front feet exploded through the surface of the puddle, throwing up a cascade of muddy water into her face, and Lisa's. Her eyes closed instinctively against the water and she was forced take off blind, only recognising at the height of the leap that the fence was a spread. Again, her instincts cut in and she paddled her front feet to clear both bars. She caught the back bar with her hind legs. Somehow she managed to stay on her feet and, even more miraculously, Lisa stayed on board. Chelsea surged away from the jump, but Lisa quickly slowed her and, as soon as she had regained her balance and brought Chelsea under control, she patted the mare's neck reassuringly.

"Brave girl. You looked after both of us then. Let's have another go."

The fence was quickly rebuilt and they circled back round to it. Honest horse that she was, Chelsea adjusted her stride to miss the puddle and cleared the jump perfectly with not a moment's hesitation. Lisa decided to leave it at that and walked Chelsea around a couple of times until she heard her number being called: "Fifty-five to the door. Sixty-one stand by." She was fifty-five.

Accompanied by Andrew, she walked the short distance to the large sliding door of the indoor arena. The dreadful conditions persisted with rain driving ferociously at the metal walls of the building, strumming cold fingers at the noisy surface. The officials were sympathetic, recognising how miserable it was to wait outside so, rather than make competitors stand in the rain, they allowed the competitor who was next in line to wait just inside the door behind a gateway into the competition ring. It was a small space, claustrophobic and cluttered with officials and those associated with the active competitor, so Lisa was unsure whether she should accept the offer, eventually deciding that it was the better option. At least she was out of the rain.

The decision was correct because Chelsea was unperturbed by the cramped space and milling bodies. In fact, Lisa could not resist a smile – there she stood, tall and square, totally composed. Not for the first time did she remind Lisa of images of athletes preparing to compete, like Linford Christie focusing down his lane at the start of the 100 metres. Learning from Chelsea, Lisa remembered her own athletics days and composed herself for the round to come.

They did not have long to wait. The horse in the ring knocked down the fourth fence and was thus unable to proceed to Phase 2. The gate into the arena opened and Chelsea walked in, passing the outgoing contestant before breaking into a canter in an immediate response to Lisa's light nudge. Then time took on a new dimension and everything happened in a blur of instinctive, half-remembered activity like a dream that almost makes sense at the time, but in retrospect is impossible to piece together. The bell sounded almost immediately and they circled round to the first fence. This they must have cleared because there was the next fence, then the next and then the next. Later they would see from the replay on Andrew's video that they had flown round all six fences effortlessly.

Lisa had to admit, "To me, it was all a blur, but a blur of perfection, if that makes sense. I knew we were clear and just swept straight on to Phase 2." They broke the beam to start the clock for the timed phase. "Somehow Chelsea realised that we were now against the clock because she upped the pace." Then even Lisa held her breath as they sailed over the fences, turning in the air to save precious fractions of a second. They galloped through the finish and Lisa had to complete a couple of small circles to bring Chelsea back under control before they could leave the arena. "I can remember that bit; oh yes, and also the commentator's voice."

"Well done to Lisa Graham and Chelsea. They go into the lead easily with that very fast clear round in 35.6 seconds." An explosion of applause burst from the spectator stand. Every single stable girl had stopped work to watch their home-grown heroine, not just because she was from Braehead, but because she was liked and loved for her gentle, considerate way with them all. A small flood of spectators poured from the building to be with Lisa and to offer congratulations in driving rain. Lisa patted Chelsea again and again as they walked out into the grim weather. She dismounted and turned to find Andrew.

"That was awesome" He hugged Lisa with one arm and patted Chelsea's neck with his free hand. "Whatever the final result, you can be proud of yourself today. By God, that's going to be hard to beat. I reckon you've done it."

"Chelsea was the star. She just took over."

Lisa was not showing false modesty. She genuinely felt that she had simply been a passenger. Then Karen emerged from the small gaggle of well-wishers. She was perhaps the most accomplished rider at Braehead, having competed in most of Scotland's main events. Karen, whose critical tongue could lash remorseless home truths at the unwary, spoke with such intense feeling that everybody hushed.

"Not from what I saw, Lisa. You were in perfect harmony together. Today, you and Chelsea were as one. That's why it seemed effortless. You didn't have to think what to do, and she didn't have to respond to your prompts. Your thoughts and her responses to them were merged. I've never seen it quite like that before – a moment to savour."

Karen's words were spoken with an air of reverence that stayed comfortingly with them as they took Chelsea back to her box. No more excited chatter, just absolute contentment and peace.

It was one of the joys of competing at home that Chelsea could relax in her own box between classes. At least today the jumping was all over in one session – no separate jump-off. Lisa would just need to ride Chelsea once more, for the prize-giving if her time was good enough for a place.

"But let's not get carried away. The competition has a long way to go yet."

They untacked the elegant mare, covered her with a rug and left her contentedly munching hay. Then Lisa and Andrew went to watch the rest of the class.

Lisa's fast clear had certainly upped the pace, especially with the Highland Show qualifier places at stake. More than 30 horses had competed before there was another double clear but the time was much slower than Chelsea's.

"Are people starting to go for a careful clear, just to get second place?" Lisa wondered. She was convinced that hacking out in the woods to warm up had made the difference. Chelsea had been completely loose, relaxed and going so well when she came to jump – so essential on this twisty course. "All those other horses have struggled to prepare properly in the paddock, especially after travelling to get here. Our near miss in the puddle probably helped too, sharpening Chelsea's senses. Another nudge from the Universe?" Lisa smiled again as thoughts played through her happy mind. She chuckled inwardly at Chelsea's bemused expression when she gently rubbed the mud off her face. "Both of us must have looked a sight jumping with mud spattered faces – as if we'd just come back from a day's hunting! It wasn't as if we'd done it on the hack either."

The next hour seemed interminable. In the end, Lisa could bear it no longer and wandered off to talk to Chelsea and even make a start on tidying up all the show paraphernalia. She came back into the arena and sat once again beside Andrew.

"You're definitely in the ribbons," he reported. "Only four to go and you're still in the lead. Better get tacked up again for the prize giving."

Lisa's heart pounded with excitement and she slipped away again to get Chelsea ready.

"It's just a prize giving, Chelsea. Just remember, behave on the lap of honour. It's not a race and it's not good form to try to overtake everyone ahead of you – you mischief."

Chelsea raised her head imperiously. "What do you mean overtake? I won't have to do that if I'm first anyway." Her haughty style oozed outrage at Lisa's inference. Lisa mounted up and walked quietly down to the door just as the last horse came out.

"Well done, Lisa!" The congratulations kept coming, and they were heartfelt. Everybody, even her closest rivals thrilled to the achievement. Lisa looked up and saw the small group of riders, those whom she had pipped for first place, all smiling their congratulations as confirmation came through on the tannoy. She had won – and qualified for the Highland Show. Proudly, the winning pair, Chelsea and Lisa, led the placed riders into the arena for the prize giving.

The dream continued, this time in slow motion as Lisa felt tears waiting to flow from brimming wells, breaking into tiny runnels of delight as she heard the wonderful announcement "Congratulations to our worthy winners today – Lisa Graham and her own Chelsea. We wish them all the best at the Highland Show." Lisa managed to compose herself enough to thank the sponsor presenting the prize and then receive the rosette on behalf of Chelsea who still looked appalled whenever anybody tried to pin one on her bridle. She had learned a lot, but this was one thing she refused to accept! A flutter of good-natured laughter bubbled from those within the crowd who knew Chelsea, followed by an extended period of heartfelt applause. When all the prizes had been presented, Lisa waited for the commentator. "Congratulations again to our winner. And now Lisa, if you would like to lead everybody away on the lap of honour."

The BBC theme tune sounded its buoyant accolade and, with eyes misting once again, she turned Chelsea who needed no prompting. The star mare cantered joyfully away around the arena in the certain knowledge that every bit of applause was dedicated to her alone.

"Of course. And notice, Mum, there's nobody for us to overtake. I told you so."

The Aberdeen Press & Journal – Monday 10th March
Mitchell's Diary

Braehead Beauty Bound for Ingliston

She came from nowhere and captured the hearts of each one of us. Spectators and competitors thrilled to the occasion. Tears were shed – tears of joy – in a wonderful moment of sporting drama, when an unknown chestnut beauty called Chelsea, ridden by owner Lisa Graham, emerged from a strong field and swept to victory in the Star Alliance Insurance qualifier for the Royal Highland Show. Braehead, hosts to this year's Champions of Scotland, has produced its own homegrown winner in this new Open Class qualifier event.

Who has heard of Chelsea? Who has heard of Lisa Graham? Few of us had before that glorious moment on Saturday when a fairy tale came true for a unique partnership. Together, they proved that here, at last, there is a sport in which committed amateurs can compete with the best, and prevail. It does not happen often so let us all enjoy the moment when it does. Chelsea, an Irish Draught Thoroughbred cross, is the equestrian equivalent of Paula Radcliffe. Her striking good looks and sassy traits are unmistakable. She simply oozes character. By just walking into the show ring she was a conversation-stopper. And then she performed! Gutsy confidence and athleticism combined to perfection. Where has this nugget been all this time? And therein lies a story. Lisa Graham has the answer.

Six years ago, this remarkable woman purchased a "petulant, infirm creature" and single-mindedly nurtured it through a ghastly mix of injury and arthritis to produce what we have today – equine magnificence. In that time, Lisa has also taken herself from novice rider to competent showjumper. Her modesty at this personal achievement is staggering. "Qualifying for the Royal Highland Show is a dream come true. When you really love a creature, like I do Chelsea, and you have a childhood dream, like I have, anything is possible. But it needs something special and I have been very, very lucky that Chelsea came into my life."

It was no luck, Lisa. The good wishes of the whole of the North East will follow your progress in Edinburgh. Let us all pray that your amazing example will be the catalyst for many more childhood dreams.

The Aberdeen Press & Journal – Friday 14th March
Late News Bulletin

Ingliston hopes dashed for Lisa

Star Alliance Insurance is no longer able to fulfil its sponsorship obligations at this year's Royal Highland Show. The company that has sponsored each one of this year's ten qualifying events for the Star Alliance Open Final at Ingliston has had to withdraw its support. A spokesman for the ailing Insurance giant admits that this is a body blow for all qualifiers and comments, "This is a policy decision that we deeply regret. By giving so much notice, we hope that a new sponsor will emerge." The thirty disappointed qualifiers, including North East's Lisa Graham, must now hope for a miracle.

Chapter 14

Living the Values

Marita's Story

Andrew smiled as he spoke.

"What we have to do, James, is to make the workplace beautiful for everybody in the FAB Division. Marita gave a clue to that yesterday, but I'd like to take it further. Would you work with her, as your very first assignment, to find a room that we can turn into a sanctuary? Somewhere where people can go to find peace and recharge themselves. But let's also ask Marita if she'd be prepared to work with us to find a way to make the entire workplace one in which there is space for everybody's soul."

"Have you any ideas which rooms we could use?"

James had already thought about this and was completely stumped. The only free rooms he could identify were the dark, windowless 'cupboard' like boxes in the centre of Arthur Garland House; the rooms that nobody wanted and that tended to act as temporary accommodation for Engineers visiting head office from their construction sites. At least these transient visitors did not mind their stark functionality. But they were soul-less cells, denied the energising beauty of sunshine and fresh air.

"Use my office, James. In the divisional restructuring, there is bound to be some shuffling about of offices. Let's get in first and set the tone of our intent to be serious about this."

Ten days later, James and Marita sat in a transformed room. Andrew's office thanked them for their efforts, by continuing to hold the former occupant's own energy, so now the two humans felt an inheritance of natural buoyant joy. They had built on that, using plants, comfortable chairs, calming pictures, and a water feature that gently joined with the sanctity of silence by adding its own unobtrusive tinkling purity. At one end of the room was a small table, decorated with yellow and blue flowers – today carnations mingled their cheerful sunny heads with the more serious sombre irises. On the table were gifts from the staff, pebbles picked from beaches, feathers from plain and exotic birds, cards with inspiring words, and candles waiting to be lit. Around the room, on carefully positioned shelves, more candles were scattered about so that the room could always be transformed into a different, cosier world on cold, dark evenings and early mornings. The floor was littered with cushions and a bowl of shiny green apples and bright yellow bananas sat on a table beside the door.

"Tell me your story, Marita; if you feel like doing so, that is."

James smiled with affection at Marita who sat on the soft, carpeted floor, her plump body curled into a ball as she hugged her knees with delight; until her faced clouded and the essence of joy was lost in painful memories.

"Grace fought leukaemia for six years; she was the bravest, most beautiful and gentlest of all people."

Immediately tears misted Marita's black eyes. As the story unfolded, the salty wells overflowed and crystals of emotion rolled down olive cheeks. Then the sunlight reflected a teardrop and James felt the presence of God, bringing Grace back into the room to share her mother's words. The three of them sat, as one, and he heard about a fourteen-year-old shining beauty, whose only calling in life had been to become a nurse, and whose loving generosity would have attracted any number of boyfriends. She would have broken many teenage hearts but the onset of cancer had prevented her from sharing adolescence with others; instead hers was the heart that was broken – by all the injustices and suffering that she witnessed in the world.

After the first bouts of treatment, she sensed, even in the face of so much love and encouragement, that her time in this life would be short. So she volunteered that time to any cause that wrung her heart, which meant any cause at all that helped her fellow creatures. She worked with animals, in children's hospitals, hands-on help and also fundraising, even organising protests and demonstrations against the iniquities of the world. And always, she worked from a basis of love of her fellows. There was simply no other agenda. On several occasions she returned home from her forays against suffering, tears of compassion, or anger, or dismay accompanying her own accounts of the day. She managed all this, whilst still achieving her ambition to become a nurse, and she had qualified just weeks before the final return of the disease.

"We all expected another long battle."

Marita wept openly, yet the room was suffused with so much love that she felt strong and spoke with few interruptions, occasionally only blowing into tissues and wiping tearful eyes, but otherwise cleansing herself in the memories and feeling a huge release of turmoil.

"I seemed to live in two worlds. In one, I'd visit her in hospital and the compassion of the staff was like a strong arm holding me up and keeping me going, cheerful and attentive, so I could in turn support Grace. Then I'd come to work and the arm would change into a fist, pounding me more and more, a relentless demand on my time, crushing my ability to perform. I remember asking if I could be excused from presentations in Manchester, but was told I was too invaluable. I remember Mr. Boardman's words to this day. "We all have personal problems, but we must not let them affect our efforts at work, especially in these difficult times. The firm's survival must come first." Can you believe it, James?"

"Yes, I can."

"So I went with Mr. Boardman to Manchester. When it was clear that we had failed to satisfy the client, he became so aloof and cold. I felt compelled to cancel my leave in the week that followed, so we could put right 'the inadequacies of your initial calculations', as he put it. That was the week that Grace died. I would never have agreed to cancel my leave. I was so certain she had a few months still to go. But it just happened one morning. Grace simply faded away. Thank God it was in peace and free of pain. But it was without me. Oh God, James. I wasn't there to hold her hand at the very end, or hear her last words."

This time Marita's shoulders shuddered with uncontained grief.

"What were her last words? The last time you saw her."

"I love you, Mummy. I've been so lucky having you and Dad."

Marita choked into silence. Somehow she managed to speak the words with the same intensity as she'd heard them all those weeks ago. Grace was there to help, and God cupped his hands around them all.

"Then those were her last conscious thoughts too, Marita."

A gentle zephyr brushed the curtain and caressed Marita's cheek. Touched by grace, Marita looked up and smiled at James. Her face shone with beauty and, for the first time since her daughter's death, the joy of certainty and release burst forth.

"I know. At last, I know."

Perfect silence enveloped them. Then Marita continued.

"I'm staying on James. Nobody knows this, but I have been offered a wonderful opportunity with Slough Borough Council. Nothing to do with engineering but it's what I've always really wanted to do – the personnel side of things. But no, I'm going to stay on here. That meeting we all attended, plus what's followed, has swung it. I'm still going to change tack completely, but I'll stay on and use Arthur Garland's offer of training to become HR Manager here. I know I can do it just as well as anybody."

"So do I, Marita. Go for it."

Five years later Marita achieved her ambition and became a respected and loved Human Beings Manager – her own title. "They're not resources, they're souls." She introduced her own philosophy and programme of events, eventually making them company wide, not simply limited to the FAB Division's activities. Inevitably, she worked hand in hand with James who was encouraged at every turn to continue with his 'opportunities for personal growth' strategy.

In the years that followed, Marita changed the lives of hundreds of employees, always for the better, simply because she never faltered from what drove her.

"The soul flourishes in beauty. In beautiful places, human performance is transformed. I want to create a sanctuary within the workplace where grace underpins performance. That way each and every person will integrate with everyone else, and that includes our clients."

Oliver's Story

Oliver asked to see James one year after the divisional restructure.

"Hi there, James." I want to join your in-house training team. Can you get me the hell out of CATS?"

"Whoa there. Start from the beginning. But first off, I'd love it if you referred to us as the 'Growth' team, not the 'Training' team."

"Right ho! OK, then – here goes."

And Oliver launched into his story.

"I'm a natural extrovert, James. Sometimes it gets me into trouble, but often people say they like it. Lightens the atmosphere and all that. So what's my job? I'm a blinking CAD operator, tucked away in a corner and expected to churn out designs. But it drives me crazy. Also, I'm bloody bright. Don't get me wrong – not a big head – just a guy who always sees things quickly. So this CAD stuff is a piece of piss. I'm bored already. But some of the guys are hopeless at it, so I thought that, if I find it so easy and I'm bored, and they find it so difficult and are not productive, why not put two and two together? So, off I go to see our lord and master – Mr. Mike effing Braindead – and I put it to him. What does he say? Just that he's already invested once in everybody's training and it's up to them now to make it happen. And anyway, he wants me to stick to the design stuff because I'm so productive at it. So I've worked myself deeper into a mire of boredom. That's what I call it – mire. Just because I'm good at it means I'm stuck in it. But it's driving me crazy, and I want out."

Oliver paused briefly, but was ready to surge on. James laughed.

"When exactly are you going to take a breath? To be serious – just a couple of things. First, I know you don't really mean it, but Mr. Brainwood is not 'effing Brain dead'. Secondly, we in FAB are not in competition with

CATS. It doesn't do anybody any good to play one off against the other. OK, we've got different approaches, but each should be given a chance. Remember, the survival of EVERYBODY at Arthur Garland depends on it. However, if you really do want to change your career, and become a coach with us, you can do so if you go about it in the right way. And be open about what you want – I can see that's not a problem! Nobody will argue if they know you want to move on for good positive reasons. So, what is it you'd love to do?"

"Computer software training; sorry – growthing."

Both men laughed at the invented word.

"Just call it coaching."

"Sure! Well, it doesn't seem to matter what application it is, I always seem able to pick it up no bother."

"Will that make you good at helping other people to pick it up?"

"People do say so. I'm helping them all the time at work, whatever Mr. Brainwood says. They all feel that the company we employ to train us in CAD is useless. All the trainers just spout out the facts and give us odd exercises. Fine for me, but not for everybody. Lots of folk say I'm able to explain it without making them feel silly. So, I guess I've got something I can offer."

"I guess you have. Let's examine this in more detail..."

A month later Oliver joined the Growth team and, not long afterwards, helped them win their first 'external' business – the software training of all staff, including those from CATS as well as FAB. Within the year, Mike Brainwood congratulated John Clarke on his 'inventive' approach to staff development. Mike's motives had been driven by the financial argument. He was getting his staff 'trained up at a better price that we did before'. Nonetheless a mood of cooperation began to dilute his long-standing antagonism and he stopped making derogatory references to the "touchy-feely" division.

"It's a start, James." Andrew was forever appreciative. "Well done for helping to break down the barriers. It's just a shame Mike could only bring himself to speak to John. I'd have loved it if he'd said well done to you personally."

The Opportunities for Growth team had found a new star. James was quick to thank Oliver.

"Well done! Your style goes down really well with everyone. It's as if your workshops are a celebration of laughter and fun. And you know what most people are saying? You've removed fear from the learning experience. Nobody is afraid of looking foolish any more, especially now that we've done away with the exam element from the CAD training. Mike Brainwood has agreed to apply a continuous assessment basis from now on, so that the slower learners can take their time, and a lot of them are starting to take responsibility for their own levels of competency. Your style has given them all a passion again. Learning and work have become fun."

"And for me. I love the banter of a coaching session, especially when we apply real-life scenarios in the workshops. Sometimes, the group as a whole comes up with fantastic suggestions for using the product. I've learned to keep quiet when that happens, to curb my chatterbox instincts. And guess what? I never stop learning too, so I can pass on the benefits to later workshops. It's just one continuous cycle of fun and spontaneity. I love my work now."

Andrew's Story

The first six-monthly meeting between the Partners and FFI was due the following week. Arthur Garland's second tranche of funding was in the balance. John Clarke was as quiet and as studious as ever. His friendship was never ostentatious, but it was solid and unwavering. As it was now as he spoke to Andrew.

"Our jobs are definitely on the line here. There is a lot of murmuring going on at the moment, not least from FFI who are anxious about the figures. Our first six months are up and all we can report is an increase in morale – not necessarily the stuff of investors." As ever, John's dry humour defused the words of any ominous undertones. "Mike Brainwood has met all his financial targets whilst we've overspent all our budgets and have not brought in the requisite income. Even so, Andrew, I am delighted with the way things are going. Really delighted."

"Thank you. Six months is far too short, as we both know. I never set much store on this first milestone, and I'm convinced that FFI will realise the same. What they want to see, before immediate and miraculous figures come in, is a solid basis of change. We can offer them that. But I am worried about one thing. The two divisions are just that – divided. FFI will not want to see that next week, although they surely can't help noticing it for themselves 'on the ground' as it were. What we mustn't do is be goaded into throwing childish barbs back at Mike, even if he goes down that route. Can we trust him to take a respectful approach?"

"Time will tell, Andrew. I've made my views plain to him so we must trust to common sense."

The meeting with FFI began with short presentations by the two divisional Partners. John led, stressing the work that had been done over the past six months, laying the ground for a recovery of morale through their philosophy of service to staff.

"I am certain that we have achieved what we set out to do, but we do need time. If it is financial considerations only that you are concerned with, I am happy to report that the haemorrhage has been stopped and that all the signs are that we are starting to move in the right direction. However, we are convinced now that, with the staff all finding their confidence once more, and with investment in their skills and attitudes, the returns that you are seeking over the next two years will not be impossible." John ended on an uncharacteristically optimistic note. "In fact, they are entirely possible and will be achieved." And he meant it.

Mike followed. "In a similar vein to John, I'm delighted to report that we are moving in the right direction. And, may I stress, we are ALREADY moving in the right direction. We have introduced changes in work practice throughout the division. From top to bottom there is a realisation, if not yet wholehearted support, for the concept that efficiency and professionalism underpin our work now. We provide for our clients' needs and, above everything, our business is focused on the generation of income. This is born out by the figures, which you will see ..."

Leonard Feitleson was delighted with both presentations. But he was a shrewd financier and years of experience had honed his instincts.

"Money's the name and money's my game" was his favourite byword. "It looks good gentlemen, but I have questions, naturally. John, clearly you are taking longer to show improvements within your division. How much longer do you mean by more time being needed. Clearly time and money are one and the same here."

John had expected the inevitable and responded honestly.

"Two years should see us through to a healthy, bottom line, profitability. We'll be holding our own within the year however. As you can see from the projections."

He was interrupted. "Tell me why further investment, and that means FFI money, in your staff is still being sought, and why Mike is already able to proceed into the next six months without being forced to make the same request?"

Mike smirked at Andrew who knew that this was a challenge – the moment for him to make a contribution. After all, much of what was happening within FAB was his own vision.

"Can I answer that one, John? At the moment, ALL the staff know that salaries have to be frozen, irrespective of which division they work in. We are in a type of honeymoon period where people are prepared to pull together, more or less because there is no option. But if we use this period to squeeze what we can out of them, to use fear as a driving force, we will lose their trust in the longer term. And the long term looks much brighter for our industry. We have weathered the oil crisis."

Andrew then took a chance. "But there is more to it than that. People come to work each day for more than just money. They come for an uplifting experience – to create friendships, to learn, to have fun. We believe that leaders of industry are being called upon to be more than custodians of corporate financial performance. They are also custodians of people's lives. And human life includes the human spirit. We, John and I, and I am sure Mike too, although we each do it our own ways, have a duty to inspire others, so that they want to work with us, instead of having to because of financial pressure. Now is the time to inspire them with our leadership, not as subordinates but as willing followers."

Mike was unable to resist the temptation to interject.

"Now is the time to make them realise that we do not have limitless funds; that effort is required and yes, sacrifice, so that we can all enjoy the longer term future that you're talking about."

Andrew did not take the bait.

"In many ways, you are right, Mike. We are fortunate to be able even to talk in terms of a longer term. I am asking Leonard for trust in our strategic approach, but I do understand the pressures. Leonard, John has given assurances. You've seen a marked improvement, and our projections. Will you give us the additional resources?"

Leonard turned to John Clarke. "I will indeed. FFI are in this for the long haul as well. But understand that we are not a charity. You have your six further months. I am doing this on instinct alone. When you've been in this business for as long as I have, you meet all types. I can tell a shady one from an authentic one. I trust you, and you Andrew." Then he turned to Mike. "Well done. I hope that these figures can be maintained?"

"Yes, indeed. The shake up has worked and the future looks good."

"Excellent. Delighted to meet you gentlemen. Now we can all look forward to the next financial review. Meantime, what about lunch?"

A week later, Andrew visited Arndale Nuclear Fuels to negotiate a contract. ANF had invited tenders for the design and supervision of construction of an underground facility for the safe disposal of low-grade nuclear material. He was worried. This was a sensitive area and it went against his instincts to continue Arthur Garland's relationship with the nuclear industry. He had argued in vain with the Partners, including John Clarke, that the firm should cease operating in areas that deeply concerned many of the staff, including himself. He had cited the Arms, Tobacco and Nuclear industries. But he had been over-ruled. Now it was his duty to iron out aspects of their tender to ANF, and his heart was not in it.

Nonetheless he was realistic, aware of the immense pressure on his shoulders following the meeting with Leonard Feitleson. This contract would certainly provide a kick-start to the second six-monthly probation period. In fact, it was a vital piece of new business at a time when the civil engineering industry was still rocked by recession. This contract would safeguard the jobs of many employees and, using his common sense, he recognised that the project was not intrinsically unethical. It simply involved the safe storage and disposal of very low-grade materials, such as protective clothing and hospital waste, and was not in any way concerned with the construction of new nuclear installations. Even so, he felt soiled, knowing that his principles were being compromised. Nuclear was nuclear. You were either associated with it or not; there was no halfway house of 'acceptable association'.

"Andrew, Garland's tender looks excellent. Needless to say you have, as expected, provided very detailed information and have catered for high levels of safety and security. However, you have also priced yourself above your only competitor …"

The discussions continued. It became clear that ANF wanted a reduction in price, even at the expense of some aspects of safety. Their argument was based on the submission of the competitor's tender.

"If they can do it, and still not compromise safety, why can't you?"

Andrew held his ground. He felt bolstered by the rightness of his approach and shuddered at the alternative – images of shoddy workmanship resulting in scandals in years to come, court cases, all the negative publicity. At the end of the meeting he returned to his office with mixed feelings – proud of his business ethics but concerned about the consequences. The ANF director's parting words still sounded clearly in his mind.

"There is a great deal of future business on the line here. Think it over, Andrew, and get back to us before the end of the week if you wish to reconsider."

The Partners summoned Andrew to their meeting and the atmosphere was icy. John Clarke supported Andrew's refusal to lower standards, but Geoff Boardman was adamant.

"It is in our power to over-rule you, Andrew. You know that. Even if you are correct and we cannot find ways to cut quality and safety, we could always maintain the same standards of construction and lower the tender price, accepting the loss in the certainty of future business. I sometimes wonder at your commitment to this Partnership."

The accusation shocked Andrew.

"I think that is a dangerous road to take. There is never any certainty of future business. Can we really rely on that undertaking? Furthermore, we would be sending a clear message that we are either desperate for work or are prepared to compromise our standards. However, I do not in any way wish to embarrass Arthur Garland and would understand if you felt that my presence on the project was making it difficult for you."

"It may come to more than that, Andrew. In fact, I am beginning to think that you have sabotaged the ANF negotiations because of your misguided belief that the nuclear industry is immoral, which of course it is not. It has provided the firm with a great deal of lucrative work over the years and ANF is the one client that has not reined in its operations throughout the recession. Try to remember where your bread is buttered, or move on."

A stunned silence hung momentarily over the room. Andrew saw a sea of hostile faces. Then John Clarke spoke once again, the only Partner to lend him support.

"Andrew has been open with us from the outset. He has been utterly authentic throughout all our discussions and it is unthinkable to suggest that he has sabotaged the contract. Now, I do not go along with all his views regarding our involvement with ANF, but I do accept his right to hold those views. Let us be grateful that he is open and that he is not so easily cowed by a need to please his bosses. That authenticity is what we need for the future."

Paradoxically, Geoff Boardman was partly correct. Andrew had not intentionally sabotaged the contract, and yet Arthur Garland would never again work with clients from the nuclear industry. But two years later Andrew was vindicated, when the scandal broke. ANF had allowed nuclear waste to contaminate a local water supply. In the resulting enquiry, it became clear that the site of their low level waste facility in North Yorkshire had been inadequately surveyed and the protective casing, deep under ground, had cracked allowing small amounts of material to escape into the groundwater and hence into a small rural community. The consequences were not fully known, but the certainty was that the issue would rumble for years as residents waited anxiously to know the full extent of the contamination.

John Clarke sent a memorandum to all Partners, praising Andrew for his foresight and courage two years earlier.

"It could have been us. It would have been us if we had compromised on quality and safety. 'There, but for the grace of God' is not putting it too gravely. Let us learn from our good fortune and never allow ourselves to be compromised, nor to be tempted to bully those who have strong values and who have the courage to uphold them."

Andrew never saw the memorandum, but the personal thanks from John Clarke meant a great deal to him. He continued to work as an associate for a further two years before accepting, with appreciation and delight, an offer of Partnership. For several more years he continued to champion the way forward using Values as a basis for his leadership.

Then, one day, he confided in John Clarke, "Something is telling me to move on. My wife and I have always dreamed of a return to Scotland. Now's the time. It's right for both of us. Life here with Arthur Garland has been truly wonderful and what has kept me going for so long is the desire to see through to completion our plans for Values Centred Leadership. For that I have been rewarded beyond measure. And I must admit, it has also been a most rewarding time of my life financially. But you know, I've always held to the view that what really matters is 'people over things' and Lisa and I want to follow that ideal, to see more of each other, and be entire with life, treating work as simply one facet of a glorious whole. We now want to work in a way that better integrates our jobs with everything that we do. It's time to move on and to achieve what we are drawn to – Scotland. I have loved my time here. I have loved working for the wonderful staff that makes Arthur Garland what is today. And John, I love you, my old friend. I love your sincerity, and your brain and your unfailing support. I pray that you will not feel let down. It is simply time to move on."

Andrew Graham was the first Partner to leave Arthur Garland with a full-blown farewell party that involved every single member of staff. The champagne flowed and the farewell wishes were as sincere as the pain felt by each person who spoke to him. And there were hundreds of them. It was an occasion that very quickly topped the annals of the firm, even the Queen's award for Industry, even the death of 'Old Man' Garland, even the knighthood of Sir John Clarke, and even the now fabled meeting that launched the FAB Division. James Anderson and Sir John made speeches that moved many deeply, but also filled the room with the laughter of joyful reminiscence and filled hearts with an abiding love of the man who had made acceptable the unthinkable.

Then it was Andrew's turn to speak. In his final words of thanks and farewell, he concluded, "And my last act as Partner is to announce with a pleasure I cannot begin to describe that I am, much as my ego cries out to object, NOT irreplaceable. In fact I am to be replaced even as I stand here in front of you. The Partners have decided to appoint a new Partner. James Anderson was the catalyst for our survival. He will deny that, but he was. James had courage at a time when many of us felt deep-seated fear – he revealed his humanness to a room full of people and faced ridicule. I know a lot of you were not here when he did that, but many of you were, and you know what I am talking about. In fact ALL of you will have heard that story, many times over. James, come up beside me and accept the hand of a happy, grateful friend. We will always remain as one in many ways. Ladies and Gentlemen, your new Partner is James Anderson, who has insisted that his acceptance of the offer of the Partnership is based on one condition – that he is known as the Partner of People's Happiness."

The room exploded with genuine delight. Here was a true leader whose appointment had already been ratified in the minds and hearts of those working around him. One journey was over and a destination had been reached. But a new keeper of the belief was there to nurture the values.

Mike's Story

The second six-monthly meeting between the Partners and Leonard Feitleson was due the following week. Arthur Garland's continued funding from FFI remained in the balance.

Mike Brainwood looked across his desk at Giles Marsden.

"What's going wrong, Marsden? This sort of news should not be cropping up at a time like this. I rely on you to anticipate trouble and nip it is the bud." Mike was deeply troubled, but he hid his feelings behind a façade of businesslike aggression. His lack of warmth was ever present, but now it was sharpened by a tone of menace as he continued to harangue Giles. "Your job is definitely on the line here. I didn't promote you ahead of others for this to happen. If there is restlessness in the ranks, sort it out. Is there any way we can gloss over this before our meeting with the Jew boy? Work on it, man. And I'll want you in the meeting to handle the issue if it arises. I have to say, I'm not amused with the way things are going. Not at all amused."

Giles cringed, feeling the claw in his guts tighten its clench on his entrails. How he hated that sensation – but it was now a constant bedfellow.

"I'll see to it, Mike. But six months is too short a time for us to be certain that the trend is irreversible. I'm convinced that FFI will realise the same. It should not be too difficult to gloss over, as you say. These things happen in all businesses; it's simply a blip at a bad time. What we mustn't do is allow John Clarke to put the spotlight on the issue during the meeting. Can we trust him to take a responsible approach?"

"Time will tell, Marsden. I've made my views plain to him. Told him we must act like a team so you will have to hope that he shows a little common sense. Otherwise, well I don't have to be specific do I?"

The meeting with FFI followed a similar pattern to the previous one, with one difference. The two divisional Partners made their presentations, as before, but this time Mike insisted on going first. Naturally, he concentrated on the positives, stressing the efficiencies that continued to reduce the division's outgoings.

"And, as far as revenue is concerned, you can see that we continue to hold to similar levels as those we turned in over the previous six monthly period; all in all, an excellent basis to prepare us for the imminent upturn. In fact, we are now in the fortunate position of facing a rather pleasant situation, namely how to meet the challenge of resourcing all the contracts that we are likely to win over the coming months?"

John followed.

"I am delighted to report that we are also well on track. By all yardsticks, we are showing that the recovery programme is working, sooner than expected which I think you will find rather agreeable." Andrew smiled inwardly. Good old John – there was genuine humour behind those dry words. "I'd particularly like to thank Andrew for his support, and dedication through the difficult times. Now, to be specific about the areas of recovery. If you'd kindly look at page six, you will see ..."

Leonard Feitleson smiled with satisfaction.

"Thank you gentlemen. I've done the reading carefully and have only brought to this meeting a single question. I'd like to ask you, Mike, why is it that you appear to have such a high turnover of staff?"

"Ah, yes. I'll ask Giles to field that one. He has been looking into the issue and assures me that there is no cause for concern. Giles, would you give Leonard the benefit of your investigations."

"Thank you, Mike. I think it is time for honesty. Here, at Arthur Garland, we must admit to one failing that nobody has addressed since we invited FFI in to help us build for the future. We have never been strong on personnel issues, and by that I mean, we have never had a strong HR Department. Thus, in the past we have not carried out leaving interviews, to identify what it is that makes people feel that they want to move on. In truth, and to our credit, this never used to be a problem. But a worrying trend seems to have developed and I have made extensive enquiries amongst our existing staff as to why it is that, of late, so many of their colleagues have chosen to leave us. I think, in short, I can report that the over-riding reason is simply that people no longer feel secure. They seem to be less prepared than in the past to rely on our commitment to their welfare. Now we all know that this is a perception that can be quickly…"

"And how much revenue has been lost as a result of staff shortages?"

"Ah yes, well that is not quite so easy to …"

"I'm addressing Mike now. You do have the figures, don't you?"

"Leonard, I'd be pleased to have Giles work on that answer and give you our findings within a month. But you must understand that we are the victims of our own success. As I sit here now, I cannot honestly say how many revenue-earning opportunities have been lost specifically due to lack of resources, or …"

"Or how many complaints you have been getting from existing clients who are worried by, and I now quote from a specific case 'the diminished levels of service that we are receiving from over-stretched resources'? Now, I recognise bullshit. Seen it before and will see it again, no doubt. Point is, what are you doing about it Mike?"

"Well now, I take your point. Can I get back to you?"

A calm voice interjected.

"You know, Leonard, I sympathise with Mike. Inspiring people who have lost faith is a close to impossible task. The changes that happened a year ago shook everybody to the core and, in a strange way, those people who kept their jobs had a worse time than those who were forced to move on. Those remaining here have had to endure an atmosphere of gossip and conjecture, of uncertainty and of lack of confidence in their employer – us. Those who left at least knew what lay ahead and many will by now have been re-employed and, by that very process, will have recovered their self-confidence. So let's all hold our hands up at this point. As far as your specific question is concerned, I think that Mike and I should work together, not as two separate entities, and jointly share what is best in what we have both achieved. Together, for the overall benefit of Arthur Garland, we will devise a strategy for staff retention and inspiration. And I do mean inspiration. I'm not going to use the word motivation any more – it carries too many negative connotations, and smacks of coercion of others for one's own benefit. I say this much with certainty now. We will only succeed if our people know we genuinely have their interests at heart. I'd like to suggest that Andrew and Giles put their heads together. That will be the single challenge we take from this meeting."

A month later, Mike sat in another meeting, not for the first time that year facing an irate client. Henry Price-Jones, the Contract Awards Manager of the Department of Transport's Highways Division was fast losing patience.

"Yes, we agree that Arthur Garland has provided us with a quality service over the past fifteen years. But not over the past one year and that is the relevant point. I am no longer able to acknowledge past glories. That tune has long since played itself out, Mr. Brainwood. We have current problems that have run for too long now. You understand well enough what I am talking about. Now I must look to the future. That is why, irrespective of your competitive bid, we no longer have confidence that Arthur Garland will perform what is being asked of them. On the face of it your tender is acceptable, but your reliability is what we now question. We no longer trust you."

Mike's face flushed in anger and humiliation. Nobody had ever spoken to him in such insulting terms – rudeness and aggression had been his prerogative and he was not prepared to be on the receiving end. He opened his mouth to speak, outrage bristling – an irate, frustrated voice determined to be heard, to stop the flow of insults.

"I really must protest …"

"No, Brainwood. I am the one protesting now. You have had too many chances. Be quiet. I will not be bullied."

Colonel Price-Jones emphasised the 'I', heavy with implication. Mike's overbearing nature, a mixture of sharp humour, persuasive charm and forceful certainty had cowed many of Henry's staff. But it would not succeed with Henry Price-Jones, OBE, old Etonian and former Guards officer. He had been born to privilege, had never known anything other than the class comforts of the higher echelons of the British establishment and, certainly, was not prepared to permit this uncouth, overbearing businessman to prevail. And he held the trump card. He was the customer and could say what he wished. One day, and this was that day, a Henry Price-Jones was always going to enter the life of a Mike Brainwood. That was the way of things. The one attracted the other as inevitably as iron filings rush towards the embrace of a magnet. And here they were, two similar people, heavyweights in both status and personality, crossing swords in a battle that could only have one outcome.

"To continue, I am awarding the Motorway contract to Ericson & Peters and that is the end of the matter. Arthur Garland will remain on our list of Consultants for the time being, but we will be wary of passing work on to you without concrete assurances, particularly in respect of resource availability for any future work you undertake. NOW, do you have anything to say, bearing in mind that I have already made my decision in respect of the M970 Motorway contract?"

Mike was cornered and defeat tasted sour. He wanted to lash out. But he was an experienced businessman who never allowed emotion to rule his head. The words he spoke were carefully modulated, but carried the searing heat of hatred into the urbane surroundings of Henry Price-Jones' office.

"I regret, deeply regret, that you have been forced to make that decision. We at Arthur Garland will endeavour to regain your confidence and I will take steps immediately in that regard. But …" these statements always contained a 'but'. Henry waited with interest to see how Mike would continue. So far, the encouraging words were too far out of step with the cutting tone. "… But you must be warned that Ericson & Peters have a reputation for financial irresponsibility, unreliability and double-dealing. On the Camfield Marsh Dam project, it is public knowledge that they …"

"You will never prevail over your competitors, Brainwood, if you slander them. These things come around in full circle and I assure you that, in the months ahead, I will be hearing similar tales about Arthur Garland. And I will ignore them, just as I intend to ignore your own shameful attempt to vilify your competitors. And, as far as 'unreliability and double-dealing', to use your own words, are concerned, I suggest you take a closer look at home. Now, are we finished?"

The farewell handshake was formal, and the clipped tones of both men lacked any warmth. This parting of the ways could only be permanent. Henry Price-Jones' cold, implacable stare drilled into Mike Brainwood's eyes and found only a burning humiliation.

Over the course of the next year Mike was forced to work more closely with John Clarke, and Giles with James. That is what he had promised Leonard Feitleson. And in that process, the flow of opinion swung slowly towards a recognition, at first grudging, and then gradually an acceptance, of the practices of the FAB Division, or 'Group' as John Clarke preferred to call it.

"The FAB Group," he mused dryly. "Takes some getting used to. Next we'll be signed up to perform at the Reading Pop Festival."

Marita's work with the Sanctuary, and her move into the common Human Beings department, contributed greatly to the growing feeling of unity within Arthur Garland. Oliver's cross-division coaching sessions led the way towards establishing a company-wide Personal Growth programme, headed by James who patiently worked towards the introduction of a variety of deeper, more personal, sessions that he himself facilitated, helping the staff of both Groups to find and pursue passions. Slowly, the staff turnover of CATS dwindled and the drain of knowledge and expertise was stemmed.

Mike Brainwood began to change.

With a brief tap on the door, Audrey Coombs entered Mike's office with the message. He was on the phone and looked up at her pretty round face and cherry-ripe cheeks. He smiled at her, and at the good memories...

After a succession of secretaries, Mike had at last found his gem and he was determined not to lose Audrey. Coincidentally, she had arrived on the very day that Mike had congratulated John Clarke on the excellent work that Oliver had done with the CAD operators. She had heard his complimentary comments and, with her natural, infectious good cheer and a complete lack of formality, she had said to her new boss, "Cor, Mr. B, you ain't half in a good mood today, ain't ya."

The Mike of a year ago would have been appalled by such uncalled for familiarity, but darn it, he WAS in a good mood, discovering how refreshingly pleasant it felt to regard his fellow Partner as just that – a partner, and not a rival. The momentary flash of alarm had disappeared in a burst of laughter.

"I reckon I am Audrey. I reckon I am. Nice to have you on board. Just one thing though; call me Mike, if you don't mind. There are too many misinterpretations to Mr. B."

On the day he had rejected sarcasm, suspicion and innuendo in his dealings with John Clarke, the gift of Audrey Coombs was presented to him. And what a gift – efficient, discreet, friendly, hardworking, the list of qualities had no end.

As time passed, another quality emerged – that of intense loyalty. She saw no faults in her boss and, because of that single unrelenting belief, there WAS no bad in Mike Brainwood.

"No, he ain't no bastard. He's a hardworking, fair boss. He ain't done me no wrong, and that's that."

Soon the expressions of sympathy that Audrey received for having been lumbered with Mike faded away in the face of her single, outspoken voice quelling the mistrust of the masses…

Audrey smiled back. Not wanting to disturb his phone call, she wordlessly laid the message on the desk, beside the two daffodils she had placed there that morning. Mike waved his thanks and then caught sight of the note, seeing Audrey's flamboyant, looping handwriting and the words 'Ericson & Peters'. He hurriedly waved an arm to attract Audrey and pointed with a despairing finger at the words, rolling is eyes in an expression of mock horror. Audrey smiled and gave him a thumbs-up. "It's OK," she mouthed, and then flicked a speck of dust from the desk surface and fussily repositioned the picture of his family before retreating from the room, happily humming the tune 'Yellow Submarine'.

An hour later, Mike popped his head round her door.

"I'm off to see Dave Collins of Ericson & Peters, Aud. I won't be back so you can close up shop whenever you like."

"Right ho, Mike. But I've lots to do so, with you out me hair, I'll just crack on."

"She's too good to be true," Mike thought as he walked into the car park, humming an old Beatles tune.

The next morning he burst into Audrey's office, flushed with excitement and carrying a bottle of Champagne. "Hey, Aud, this is for you. Guess what?"

"You've been invited by Ericson & Peters to submit a joint proposal for the London Docklands Redevelopment contract, only a one hundred million pound consultancy project that'll guarantee work for the whole of CATS for the next few years and …"

"How did you know?"

"Well I am your secretary, ain't I?"

"Yes, but be serious for a moment. How did you know? Only yesterday I was preparing our tender as a competitor to E&P. You had no inkling, or did you?"

"You won't be cross, will you?"

"No, never, Aud. What's all this about?"

“OK. Remember you said at the last meeting of the Engineering Team Leaders that people should never be afraid to be ‘proactive’, that you’d never take them to task for trying? I took the minutes, I should know. Well, I reckoned you meant everyone, see, not just team leaders, so after I looked up ‘proactive’ in the dictionary, I thought, why not me too? Well, my boyfriend, Gerry, he works for E&P; he says that they all think us lot at AG are the pits and got bounced from the M970 contract because we done the dirty on the Ministry. I tell Gerry, it ain’t true and that’s just daft people talking, so I decide to put things right, see. Well, it’s a long story – you wanna hear it? You know, somebody knows somebody and that somebody knows some other body.”

“Audrey, forget the full chain of events. What happened?”

“OK then. So there’s this Engineer, Neil something-or-other. Used to work for us in Uganda. He’s now with E&P because he couldn’t keep his job with us when he returned from his posting, right at the start of the bad times. Anyway, Neil knows James Anderson, so I get Gerry to talk to Neil and he and James meet and, well they decide it’s nuts for two companies to be competitors when there’s opportunities for each to help the other. Anyway, they speak to other people and here we are.”

“Let me get this right. Neil McDonald, I know him well, met James Anderson because Audrey Coombs tells her boyfriend that two companies should get on better with each other.”

“Yeah. That’s about it.”

“Aud, this bottle of champagne isn’t enough for you. You are a gem, a real twenty-four carat diamond gem. You’ve saved us thousands in tender costs, and you’ve made it pretty certain we’ll get the LDR contract. What can I say? Thank you for your efforts and for your wonderful, wonderful loyalty. What can I do to show my appreciation?”

“Well, you can open that bubbly at lunch time for starters and have that James Anderson round here to share it with us. He takes most of the credit, at least on our side. He’s a bit of all right you know. That scar ain’t half sexy. Shame he’s married.”

Mike shook his head in happy bewilderment and began to retreat to his own office. He stopped briefly at the door hearing Audrey’s final words.

“You ain’t too bad yourself, Mike. I did this coz I love working for you.”

And Back to James' Story

James' first undertaking as assistant to Andrew was to work with Marita to prepare the sanctuary. The room was born out of sincerity, Andrew setting his own example of authenticity by making his own office available for a soul space that was soon transformed into an island of solace and peace. In that room for the first time, Marita told James her own story, the one that had caused her to make the suggestion, to plant in the minds of her employer an idea that had so quickly manifested this wonderful reality. In listening to the story, James experienced the wonder of quiet openness, so evident in Marita's deeply held feelings, and the honesty with which she had been able to express them. James felt an overpowering desire simply to listen and be supportive in a way that would have been impossible in any other 'ordinary' room.

Whenever he entered the 'Soul-space', as the room was now called, his feelings of awe never diminished; rather they were heightened. He had wondered whether familiarity would breed complacency, if not contempt, in the same way that it often lulled people into taking for granted other aspects of life, like friendship, a beautiful view or painting, or the much loved words of a poet. But the room seemed more than simply alive; she became a place that was itself evolving through change and growth, absorbing a little of each human experience to which she was host. And because, in her own way, she became a servant to the human soul, she was revered by her occupants who never once sullied her purpose. Never once did she become a 'breakout' room for a business meeting, nor a place into which anger was brought, nor idle gossip. Instead, as the days passed, James witnessed scenes of beauty and healing, of tranquillity and soothing, gentle peace, and of openness of heart and pure, all-embracing love.

Soul-space asked each visitor, through soundless whispers of energy, to respect her rules. Sometimes she was filled with several people, simply recharging themselves for what lay ahead in their busy days. At these times nobody spoke, each respecting the other's need for quiet reflection. Sometimes people prayed and others meditated without feelings of self-consciousness – the room accepted anybody whose intentions were pure. Sometimes one person would find herself there, alone, and would emerge in some way gentler, with kinder intentions to others and less concern for ego or personality. Sometimes another person would find himself there, alone, and would discover, in the peace and beauty of Soul-space, answers to problems, salves to pains or simply a greater inner peace. Sometimes, like Marita with James, two people would share Soul-space's company and would reach heightened levels of openness and honesty, and through sharing and listening, give and receive such comfort and support as would be impossible to find in the harsher, less real world outside. For what could be more real than the essence of a human soul? No rules of use were ever written for Soul-space, nor were they considered necessary, and the sceptics, even the cynics, felt no need to challenge her existence, or mock her presence, let alone sully her atmosphere with inappropriate behaviour. She became a symbol, the first visible step towards truly inspirational leadership within Arthur Garland's Partnership. And James was so proud to have been Marita's assistant in bringing this about.

In the years that followed, James worked tirelessly with his Opportunities for Personal Growth programme. 'OPG' or 'Growth' became terms that eventually comprised a familiar, often used language within Arthur Garland. This language embraced other words, like love, inspiration, authenticity, service, truth, and even efficiency, bestowing on each term its own unique meaning within the firm, often quite different from its use in the outside world. But it all took time. To begin with there was friction, particularly between the two divisions. Amazingly Soul-space was never challenged – with her, humans rose above their own frailties. But not elsewhere. Led by Mike Brainwood, cynicism with OPG was rife from the outset especially amongst most of the Partners and Associates, and it fell to John Clarke together with Andrew, two gentle rocks of certainty, to support James in his endeavours. But not once did an ordinary member of staff object to 'Growth'.

James worked tirelessly, at first preparing 'Growth' sheets with their lists of challenging, thought-provoking questions, that would help individuals give serious consideration to where they intended to take their careers and lives. At the top of each sheet James' typed reminders, like:

'TO MAKE ME EMPLOYABLE WHEREVER I MAY BE', or

'TO BE HAPPY AND FULFILLED', or

'TO KNOW WHAT REALLY MATTERS IN MY LIFE'.

James looked again at all Arthur Garland's existing training sources and assessed their methods and effectiveness, speaking to staff for genuine feedback and then encouraging all suppliers to adapt to a coaching style, rather than imposing the more traditional lecturing, instructive one. Many followed James' request and improved their programmes to the immediate benefit of Arthur Garland's staff, whose enjoyment of the experience was clearly evident and whose levels of skill, mainly hard skills like project management and effective use of software, increased perceptibly. Some training companies were honest enough to report back to James that the new techniques had been used with other clients, with similar positive results. James began to run his own workshops, helping his people to work towards better relationships within the workplace, improve their assertiveness, and find clarity in their lives. This was where he experienced starkly contrasting reactions. The FAB employees, at least the majority who took up the offer, loved the experience and showed an immediate preparedness to take control of their lives. The leaders within Arthur Garland, other than John Clarke and Andrew, constantly questioned the costs involved, asking for proof of the efficacy of the workshops and, finding it difficult to change their own mindsets, preferring to echo Mike Brainwood's challenging voice.

The breakthrough came when Oliver's approach to James enabled the first step to be taken in bringing together CATS and FAB under the same 'Growth' umbrella. It had not been easy. Mike initially rejected James' request that Oliver be transferred.

"Go away, Anderson. It's not in your remit to poach my staff."

But Andrew, and later John, interjected on James' behalf, making it clear that it was Oliver who had made the first move and that his skills would be completely lost to Arthur Garland if they were not harnessed in a way that fulfilled the young star's aspirations. Mike had immediately responded to that argument, clearly mindful of Leonard Feitleson's directive.

And later that year, Mike made his first gesture of recognition of James' efforts. His thanks and compliments to John Clarke had been genuine, coming at an important time when he could at last show to Leonard Feitleson clear evidence that the 'brain drain' from CATS had been staunched. The moment had been significant, a watershed when all the vitriol and lack of cooperation had been diverted into the catchment area of a forgotten past, and Mike's reprieve from humiliation had opened his mind at last, and changed his character, attracting at the same time his first truly loyal supporter, the unquenchably direct Audrey.

James never forgot to pass his own thanks on to Oliver, and to share with the young coach his own appreciation of the significance of Oliver's contribution to more than just the firm's training needs.

"You were also instrumental in changing mindsets."

In the years that followed, with the 'proof of the pudding' duly established, support came to James from every quarter, none more so than from Marita, whose move to the Human Beings Department had ensured that the Growth programme would always be given her full backing. Together, and with the enthusiastic support of Arthur Garland's new Senior Partner, John Clarke, following the retirement of Geoff Boardman, James and Marita introduced a truly inspirational programme, using the services of a like-minded coaching organisation, Leadership Coaching International. LC International helped the leaders and senior managers within Arthur Garland understand, and develop in wonderful and creative directions, the deeper concepts of Values Centred Leadership.

Andrew, now a Partner himself, thanked the two new Associates.

"It was a brave move to bring in LC. You were quite right, Marita, to use an external organisation. Respected, as you are James, you were wise to accept that this programme should not be run 'in-house', especially by a 'humble' Associate, as you put it yourself. But all the Partners are aware of your help with the subject matter and none are taking umbrage – a sure sign, in itself, that the inspirational values we are trying to espouse are being taken seriously. For the first time ever, across the board there is not a single voice of dissent amongst our leadership team. It's a great day. Thank you both, from the bottom of my heart."

Several months later, John Clarke received his knighthood and the whole of Arthur Garland celebrated. Sir John took a well-earned holiday, followed by a sabbatical that involved a world speaking tour. The turnaround in Arthur Garland, and its association with unfamiliar methods, had attracted worldwide attention, particularly in the open-minded but very 'bottom line' driven North American business world. In the face of ridicule, particularly from the British press, Sir John insisted in titling his lecture series 'Love is all you need'.

During Sir John's absence, Mike struggled with his conscience. He knew that the LDR tender was draining his resources and that a joint venture with Ericson & Peters, their main competitor, was an obvious solution for both parties. But he could not erase his gaffe, which he now deeply regretted, that he had once shamelessly used slander in an attempt to sway the Ministry of Transport from their decision to award work to E&P. These things have a way of haunting people. Privately, he was ashamed of his behaviour but, as a proud businessman, he could see no way around the issue other than to ensure that never again would any client have an opportunity to criticise Arthur Garland's professionalism. James was unaware of this background so, when he received a phone call from Neil McDonald, he was pleasantly surprised, and puzzled that a competitor should wish to speak to him. His first thoughts were that his old boss was headhunting.

"Hello, James. How are things?"

The broad Scots accent cut its familiar swathe through the ether.

"Faer Fa, your honest soncy face, laddie."

"And is that a compliment, Neil? Or am I about to be likened to the 'puddin race', a haggis maybe?"

James laughed, enjoying this memory of the good old days, on site in Uganda with genuine folk like this huge, no-nonsense Scot whose earnest endorsement of a young man's qualities had ensured that James would survive the round of redundancies that eventually swept his benefactor out of Arthur Garland. Life was unfair, and yet was there not a reason for everything?

"I'm fine. How are you, Neil?"

"Never better. I mean it. E&P were in need of me, and they offered better opportunities than AG would ever have done."

The chat continued, a good-natured exchange of long overdue news and happy memories, until Neil suddenly turned serious.

"I was going to phone Mad Mike, and then all but dismissed the idea. He's definitely 'persona non grata' here at E&P – doesn't deserve a look in. Then I saw that your name has crept onto the AG letterhead. Congratulations by the way, AG must be on the right track at last if they've seen fit to make you an Associate. Look, can we meet. Today, if possible. What I have to say may take time?"

"Just give me a clue, Neil. If it's that important, I'll clear my diary."

"Oh, it's important. Let's just say – important enough for the E&P/AG hatchet to be buried once and for all."

"I'll be in your office within the hour."

James spent two hours with Neil, explaining the extent to which Arthur Garland had moved in striving for values in the workplace. He admitted, truthfully, that he knew nothing of Mike Brainwood's shoddy dealings, but defended his Partner vehemently.

"The Mike you are talking about doesn't exist any more. He's become less competitive and overbearing, even much more human than you could ever imagine. I'm in a position to vouch for him, unreservedly, just as you so kindly endorsed me all those years ago. These things are never done lightly, but I'll put myself on the line here. Trust me. Let's clear up this feud between the companies. I'll do what I can at my end."

"OK. I'll do what I can too. My problem will be Dave Collins. He's senior Partner here and is vehemently anti-AG. It will take some doing."

It did take some doing, but after meeting James and seeing authenticity shine through the young Associate, Dave Collins relented. He finally admitted that E&P were desperate to enter into partnership with a strong, reputable fellow consultancy – "a good, solid firm with the clout to carry us both into the LDR project."

Again, James offered 'any help at all'. "Anything I can do from my end."

Dave Collins cut him short with an appreciative smile.

"Thank you, James. You've done almost enough, but one last piece of proof is needed to convince me that AG is just the partner we need. Let me call Mike. His reaction to my call will be the clincher. Can I trust you not to prime him?"

"You can trust me not to speak to him for a full day, Mr. Collins. But I can't be your mole in Arthur Garland. They are my employers and my loyalty is ultimately with them. Unlikely as it is, if anybody does approach me about my meeting here today, between now and the end of tomorrow, I will have to speak the truth. But I reckon my conscience can survive twenty-four hours of low profile! It's to everybody's benefit."

"Fair enough, James. Thank you. I look forward to renewing my dealings with Arthur Garland in the future, particularly if that involves seeing more of you."

The two men shook hands warmly.

Neil accompanied James in a leisurely walk from the building. They stopped at a young Engineer's office.

"I'd like you to meet Gerry Chaplin. Gerry, this is James Anderson from Arthur Garland."

"Delighted to meet you, Gerry. I'd like to thank you for speaking to Neil in the first place. You set in motion quite a chain of events. Well done. It must have taken some courage. Tell me about it all."

"It wasn't courage, sir. I'd have needed more courage to face my fiancée if I'd done nothing!"

"I know what you mean. Audrey's a real star. Everybody at Arthur Garland loves her, but we sometimes have to toss our hats into her office before risking an entrance! She's irreplaceable but by God, you always know where you are with her. Tell me one thing, Gerry. How come she can turn on such a perfect telephone manner, accent and all, and then revert to good old cockney when you meet her in person? I hope you don't mind me asking."

Gerry laughed with delight.

"That's easy to answer. To use her own words, 'I'm buggered if I'm going deny me roots ALL the time. What you hears is what you gets. And that's that, see'. So I guess we all have to live with it."

"More than that, Gerry. I love it. That's a genuine person with self-confidence speaking. Something I never had at that age. Reminds me of my wife, Harriet. I know Audrey will make you happy. We men sometimes need an Audrey in our lives – prevents us getting above ourselves. You've got yourself a winner there."

James' second proudest moment at Arthur Garland was to be offered a Partnership, the first son to successfully follow his father's footsteps. Jim Anderson, long since retired, hugged his son. A stroke had affected his speech, but the few words, "Son, I love you," dribbled out clearly and meant more than anything in the world to James who, momentarily, became an affection-seeking child again, desperate for that very moment of recognition and approval, and genuine love. He hugged the frail frame as tight as he dared before moving across to his darling mother and holding her in his arms.

"You stayed by me all my life, Mum. I owe this to you." Helen wept tears of joy.

Without doubt, James' proudest moment of his years at Arthur Garland was to join Sir John Clarke in making a farewell speech to the man he loved most of all. Although he had prepared well, when it came to the moment, he found it easer to speak from the heart and the words simply flowed with genuine ease. And so did the sincerity. The room was hushed momentarily after the closing sentences.

"And so, it is not farewell, for you will never leave our hearts, Andrew. But, for now, au revoir to our dear boss, our inspirational leader, a true and authentic friend and …," James paused, clearly emotional, "…allow me my own indulgence here … my Azenzio."

A thunderous cheer and an extended ovation enveloped them all. Only one person in the room understood the reference to Azenzio. The one person with whom he had shared the full story. The one person who really mattered. Andrew's eyes were misted.

Amid the hubbub, James saw Mike Brainwood smile at him. In the past, James had seen such intimidation, often gloating, in that smile. Today, he saw only genuine affection and knew that Andrew Graham had indeed made a difference to everybody's lives.

James and Andrew kept in close touch with each other. Harriet and Lisa became inseparable. Distance did not prevent constant contact and there were several visits to and from Scotland. But one day, years after the famous farewell function, James received a phone call and heard the familiar voice of his friend.

"James, I need your help."

"Anything, old friend. What can I do for you?"

Chapter 15

The Power of Gentleness

Horse & Hound – Thursday 24th April

English Engineering Company Sponsors at Scotland's Premier Event

The Arthur Garland Partnership, London based consulting civil engineers, has turned its back on tradition by offering to take over sponsorship from Star Alliance at the Royal Highland this year. In March, the Insurance Corporation was forced to withdraw from its own Star Alliance Open Final class. Then, Arthur Garland's forward-looking Partner, James Anderson, saw an opportunity for his firm to "Live its values." In an unprecedented move, equestrian sport will, for the first time, receive sponsorship from a private company within the conservative world of civil engineering consultants.

James Anderson comments, "When we first heard that so many people had been let down, we felt drawn to help. This is a competition that clearly touches ordinary people. The disappointment for many of those thirty outstanding qualifiers was heartbreaking. So we looked into it, and discovered that the class had attracted competitors from as far afield as Ireland and Europe, not to mention England. This is clearly a prestigious event, fielding not simply the cream of Scotland's showjumpers. With its mix of professionals, Edgar Gibson and Dieter Hamann are household names, and a number of very promising amateurs, we could see an opportunity that should not be missed. We couldn't allow so many dreams to be shattered. But it's not just the competitors who will benefit. We, at Arthur Garland, feel that this is a perfectly acceptable means of increasing our own profile, but in a way that allows us to live our values. This move has excited and thrilled our staff, many of whom follow equestrian sport. We believe that people should be allowed to follow their passions, and we've certainly unearthed a real passion here. It seems quite evident that everybody will benefit."

The Open event will be renamed the 'Arthur Garland Challenge'. James Anderson promises that this is not 'a one-off wonder' and he has committed Arthur Garland to making the competition a qualifier for the Horse of the Year Show at Wembley, one of Britain's biggest equestrian occasions. He also undertakes to continue full sponsorship of the same events for the next two years. With their intervention, Arthur Garland has, in one stroke, increased the profile of this year's showjumping programme at Ingliston. Edinburgh welcomes its English friend.

During the spring and early summer Lisa focused on preparing for the Highland Show. Riding became an all-absorbing part of her life, more than ever before. She concentrated on her jumping technique and competed in several shows, many away from home to accustom Chelsea to travelling and to help her become used to a variety of different environments, including overnight stays. In this one respect, Chelsea had been spoiled, having enjoyed for many months the luxury of her own box at night. When Lisa saw the schedule for the Highland Show, she realised that it would be sensible to make the one hundred and twenty mile trip to Edinburgh on the day before their class, which was due to start at midday. An early departure on the day of competition would have been perfectly possible, but Lisa was determined to take no chances. She wanted peace of mind, not to be plagued with nagging doubts about the notoriously bad traffic congestion around the Forth Road Bridge.

"I'm going down on Wednesday. Nothing is worse than sitting in heavy traffic, with a deadline ahead, wondering if the jam will loosen up. I've waited a lifetime for this day. More than anything else, I want to enjoy it, to relish each and every moment."

For that same reason, Lisa cleared her diary for the whole week of the show, 'so there's plenty time to prepare'. Nobody argued.

As the big day approached, Lisa was delighted to find that she was to be accompanied to the Royal Highland Show by one other person from Braehead. Since the previous summer Jane and her gorgeous little working hunter pony had gone from strength to strength and were delighted to have qualified, only recently, for the Highland. The elfin-like eleven-year-old had been jumping since the age of six, but 'showing' classes were still a novelty and she had achieved wonders to qualify. Lisa's motherly instincts took over. To their delight, they found that their classes were both scheduled for the first day. "We can all travel together – the Braehead world beaters." Jane's enthusiasm was a delight, pure openhearted excitement, injecting them all with a healthy dose of joy. 'All' included Andrew and both of Jane's parents – Angela and Tom. The expedition was planned meticulously. In order to have sleeping space for everyone, Jane and her parents would take their own transporter, and Lisa and Andrew theirs, but the horses would travel together.

"Let Chelsea come in ours, oh please," Jane enthused. "It's bigger, AND we've got air conditioning."

Lisa smiled, and looked at Angela who laughed aloud, "Of course, darling. If Lisa is agreeable."

And of course Lisa was agreeable, adding: "Besides, the horses will enjoy travelling with each other." Lisa knew that Chelsea would be well cared for. Tom was an excellent driver, more experienced than Andrew, and Jane was a perfect companion, a mix of horse-lover and expert beyond her tender years, altogether a very competent little horsewoman, under the watchful eye of her equally competent mother. Jane's face flushed with pride. To be entrusted with both Chelsea, and Star her own pony, simply added to the thrill of the occasion. Lisa was happy to add to the girl's joy. Even so, her practical nature had already concluded, "We can easily cope with a drama, not that there'll be any. Andrew and I won't be far behind – and we've always got mobile phones!"

Wednesday arrived! Lisa and Andrew appeared at the yard just after midday and loaded their lorry, the ever-meticulous Lisa ticking items off her carefully prepared list – saddle, bridle, numnahs … show jacket, hat … hay nets, feed … matches for the stove, food … water. It seemed endless. With no horses travelling in their lorry, Lisa used the space to take hay for both Chelsea and Star, enough to last the round trip. Hay was always available on site, but both Lisa and Jane had conferred and, between their two great minds, agreed that they wanted to take their own supplies! Competition horses can easily suffer stomach upsets from even slight changes to their feed.

Then it was time for Andrew, the number one horse catcher, to bring Chelsea in. She seemed to be aware that there was an adventure afoot and came without question. Secretly, Andrew felt a faint disappointment. He'd have much preferred a challenge; at least a few minutes of 'catch me if you can'. He loved that private moment with the mare when they each enjoyed the fun of their own special relationship, a mixture of impertinent independence, leading to eventual affable companionship. Lisa gave her a quick bath and asked Andrew to walk her around, 'to dry her off'. It was a glorious day so the process didn't take long. Then Lisa covered the mare with a light fleece, ready for the journey, and left her happily munching hay whilst also keeping an eye on proceedings confirming, in her own way, that something important was in the making. She understood, for certain, that this was no ordinary afternoon. Jane and Star were soon ready as well.

Both horses loaded effortlessly, although Chelsea first took a moment to look down at the tiny Welsh Cross pony with a mixture of disdain and benign tolerance.

"What sort of a competition can this be? Surely I'm not competing with that!"

Before long, all was ready. "As ready as we'll ever be." So, just as planned, with both lorries proudly displaying their Highland Show Competitor passes on the windscreen, they left Braehead in the mid afternoon, and headed south, missing the Aberdeen rush hour. They had agreed not to travel in convoy, knowing that this would annoy other drivers, but the plan was, if possible, to keep each other within sight. This was easy once they left the city and hit the open A90 motorway. After an uneventful journey – the traffic had been judged to perfection – they reached Ingliston in the bright daylight of a glorious still June evening and drew their vehicles into the competitor's lorry park. The sun shone from a clear, blue sky, continuing to bathe the show ground with its warmth, providing just the welcome they all wanted. And, being close to the longest day of the year, it would not be dark until well after ten o'clock, giving them plenty of time to settle the horses in for the night, and themselves too. Everything was falling nicely into place.

Arm in arm, Jane and Lisa strolled off to find their allocated stables. Happily, their boxes were next to each other. Lisa was delighted. She sensed that at this special event, only the highest standards would apply. Even so, she was touched by the thoughtfulness of the organisers.

"There aren't too many other horses around yet. The stables will be much busier once the show gets underway tomorrow. But, for tonight, Chelsea and Star will be quiet and will get all the peace they need."

The girls returned, unloaded the horses and led them to the stables, just a short walk away. Then they removed the travel gear and left them to settle in with plenty of hay and full water buckets. Meanwhile Angela, who had appointed herself as catering manager for the party, had begun to prepare a late evening meal. She was an old hand at this game, having ridden at many shows as a child and into early adulthood, before raising her family. So she knew the routine well and was a wonderful, quiet, 'just get on with it' support. During their meal, a ham salad and delicious new potatoes dripping in melted butter, Lisa enquired whether she missed competing.

"Not really. I'm happy to do a wee bit of Riding Club competition with old Jasper; and it's fun to enter the occasional Mother and Daughter classes with Jane. But these days I just enjoy helping in the background."

"Well, it's much appreciated."

After supper Andrew and Tom, who had soon found much in common, slipped off to enjoy a quiet beer away from the constant 'horse chatter'. In truth, Andrew enjoyed such chatter, but he was happy to follow Tom's lead. Jane's kindly father made the suggestion, and both men slipped away. Yet Andrew was responding to a stronger impulse – something deep within his heart told him that Lisa needed to be alone this evening. He could not help thinking, "She needs solitude at this single incredible moment of her life. Something is about to come into full circle. But what?"

Lisa continued to chat to Angela for just a few more minutes before leaving mother and daughter to settle down for the night. Jane's eyes were heavy, reflecting the extent to which the efforts of a long day had at last caught up with her. Overwhelmed by tiredness, the excited energy that had kept the delightful youngster going for so long was melting away before their eyes. It was time for bed.

"I'll see to the horses. You both get heads down."

Yet, something stronger was drawing Lisa.

"I've got to be alone with Chelsea." She was unable to explain the feeling. "Something needs to be resolved. But what?" Lisa walked towards the setting sun, drawn by the very power of the Universe, suffused with its benign energy. "Something incredible is going to happen. I just feel it."

Fortunately, the lorry park was quiet that night. On any other night, with the show in full swing, it would have been filled with noise, humming with activity and anticipation, and excitement as friends met and socialised, partying long into the night. Lisa continued to let her thoughts run free.

"I'm glad I was so determined to come a day early. The atmosphere tonight is so special, laid on just for me, I can't explain why."

Ahead she saw a figure, also walking towards the stables. The sun's late evening rays flashed weakly on the tents and temporary wooden boxes, fleetingly painting them a deep ochre. The figure passed the side of a tent and sunlight caught his hair, which flared momentarily into a shining bright red aura. Then he passed once again into shadow and Lisa could see, just barely, his natural ginger colouring. She continued to follow, but more slowly intentionally falling behind, waiting for him to pass by Chelsea so she could have her moment of peace with the mare. With his head down, deep in thought, he didn't notice Chelsea, in line with several other horses, all peering out at the peaceful evening sights. But she saw him and nickered in recognition. Not hearing, he walked on.

Lisa froze, fascinated. Chelsea became agitated and retreated back into the box, trying to walk a few paces, parallel to him. Then her head reappeared, and she became increasingly frantic. The nickers became louder, broken by anxious intakes of breath, excited gasps interspersed with louder and louder nickers. "I'm here, I'm here," the mare's desperate cries continued. The man stopped and turned around, revealing a kind, puzzled face and, barely visible now in the fading evening light, a freckled nose. Then he walked back to Chelsea, whose lips quivered with more nickers, this time soundless, joyous mutters of welcome. Eric patted Chelsea. He held both sides of her face and kissed her, and kissed her, and kissed her, before finally laying his head on her neck and weeping openly. After all, nobody was watching so his emotional Celtic temperament was free to express itself.

"Hello!"

Eric jumped with embarrassment. He self-consciously rubbed a dribbling nose, and then wiped his hand on the seat of his pants. Lisa smiled, hoping to put this delightful young man at his ease.

"It looks like you've just found a long lost friend. That's Chelsea. I'm her owner."

"Hi." Eric could manage no more, but he offered his hand to Lisa. Then at last, "I'm Eric. Oh God, what can I say? She's still called Chelsea. That's wonderful so it is." The Irish lilt was unmistakable. "I christened her that. Oh …"

Once again, Eric was speechless. He gulped with emotion and tears welled into happy, bewildered eyes. "Forgive me, lady. I need time."

Lisa looked at Eric with deepening affection. She had witnessed something so special and felt drawn to this strange new companion.

"Take all the time you want Eric. I've had seven years of wondering. I can cope with anything. Would you like to come back to my vehicle for a cup of tea?"

"No. Thank you ma'am, but no. I want to stay here with Chelsea. Can we stay here to talk?"

"Of course. But please just call me Lisa."

And so they stood, one on either side of Chelsea who listened to them both, and shared two amazing stories, so different, yet linked by a common golden thread – of gentleness and love. Eric spoke first.

"I was with Chelsea the day she was born …until she was four … loved her to bits … terrible fall in Dublin ... couldn't afford to buy her … dreadful dealer … lost touch … often thought of her and wondered how she was – or even if she was still alive.” Eric spoke for an hour. His voice reflected each emotion that the mare now conjured – the joys of her successes and warmth of her companionship, the pain of the disasters, the gut wrenching sadness of separation, and the anxiety and awful, awful fear of uncertainty. So much of what he said confirmed Lisa’s picture of Chelsea’s life in Ireland, but much more, so very much more was added and Lisa’s heart went out to this magnificent creature who was now a part of her life, a gift from creation itself. The sun dipped below the horizon, its job done.

And then Lisa spoke and Eric listened, in rapt attention, weeping deep inside when he heard how Chelsea had been damaged, in so many ways, by her experiences in Ireland, smiling with undiminished joy at the miracle that had been worked since, then weeping again, now openly, unashamedly, when Lisa closed with the words, “But, you know Eric, I can’t take all the credit. Always, even at the worst times of pain and mistrust, Chelsea had a core of strength to carry her through. That core came from you and her first experience of love, the true, deep, wonderful, gentle love that you showed her in those first years. Like a flame, that love flickered but never died. You passed it on to me and, yes, I’m proud to say that I rekindled it to produce what we have today.” Lisa hugged the weeping, emotional young man. Together, they wept as Lisa finally choked, “We did it together, Eric. You and me.”

Chelsea nuzzled them both, joining her two most loved of all humans in that precious moment of oneness.

“And me too.”

It was after midnight when Eric and Lisa parted, hugging each other and cementing a bond of friendship. Eric slipped off to say goodnight to Titan. Edgar Gibson had brought three horses to Britain, intent on touring the summer circuit in a final effort to establish his reputation as a top-flight showjumper. He had asked Eric to join his small team, as groom for the horses. Eric had been delighted to oblige, keen to keep his hand in and to continue working with horses, a source of so much joy in his life. His only regret was in leaving behind his lovely wife, Mary, but she had agreed happily, remaining in Killarney to care for their two-year-old daughter, and to manage their growing business, ‘Tack it from me’, a retail outlet for tack, clothing and footwear.

Lisa said her own goodbyes to Star, who had watched the evening's activity with a pony's intelligence. Then she spent another precious moment with Chelsea, calm and so at peace with the world, before slipping contentedly away.

"Sleep well, you two," she whispered quietly. "You'll need all your energy for tomorrow. It'll be a long day."

Andrew had not been concerned by Lisa's disappearance. He sensed that she had needed this time alone, and Lisa loved him all the more for not pressing her. But she was enthused now, wide-awake and yet in a strange contented daze. Sleep would not come easily tonight.

"Are you sleepy, darling? Can I talk? I have the most amazing story to tell you."

In the end, well after two in the morning, Lisa and Andrew drifted into contented sleep. Lisa dreamed of a spindly-legged foal, welcomed into the world by a loving mother and a caring, gentle young man. Not once did she awake, as she had feared she might. Nerves and tension could find no place to intrude that night.

Everyone else, including Chelsea and Star, slept surprisingly well considering the excitement that lay ahead the next day. Jane and Lisa were delighted to find straw and stable stains on the horses' rugs – a sure sign they too had been relaxed, confident enough to lie down in their strange overnight home.

Jane was the first into action. She had an early start in the show ring and so, even before breakfast, she took Star for a brief ride. Then, after a quick foray into a packet of cornflakes, 'Jane, dear, it's not a nose bag', she dashed off to make a start on the serious preparation that would transform a scruffy, lovable little pony into a polished show ring performer. Lisa couldn't resist a smile, sharing her thoughts with Angela.

"Jane's just like Star. Scruffy and lovable one minute, and polished and ever so proper the next. I'm genuinely fond of them both. Having them around is perfect preparation for me and my nerves."

Then Lisa went her own way, giving Chelsea her morning feed before returning to join the rest of the party for her own breakfast. There was an air of excitement as the adults discussed the day's logistics. Jane's class was due to start at 9.30 am and would run through most of the morning. Lisa's class was scheduled to start at midday and would be finished by about 2.30 pm. That would give them plenty of time to pack up and drive back to

Braehead, well ahead of the Edinburgh evening rush hour. Lisa announced her intention to take Chelsea for a walk and then to do some work in the warm up area before beginning final preparations. She hoped this would settle both herself and Chelsea and keep them gently occupied. In between, she promised to follow Jane's progress.

Andrew asked permission to slip away and greet the sponsor's guests.

"But I'll be back in good time to help you with the final preparations. I'll also encourage James and Harriet to join me in supporting Jane. I know they'll be relieved to get away from the formal entertaining side of things for a while."

Each went their own way.

Lisa gave Chelsea a quick brush up and made her way to the warm up area. Chelsea seemed calm in spite of the bustle as the show came to life on its opening day. The two worked quietly together for almost an hour, until Lisa became aware of a young man, together with an older companion who might have been his father, watching them intently. This didn't bother her. She was simply intrigued – people often stopped to watch Chelsea; she had that quality, eye-catching with her glorious chestnut colouring and beautiful intelligent head. She was also smaller than most showjumpers and people were often amazed at her ability to produce big jumps seemingly from nowhere. But this time, the onlookers seemed more than simple admirers. Still intrigued, Lisa deliberately circled the mare close to her audience. Immediately Chelsea laid her ears back and broke into a brief canter, taking herself quickly away from the watching pair. Usually Chelsea appreciated an audience – another opportunity to flaunt her good looks shamelessly.

"I wonder," Lisa thought. "I just wonder."

But today was a day to concentrate, and not to be distracted, so she continued the warm up keeping Chelsea as far as possible from the watching pair.

She took Chelsea back to her box and, with plenty of time to spare, made a start on their final preparations.

Andrew saw Harriet first. Or rather, he saw a small gathering of admirers and heard that familiar infectious laugh and the friendly American accent.

"Gee, no kidding!" It could only be James' gorgeous wife.

"Hey, Harri. Hi there!"

Her entourage, all male guests of Arthur Garland, doting hangers-on, parted reluctantly to allow Andrew to join their privileged group.

"Oh, Andrew, it's so good to see you. Give me a kiss, quick, before James sees us. It's the only reason I came." Spontaneous delight quickly gave way to businesslike formality. "I'd like to introduce you to our dear guests. First of all folk, this is Andrew Graham, retired Partner of Arthur Garland and my biggest hero. Andrew, you know Mike", the two men smiled warmly and shook hands, "and this is Willie Macfarlane, from the Crofting Commission, David Collins from Ericson & Peters, …"

Eventually, Harriet grasped Andrew's arm and pulled him to one side. At last they had a moment to chat.

"God, it's good to see you. James is with Sir John in the sponsors' pavilion – so many people want to thank Arthur Garland for their sponsorship. They can't seem to escape. He's desperate to see you and to wish Lisa well." She sighed deeply. "This is great. What an occasion! I love Scotland. I know why you felt you had to live up here."

The chatting continued for five minutes. Then Harriet made a request.

"Where's Lisa? I'd love to see her, if it won't distract her from her preparations. Do me a huge favour – look after my guests for half an hour."

Andrew laughed. Harriet was ever the Harriet he knew and loved.

"Sure. I'd particularly like to chat with Willie Macfarlane. He seemed such an interesting chap."

"He is. A real gent too – he's got all the nicest traits of you Brits. Just like you, Andrew. But then, I keep telling you that, don't I? Thanks for your help. See ya soon!"

And suddenly the whirlwind was gone, leaving behind an uplifted spirit. Just sharing five minutes with Harriet Anderson was enough time to experience genuine, positive warmth. What a lady!

Still warmed by Harriet's company, Andrew found Willie and began to chat to the delightful, quiet, sincere Scot. Eventually he suggested that they watch a current competition.

"I know a great wee girl whose showing in the Working Hunter Pony class. Anybody want to join me?"

Willie was relieved to enjoy some genuine spectating at last. The two men were joined by one other, whilst the rest of the party, mainly engineering contractors, decided that it was well past time to visit the bar in the sponsor's pavilion!

As soon as Chelsea was ready, Lisa walked her to their lorry, and tethered her there whilst she returned to the horse box, to muck it out and leave the temporary stable ready for the next occupant – a small, thoughtful gesture that was typical of the person who had made herself so popular with the girls at Braehead. When she returned, she was thrilled to see her old friend, Harriet, chatting freely with Tom. Another admirer had been added to her entourage! However, he slipped away as soon as he saw Lisa, leaving the two friends to catch up with their news. Also, he was keen to see how Jane was faring. But it was a close decision! Harriet continued to chat, moral support for Lisa whose nerves were beginning to jangle, whilst Lisa completed her preparations with Chelsea. Then Lisa changed into her own gear – she had treated herself to a new show jacket and jodhpurs in honour of the occasion. When she had started to show Chelsea in hand, Lisa had bought a tweed jacket and beige jodhpurs, an outfit that had been appropriate for all their outings.

"It would have been fine for today too, but I felt that the occasion demanded something new."

It was wonderful to share these thoughts with another female, especially a good friend like Harriet. Andrew was supportive, but there were times when …! Harriet admired the beautiful navy show jacket with dark green piping and matching silk lining. Navy and green had always been Lisa's 'racing' colours – "Blue for me and Scotland, green for Chelsea and Ireland." She had also bought some elegant white jodhpurs to complete the outfit. Lisa looked a dream.

"It's perfect for you, Lisa. Wow, riding keeps your figure trim too – you look so sleek, like a million dollars."

Finally, Lisa pulled on her boots and donned her hat; ready at last to collect Chelsea.

"Shame there's no prize for best turned out today," smiled Harriet, "you two would win by miles!"

The three of them walked together to the collecting ring, where Andrew joined them, now at last with James, who hugged Lisa but was careful not to interrupt her preparations. Everybody was beginning to feel the first tremblings of apprehension, joining Lisa in a fit of pre-competition nerves.

Today there was no need to declare and select their slot. Everyone had pre-qualified and a random draw had been made to determine the order of competitors. Lisa was relieved to see that she'd been drawn early – third to go. She had often reflected on how her competition experience as a young athlete had stood her in good stead for showjumping. Just as she'd run the four hundred metres on the basis of going as fast as she could for as long as she could, and then hanging on grimly until the finish, so in showjumping she preferred to go early and post a clear for others to follow. So too, in jump-offs she liked nothing better than to be drawn first and to post a fast double clear. That was her preference, although with her wonderful mare, she never lacked confidence when drawn late, herself facing the challenge of somebody else's fast double clear.

She made her way into the collecting ring, walked the course and began her final warm up. As she did so she was delighted to see Jane standing beside the rails, waving a red rosette and smiling proudly.

"Your turn next Lisa," she called excitedly.

Lisa was thrilled. What a lovely boost just before her own competition. She rode Chelsea over to the rails and bent down to give the excited youngster a hug.

"Well done you! You really have inspired me to go for it too."

Jane reached through the rail to pat Chelsea.

"Go, Chelsea, go!"

Lisa returned to the warm up routine and lined up to take their practice jumps. As ever, Chelsea was well organised and soon found her stride. Then Lisa noticed an older man, the same person who had been watching them earlier. This time he was helping a young rider, hidden by a protective helmet, who was riding a large black horse. Lisa guessed it was a stallion but was not certain. Anyway, it wasn't that important. She concentrated on her own preparations, taking a few deep breaths to help suppress those ever-present butterflies.

Andrew gave a few last words of encouragement.

"I'm so proud of you. This is your day, your moment to realise a lifetime's dream. Enjoy it darling and remember, you're taking my love with you into that arena. Chelsea won't fail you. She knows what's going on. It's almost as if she is realising her own life's ambition, to purge those memories of Dublin. Each of you has given the other the opportunity to achieve an ambition. She won't let you down."

And then there was no time to say anything else. The loudspeaker drowned out any further words. Andrew simply laid a hand across Chelsea's muzzle and kissed her ear, whispering, "I love you too girl." In response, the mare pulled up her head, all set to go, skittering in readiness, an image of determination and power.

The second horse made its way into the arena, and Lisa and Chelsea took their place at the entrance to the ring. Chelsea, as ever, stood to attention, focusing on the task in hand. In a few moments, the gate opened for them and they were on their way. They cantered around waiting for the bell, both of them intent on the first line of jumps. Lisa recalled afterwards that she had been oblivious to the full grandstand that surrounded the show ring on two sides, even less aware of the crowds on the open side, with people sitting on the ground close to the barriers, others watching as they walked past on the path that separated the arena from the trade stands. The bustle, the fluttering flags, the applause, just for her – the oldest competitor – and even the howl from the skies above as a plane made its approach to Edinburgh airport. Nothing disturbed their total concentration.

The bell sounded and they cantered towards the first jump. Chelsea was high on adrenalin, determined not to let her mistress down. She took a huge leap, almost jumping Lisa out of the saddle. Harriet gasped, placing a hand over her mouth, but Andrew squeezed her forearm and whispered, "It's OK, she's in control."

"Steady, steady girl," whispered Lisa, regaining her seat and their balance just in time for the next fence. Back in control after their 'fright', Lisa coaxed the willing mare effortlessly through to the final fence. The applause thundered into Lisa's consciousness breaking the imposed silence of her total concentration. Together, James and Andrew leapt to their feet, a moment after Harriet who was unable to contain her delight.

"Yes, yes!"

Casting inhibition aside, Harriet released pure, undiluted joy, drawing those around her into the celebration. Quiet, sedate, Sir John Clarke pumped the air. Focused, competitive Mike Brainwood clenched his fist by his side and hissed a long intense "Yesssss." And gentle, reserved Willie Macfarlane put two arms in the air and applauded long and hard. "Braw, lass, braw," he shouted until decorum suddenly resumed its place in his world and he sheepishly looked around, relieved beyond measure that he had not been noticed.

Chelsea was momentarily startled by the reception, and bucked twice, a mixture of exuberance and alarm. But only momentarily. She responded immediately to Lisa who leaned forward and, with an arm on either side of the neck, hugged her darling mare from behind. Then she stroked her neck.

"It's OK, lass. Steady, steady. We've done it."

For one of them, a dream had come true – Lisa had competed at the Royal Highland Show, producing an inspirational clear round. Tears welled into her eyes and she looked up at the stand and saw her supporters' faces, alive with joy, sharing this precious moment.

"Well done to Lisa Graham and Chelsea, our first clear round of the day," the commentator announced calmly, seemingly the only composed voice in the entire ground.

"Well, we've been here a few times," thought Lisa as they walked into the collecting ring to be met by an excited little group – Andrew, Jane and Angela all offering congratulations and patting Chelsea.

"Wow, that was exciting – nearly too exciting over that first fence. I really thought I was going to be sent into orbit!" Lisa laughed, "To have come all this way and then to fall at the first would have been just too awful, too embarrassing to contemplate!" They all composed themselves, although Jane wanted a special hug first. "You can have two, one for your own amazing win, and one for my clear round." Lisa held the tiny frame tightly.

Gasping with optimism, Jane whispered, just for Lisa, "We're going to do it, I know we are, Lisa. We're the Braehead world beaters."

They covered Chelsea with a light rug and gathered round to watch the other competitors. Lisa was intrigued to discover that the young man riding the black horse was indeed Edgar Gibson and that the horse was the magnificent Titan. Lisa had heard of him, at one time one of Ireland's most promising young riders. But, last night, Eric had completed the picture. Edgar had not fulfilled that early potential.

"He's still a competent showjumper but these days he makes most of his money buying and selling horses. Titan is one of the few horses he's kept for any length of time. I'm looking after Titan this week."

Titan and Edgar also went clear. Lisa applauded and clapped her arm on Eric's shoulder as he waited for his charge to exit the arena.

"Well done, Eric. We're both through to the jump off."

"Aye, Lisa. And I know who I want to win!"

Dieter Hamann was last to go, riding an English horse, Fellow Craftsman. With effortless Germanic precision, he rode faultlessly, with plenty to spare and was now clearly the gambler's favourite. By the end of the first round, seven horses had progressed to the jump-off. Lisa was drawn fifth. Once again, she began to warm up, asking Andrew to raise the practice fences a few notches, "Just a bit bigger than they'll be in the final round." Chelsea responded to the occasion, soaring over the fences with a determination that Lisa had never seen before. Prickles of excitement ran down her spine.

"My God, lass, you don't need me to keep you focused today." But she also knew that she would have to be on top form, to help steer the mare around the twisting jump-off course. And all of a sudden she was no longer satisfied simply to have competed. "I want to win now, Chelsea. For you, my girl. You've helped me fulfil my dream, in the first round. Now I won't let you down in fulfilling yours. Let's purge those demons today."

Of the four horses that preceded Chelsea in the jump off, three went clear -- one with a fast time. The rider was well known on the Scottish circuit and she brought all her experience to bear with a very good young horse. Andrew called out to Lisa as she left the holding area, "Give it your best shot – Chelsea will respond!" They cantered into the ring and were greeted by an explosion of applause.

Lisa became focused.

"Concentrate, Lisa, concentrate. This one's for you, Chels."

Then there was a hush. As they cantered around, waiting for the bell, the silence was broken only by a single calm measured call from the gate leading to the collecting ring – "Go, Chels, go girl" and Chelsea responded instantly to the familiar, loved voice from the past.

The bell sounded and she galloped towards the first fence. They flew over it, effortless athleticism combined now with utter determination. Then they turned for the next. As they sailed over, Lisa was already looking back towards the third – a double that required accurate riding. Chelsea sensed Lisa's imperceptible switch in body position and turned in the air, saving a single valuable second. She stretched for the first element and then amazingly, with just one stride, took off over the second element. Another fraction of a second saved. The risk paid off. She surged clear of the double and braked quickly turning inside the wall, saving yet more time, before steadying briefly in front of the planks. Clearing them, she drove towards the final fence. The crowd cheered their support, willing them to a clear round. Chelsea knew this was the last hurdle and focused intently, leaping it with a perfect stride and natural power, with inches to spare, just like the practice jumps minutes before. This time the crowd erupted, drowning the tannoy announcement, "Well, that very fast clear round puts Lisa Graham and Chelsea well into the lead in a incredible time of 32.5 seconds."

Andrew had no more energy. He leaned on the gate and put his head in his hands, drained of emotion, waiting limply for his team to exit the arena. As they passed through the gate, Chelsea's ears pricked up, again recognising Eric's voice.

"Well done, Chelsea. Well done, my girl!"

Lisa looked down to see his jubilant face beneath the distinctive shock of red hair. She smiled at Chelsea's number one fan.

Dieter Hamann was next, experiencing a nightmare of misfortune. It would have been difficult for any rider to follow the euphoria of Chelsea's reception. Fellow Craftsman lost his composure and stumbled through the course with twelve faults. Then Edgar Gibson entered the ring – last to go, knowing that only a fast clear round would beat Lisa. Lisa stood in the collecting area as Edgar passed close by. She raised a hand, saluting a fellow competitor with dignity. Edgar nodded, returning the unspoken message of respect, a half smile breaking momentarily the determined set of his clamped jaw. Eric walked beside Titan and smiled at Lisa who mouthed a sincere "Go well."

Titan emulated Chelsea by galloping towards the first fence. With the greater power of a stallion he snatched a fraction of a second from Chelsea's time and turned for the next. Safely over, but he lost his advantage in the turn for the third, Chelsea's agility cancelling the larger animal's strength. Titan swept through the double but again lost a fraction of a second in the turn to the planks. Again the momentary gain through power was being lost to agility. They too cut inside the wall; then Titan rattled the planks. They stayed up! But that smallest of hesitations cost them a further tenth of a second, and first place. Chelsea had won!

Lisa shook as she mounted Chelsea for the prize giving. Andrew helped her with a 'leg up' into the saddle. Then emotion welled inside her as she thought of her wonderful friend, of Dublin and of this moment.

"Chelsea knows, she knows."

Tears returned as she looked down at the triumphant ears, and kindly head and muscled neck, feeling nothing but a heart-wrenching affection and thinking only of gentleness and strength. What a powerful, powerful combination. The moment was then made all the more special. Presenting first prize was Harriet, in her capacity as wife of the sponsor. Harriet saw Lisa's emotion and she too felt the welling of tears.

Watching, a delighted Mike Brainwood turned to James and whispered with good nature.

"What a wonderful moment. Just look at them. Trust a lady to weep at a time like this."

James wiped his eyes with a large white handkerchief and croaked: "Typical women. But don't you just love them."

Waiting in line for the presentation, Lisa saw Chelsea lay her ears back at Titan before edging a step sideways, away from her fellow competitor. She caught Edgar's eye.

"Bad luck, Edgar. It was a great try. It's always difficult to chase a time and you did brilliantly."

"You deserved it, Lisa. You've worked a miracle with that mare. She was with me for a little while but I found her hard work. You clearly have a way with her. Well done! And you know, apart from missing out on the qualifying spot for Horse of the Year Show, I really don't mind. I enjoyed seeing Chelsea back to fitness. It was the best prize of all."

Today, an arrogant young man had finally grown up.

Lisa was pensive for a moment. The sixth-placed horse was receiving its rosette. She only had time to say, "Let's meet up briefly this afternoon, before we go our separate ways. Let's share past memories."

And then came the lap of honour. Lisa had ridden this countless times before – in a young girl's vivid imagination.

"I hope we've caught all this on the video. That's one tape that will be worn out before long! I don't care if I look so emotional. Nothing in the world can make me any happier."

It was hard to know whose smile was larger – Lisa's or Chelsea's – as they eventually came to a stop by the gate and walked quietly out of the ring. Andrew, Harriet, James, Angela, Jane and Tom, a wonderful collection of friends, were all there to greet them and shower them with hugs and pats. Chelsea immediately reverted to her usual insouciant self.

"And what else did you all expect?"

Lisa laughed as she jumped off and patted the mare again. But soon everybody had to slip away. Angela, Tom and Jane had left Star alone in the lorry, so they could watch the jump off. They were anxious not to ignore their lovely pony any longer. Andrew accompanied Harriet and James, to say farewell to their guests.

"We'll all meet up later, at the lorry."

In truth, Lisa was glad of a few minutes alone with Chelsea. This was a precious moment. But she also needed to think – something was playing through her mind. A final decision had to be made. They made their way quietly back along the walkway towards the lorry park. Then Chelsea's ears pricked up and she stopped. There stood Eric, waiting to say his own private words of farewell. Lisa handed him the reins.

"I'll leave you two alone for a few minutes. Would you be kind enough to walk Chelsea back to my lorry when you're ready? Take all the time you want."

Eric's last words to Chelsea reflected his own deep contentment – a peace of mind that transcended any sadness at saying farewell.

"Well, girl, I always prayed that you'd meet the right owner; someone prepared to give you their time and effort and, above all, love. Lisa did all that, and more – she never allowed herself to think that you could ever be less than a beautiful miracle."

The small group gathered around Lisa's lorry. They waved goodbye to Jane and her parents. Lisa had assured them, "Don't worry, we'll take Chelsea. Don't wait for her – she's with Eric, saying goodbye."

The transporter coughed into life and began its journey home, sporting Jane's red rosette proudly in the windscreen. Lisa and Andrew sighed with contentment. James and Harriet held hands waving their own farewells to newfound friends.

Then Edgar appeared. Instinctively the four soul mates began to applaud, showing genuine respect for his magnificent effort.

"I'm ever so glad you came, Edgar. There's something I want you to hear." At that moment two redheads appeared to complete the circle. "Even better. There's something I want you all to hear. You too, Chelsea."

The mare tossed her head with delight and peered enquiringly at the circle of friends. Eric rubbed the white crescent.

Lisa continued, in a tone that Andrew knew so well; the quiet determination of utter conviction.

"I've been doing some thinking. What Chelsea and I have experienced, yesterday and today, is the completion of a cycle, a sort of coming together of unresolved issues in a way that gives me a feeling of closure."

She paused, allowing peace and silence to bind each one of them to the moment. Chelsea flicked her ears towards her mistress, waiting for the comfort of her voice.

"Chelsea has brought me to this wonderful moment – the achievement of a cherished dream. And she has carried me beyond that. It's time to stop and think of her. Right now, she's fine. Her hocks are giving her no trouble. But, if we continue jumping at this level, there will come a day when she'll pay the price. I don't want a repeat of what happened to her in the past. In fact, I would never forgive myself. She's twelve, and I want her to enjoy many more years, happy years. I'd like her to have a foal and just be my riding companion, and my friend."

There was a hum of approval. Chelsea nodded.

"So, I'm not going to Wembley in October. That means that my qualifying place is vacant. I don't know the rules, but I'd love to think that, in any case, the sponsors have some say in the matter. After all, it is Arthur Garland's own competition now. James, can you do me a huge favour and allow me the honour of suggesting that Edgar gets my place?"

"Yes, Lisa. You have my assurance on that. Thank you Lisa, for having the right values in all that you do, and for your courage in living them. And congratulations, Edgar. Your dignity in defeat this afternoon was so evident. I'm sure we'd all be delighted if you could step into Lisa's shoes."

Edgar hugged Lisa.

"I'm not sure I'll ever be worthy to do that. But thank you, Lisa, for your offer. More than that, thank you for being an inspiration to me, a living example that there is always a better way, one that is based on service. Thank you for serving Chelsea, with kindness and gentleness."

James brought them all back to earth.

"Of course, we can't proceed without the approval of one other important person."

He hugged the silken chestnut neck and looked into Chelsea's eyes for the final deciding vote. Her nose pushed him gently backwards, so she could nod her consent.

A Message from the Author

Please keep in touch with us.

Beth and I would like to thank you for reading this book. How did you find it?

Was it simply a story that entertained you and lifted your spirits?

Was it because it is a 'horsey' book and you wanted to immerse yourself in 'horsiness'? Did you feel drawn to see, be challenged by, support or even argue with the book's messages about how we believe horses could best be treated?

Or was it because somebody else pointed you to the book, and maybe asked you to read the messages about bringing spirit and values to the workplace?

Readers have already given all of these reasons. We'd love for you to do the same. Please do drop us a message and continue the debate.

Our website is www.gentleleadership.com.

You can also contact either of us directly by e-mail at aidan@gentleleadership.com or beth@gentleleadership.com.

We'd be honoured by your interest and would be happy to reply.

To learn more about **the red horse speaks** why not subscribe, free of charge, to our monthly newsletter?

Simply visit www.theredhorsespeaks.com.

Look out for more books on gentle leadership in the near future. Beth is busy on her own (non fiction) book right now, with its messages about leadership. In it you will see how 'the red horse speaks'. I will soon be working on a dialogue between our two horses (Chelsea and Susie). It will be ideal for children (of all ages!)

Until next time, love and gentleness to you all ...

Aidan and Beth